For use with Fourth Edition

bju press®

Greenville, South Carolina

Note: The fact that materials produced by other publishers may be referred to in this volume does not constitute an endorsement of the content or theological position of materials produced by such publishers. Any references and ancillary materials are listed as an aid to the student or the teacher and in an attempt to maintain the accepted academic standards of the publishing industry.

MATH 1 Reviews
Fourth Edition

Authors
Gina Bradstreet
Florence Fong
Pam Frank
Kelly Payne
Carol Satterfield
Robin E. Scroggins

Project Editor
Abby Offord

Cover/Book Designer
Drew Fields

Design Coordinator
Duane Nichols

Page Layout
Katherine Cooper
Ashley Hager

Art Director
Elly Kalagayan

Art & Design Facilitator
Jim Frasier

Illustrators
Lynda Slattery
Julie Speer
Courtney Godbey Wise

Project Coordinators
Brittany Mellen
Sam Winchester

Permissions
Sylvia Gass
Carrie Walker

Photo credits appear on page 361.

ISBN 978-1-60682-626-3

15 14 13 12 11 10 9 8 7

To the Teacher

Math 1 Reviews provides two pages of review activities for each lesson.

- The front page reviews the concepts taught in the lesson using the format of the corresponding Worktext page. This page should be used the day after the lesson presentation in order to assess retention and understanding.

- The back page of each lesson reviews concepts from previous chapters, providing continual practice of essential first-grade concepts.

- Chapter Review pages correspond to the Worktext Chapter Review pages. These pages make an excellent study guide for the Chapter Test.

- The Cumulative Review pages reinforce concepts from previous chapters in a spiral review.

The answer key for the *Math 1 Reviews* book can be found on the Teacher's Toolkit CD in the *Math 1 Teacher's Edition*.

Zero-Ten

Write the number for the set.

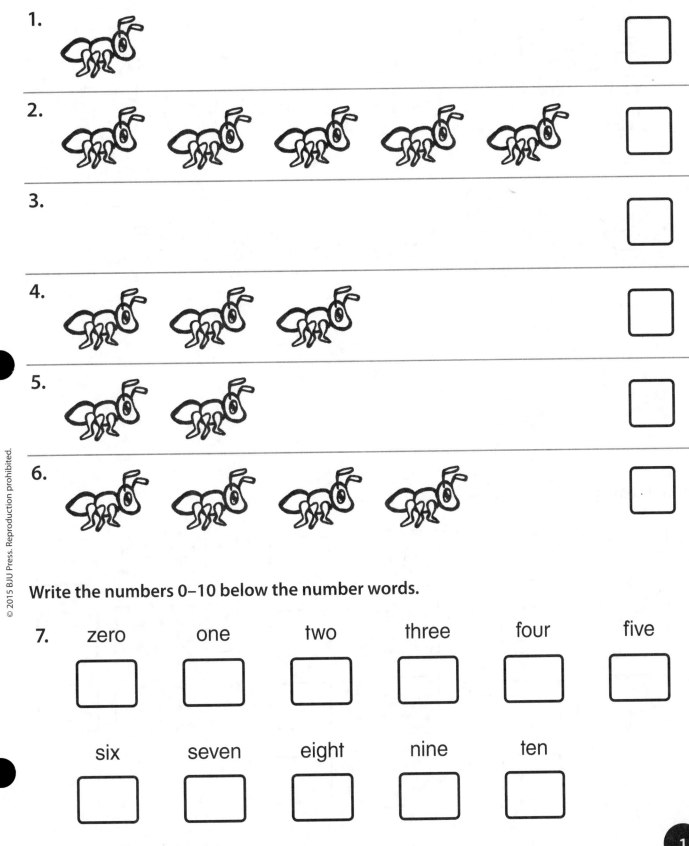

Write the numbers 0–10 below the number words.

7. zero   one   two   three   four   five

   six   seven   eight   nine   ten

Write the number for the set.

1.

2.

3.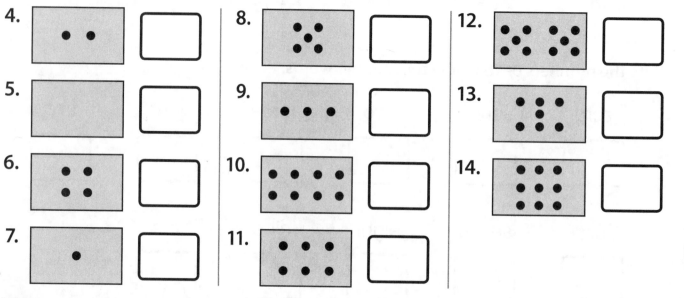

Write the number that matches the dot pattern.

4.

5.

6.

7.

8.

9.

10.

11.

12.

13.

14.

Compare Numbers to 10

Draw 1 more shape. Complete the sentence.

1.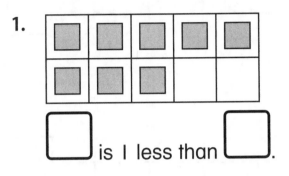

☐ is 1 less than ☐.

2.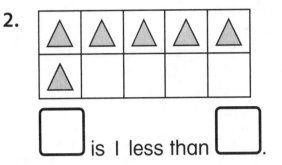

☐ is 1 less than ☐.

Write the number for each set.
Circle the set that has more.

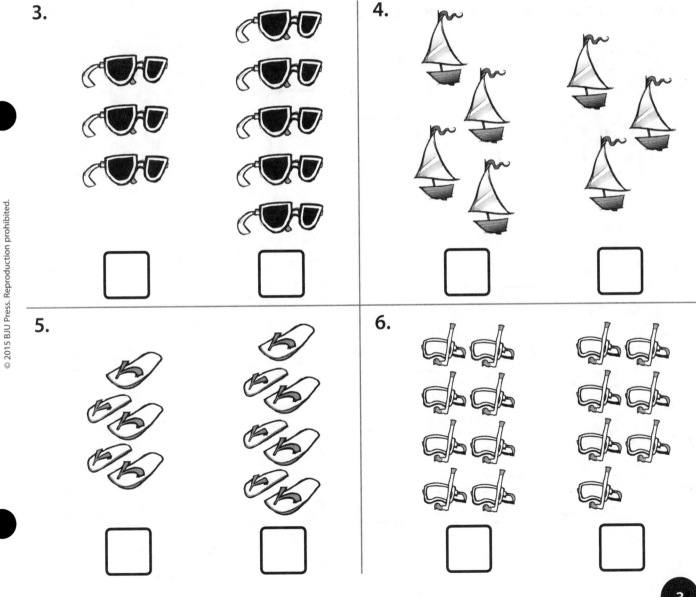

3.

☐   ☐

4.

☐   ☐

5.

☐   ☐

6.

☐   ☐

Trace the jumps. Write the number.

1.

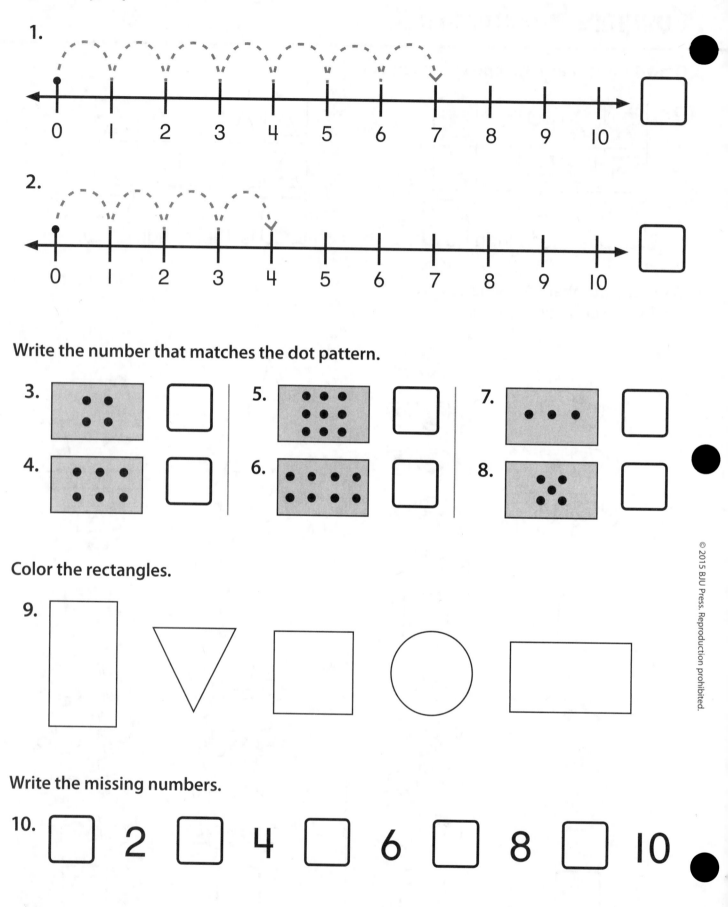

2.

Write the number that matches the dot pattern.

3.

4.

5.

6.

7.

8.

Color the rectangles.

9.

Write the missing numbers.

10.
☐ 2 ☐ 4 ☐ 6 ☐ 8 ☐ 10

Ten

Draw more jumps to make 10. Complete the sentence.

1.

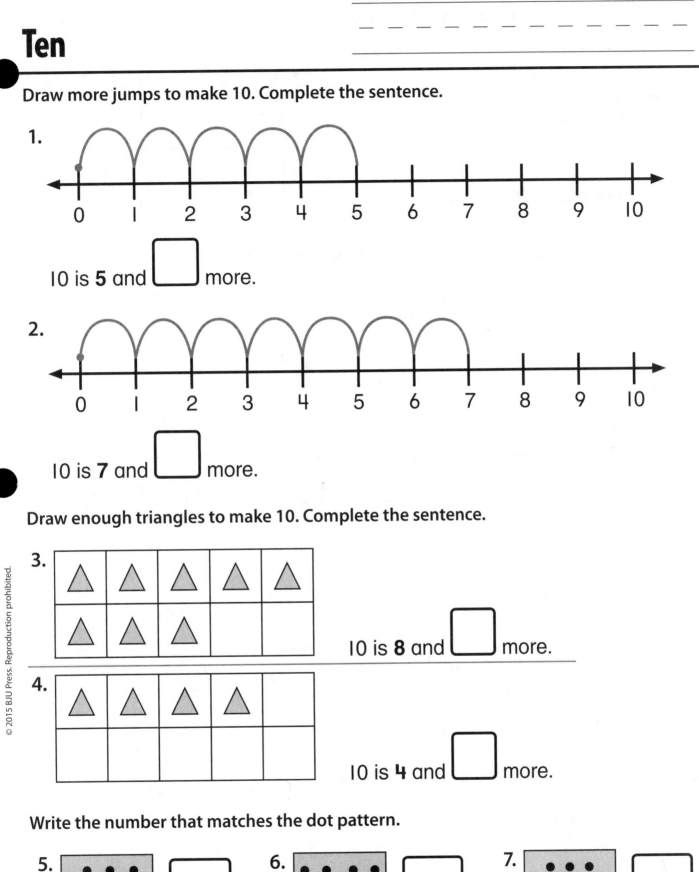

10 is **5** and ☐ more.

2.

10 is **7** and ☐ more.

Draw enough triangles to make 10. Complete the sentence.

3.

10 is **8** and ☐ more.

4.

10 is **4** and ☐ more.

Write the number that matches the dot pattern.

5. **6.** **7.**

Draw 1 more shape. Complete the sentence.

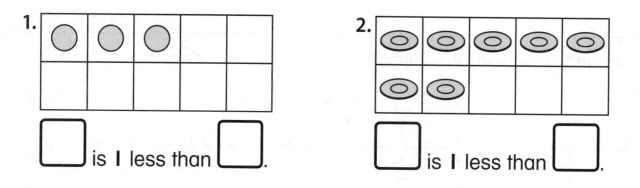

1.   ☐ is **1** less than ☐.

2.   ☐ is **1** less than ☐.

Write the number for each set. Circle the set that has more.

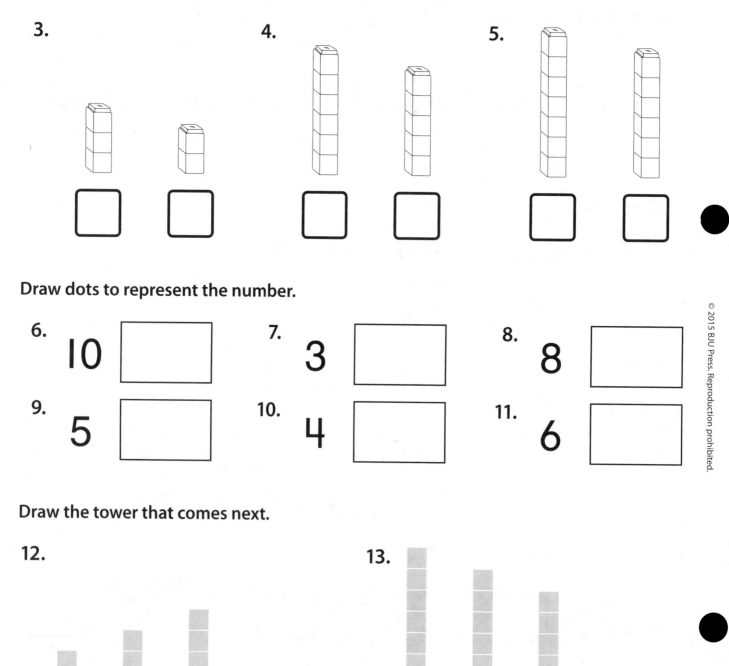

3.

4.

5.

Draw dots to represent the number.

6. 10 ☐

7. 3 ☐

8. 8 ☐

9. 5 ☐

10. 4 ☐

11. 6 ☐

Draw the tower that comes next.

12.

13.

Eleven & Twelve

Count the eggs. Write the numbers 1–12.

1.

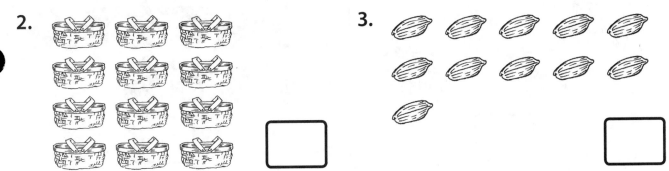

Write the number for the set.

2.

3.

Write the number for the set.
Circle as many pairs as you can.
Mark even or odd.

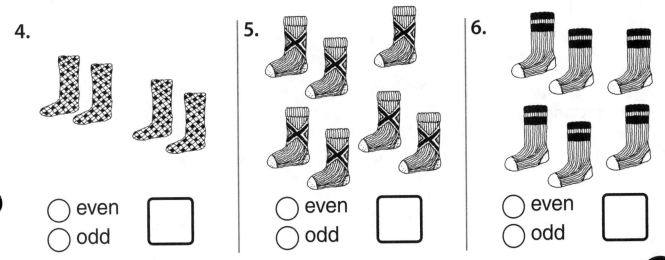

4.

○ even
○ odd

5.

○ even
○ odd

6.

○ even
○ odd

Write the number for each set.

1.

2.

3.

4.

Color the triangles.

5.

Color the rectangles.

6.

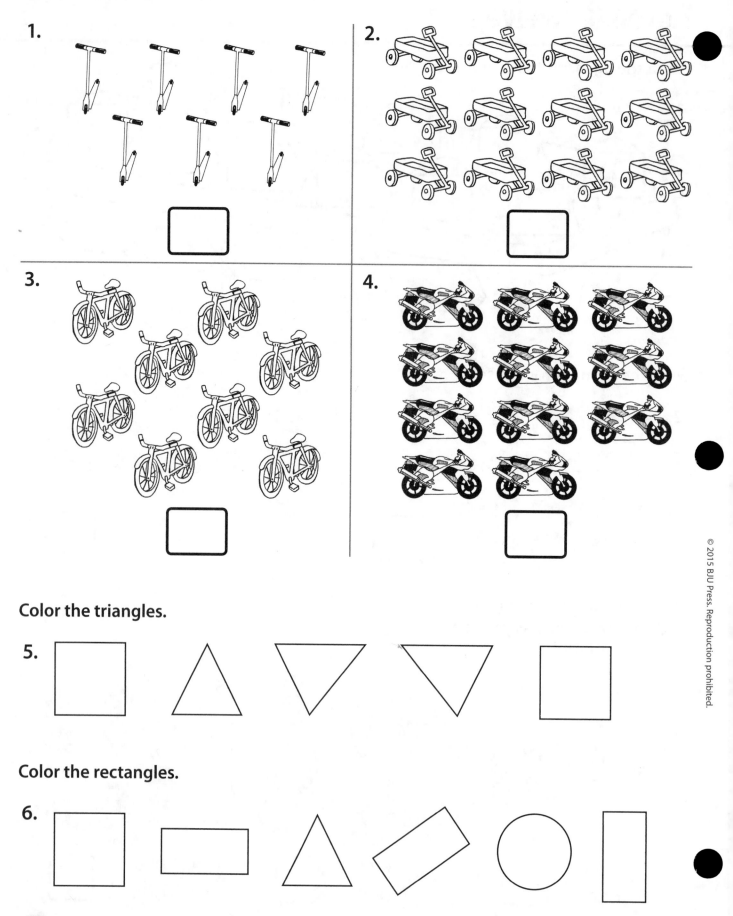

Thirteen-Nineteen

Circle a set of 10 and *count on*. Match the set to the number.

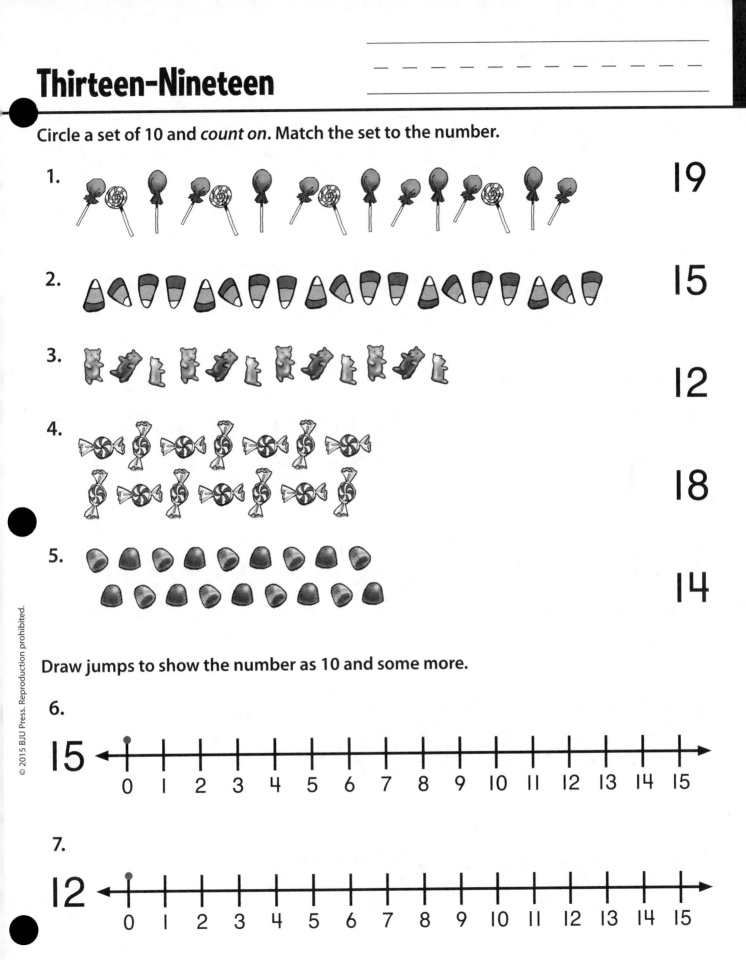

1.   19

2.   15

3.   12

4.   18

5.   14

Draw jumps to show the number as 10 and some more.

6.

15

0 1 2 3 4 5 6 7 8 9 10 11 12 13 14 15

7.

12

0 1 2 3 4 5 6 7 8 9 10 11 12 13 14 15

Write the missing numbers.

1.
5 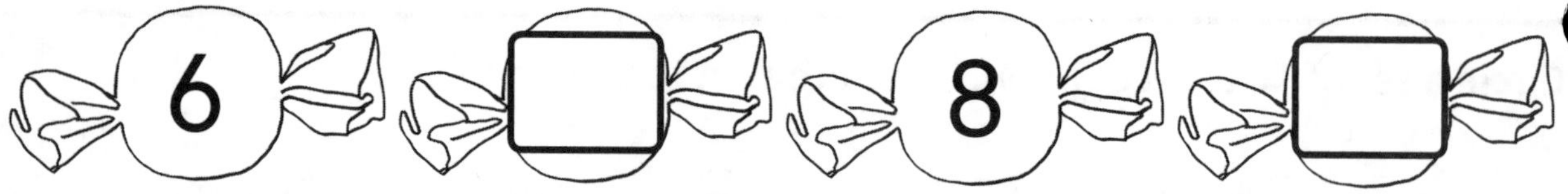   6   [ ]   8   [ ]

2.
15   [ ]   17   [ ]   19

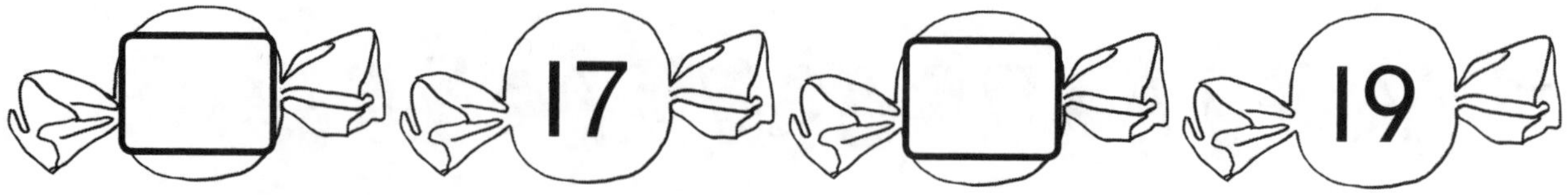

Write the number that matches the dot pattern.

3. [ ]

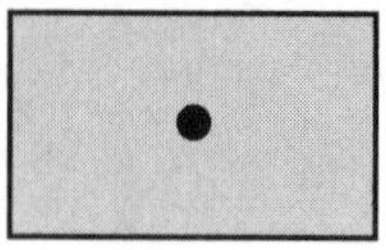

4. [ ]

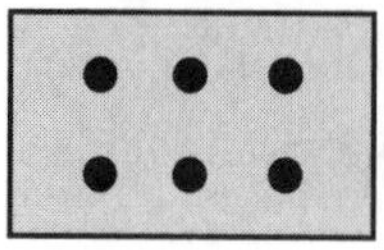

5. [ ]

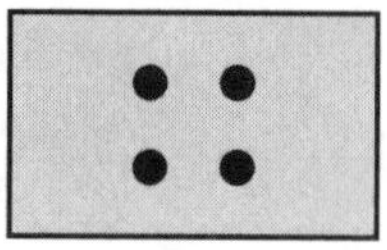

6. [ ]

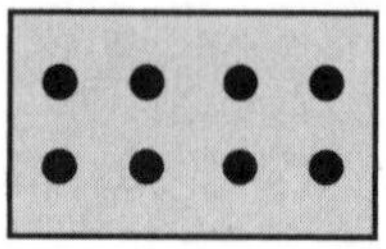

7. [ ]

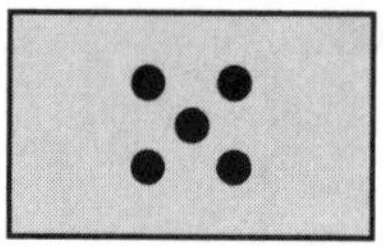

8. [ ]

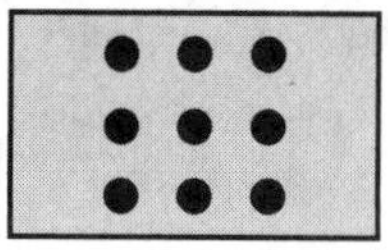

9. [ ]

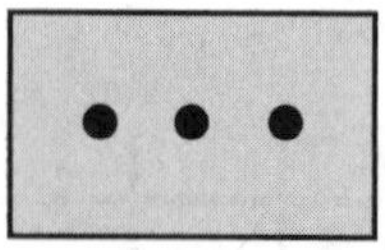

10. [ ]

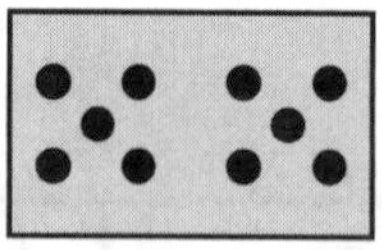

11. [ ]

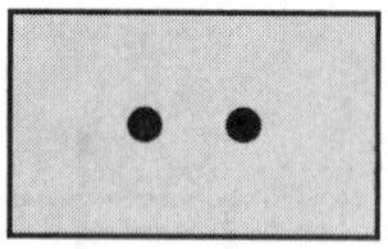

12. [ ]

13. [ ]

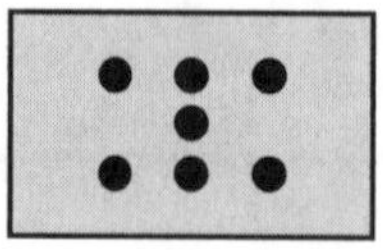

Compare Numbers to 19

_____

Write the number for each set.
Circle the number of the set that has more.

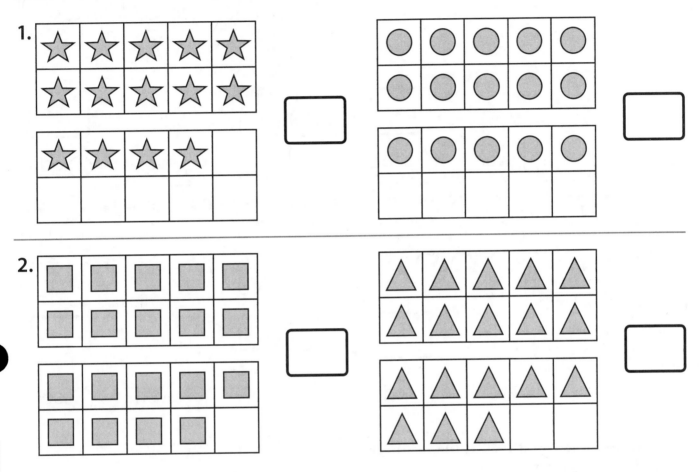

1.

2.

Write the number for each set.
Circle the basket of the set that has more.

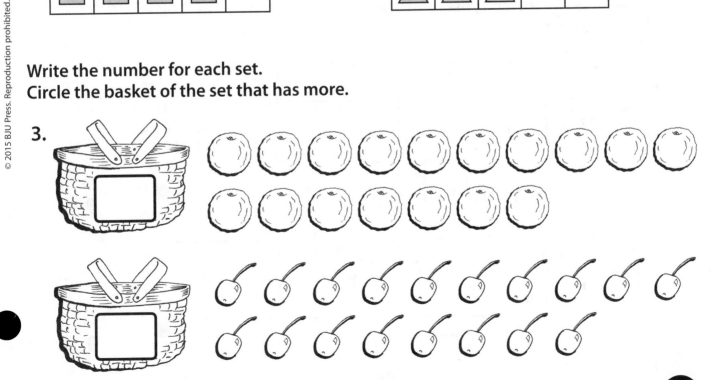

3.

Write the number for each set.
Circle as many pairs as you can.
Mark even or odd.

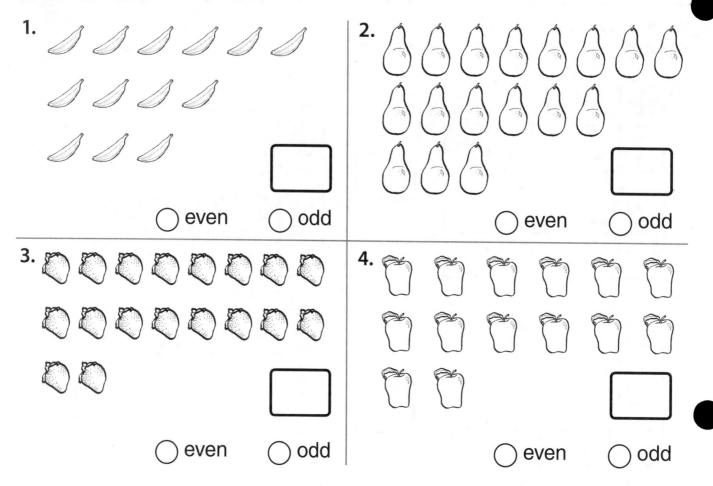

1.

◯ even   ◯ odd

2.

◯ even   ◯ odd

3.

◯ even   ◯ odd

4.

◯ even   ◯ odd

Draw more dots to represent the number.
Complete the sentence.

5.

15

15 is **10** and ☐ more.

6.

16

16 is **10** and ☐ more.

Twenty

Circle sets of 10. Count by 10s.
Write the number for the whole set.
Complete the sentence.

1.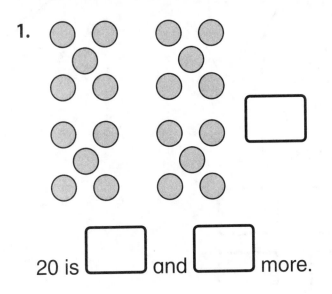

20 is [ ] and [ ] more.

2.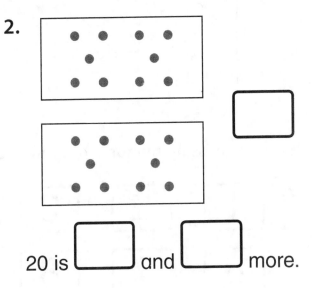

20 is [ ] and [ ] more.

Draw more shapes to make 20.
Complete the sentence.

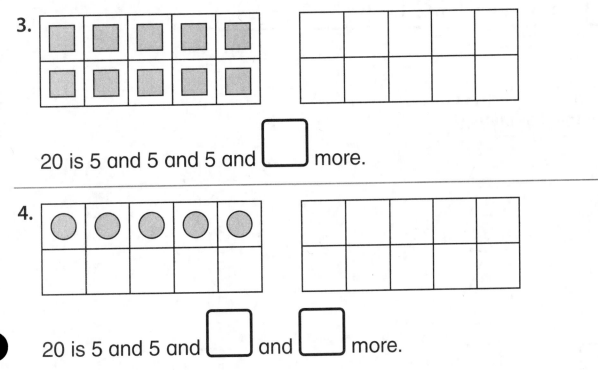

3.

20 is 5 and 5 and 5 and [ ] more.

4.

20 is 5 and 5 and [ ] and [ ] more.

Color the triangles red, the circles blue, and the rectangles green.

1.

Write the missing numbers to show counting by 5s.

2.

1	2	3	4	
6	7	8	9	
11	12	13	14	
16	17	18	19	

Write the number for each set.
Circle the set that has more.

3.

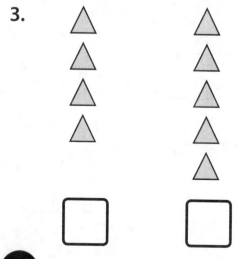

4.

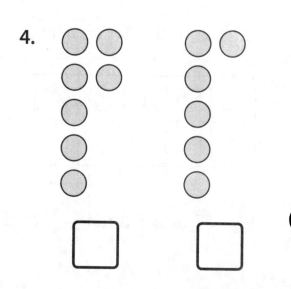

Chapter 1 Review

Write the number that matches the dot pattern.
Circle the number that is greater.

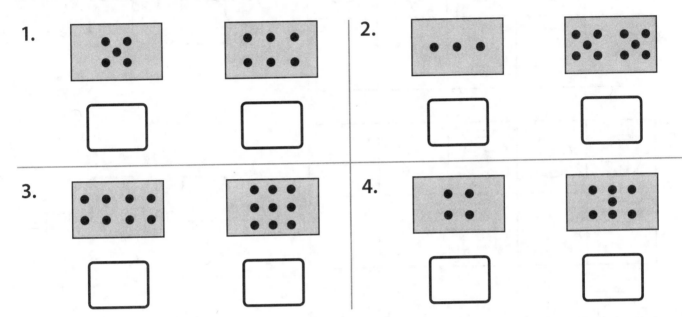

1.

2.

3.

4.

Draw shapes in the box to represent the number.

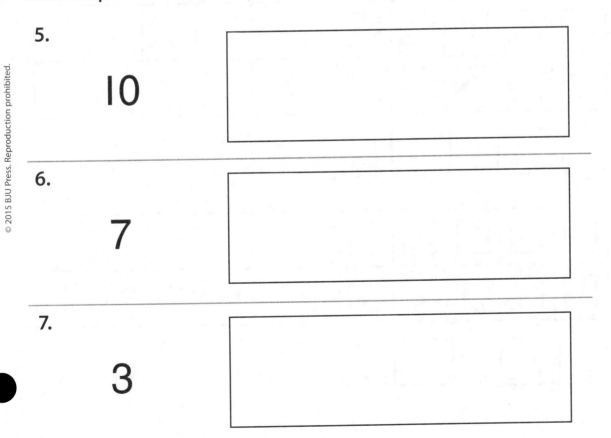

5. 10

6. 7

7. 3

**Draw more circles to make 10.
Complete the sentence.**

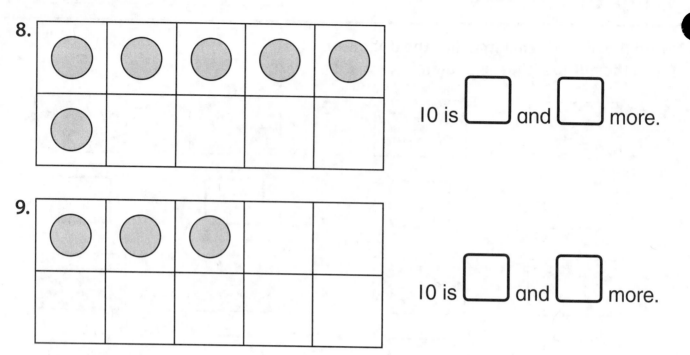

8. 10 is ☐ and ☐ more.

9. 10 is ☐ and ☐ more.

**Draw more boxes to represent the number.
Complete the sentence.**

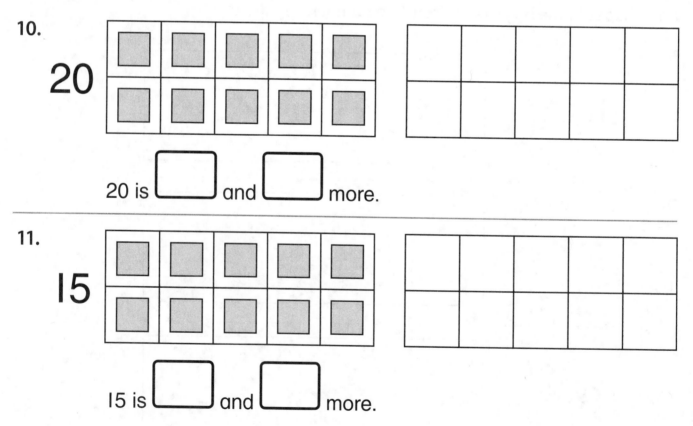

10. 20

20 is ☐ and ☐ more.

11. 15

15 is ☐ and ☐ more.

Kindergarten Review

Mark the number.

1.

⭘ ⭘ ⭘ ⭘ ⭘
0   1   2   3   4

2.

⭘ ⭘ ⭘ ⭘ ⭘
5   6   7   8   9

3.

⭘ ⭘ ⭘ ⭘ ⭘
0   1   2   3   4

4.

⭘ ⭘ ⭘ ⭘ ⭘
1   2   3   4   5

5.

⭘ ⭘ ⭘ ⭘ ⭘
5   6   7   8   9

6.

⭘ ⭘ ⭘ ⭘ ⭘
0   1   2   3   4

7.

⭘ ⭘ ⭘ ⭘ ⭘
5   6   7   8   9

8.

⭘ ⭘ ⭘ ⭘ ⭘
0   1   2   3   4

Write the numbers 1–10 below the number words.

9.

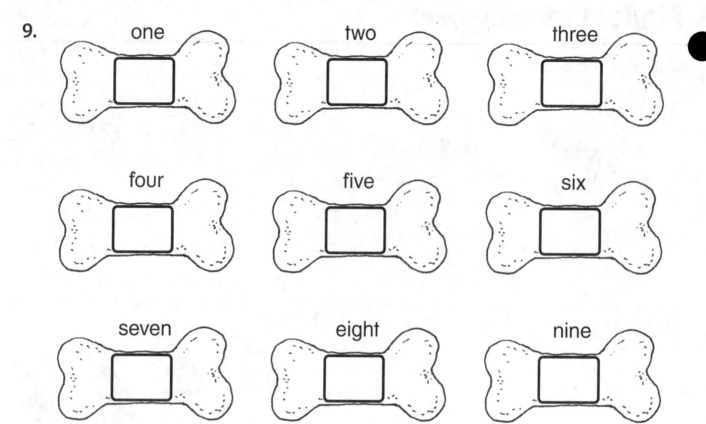

one

two

three

four

five

six

seven

eight

nine

ten

Color the squares.

10.

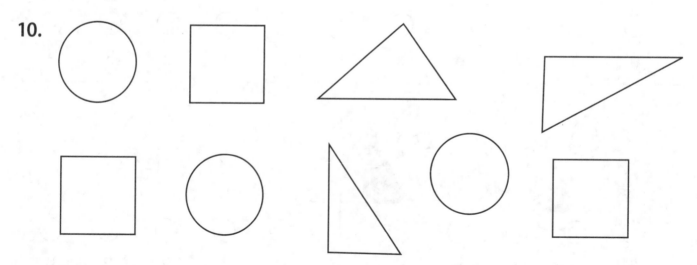

Addition Readiness

Write the number to match the picture.

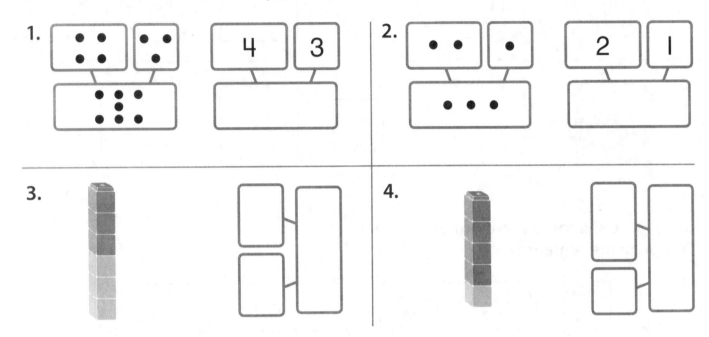

Make 2 sets using 2 different colors.
Write the numbers to match the picture.

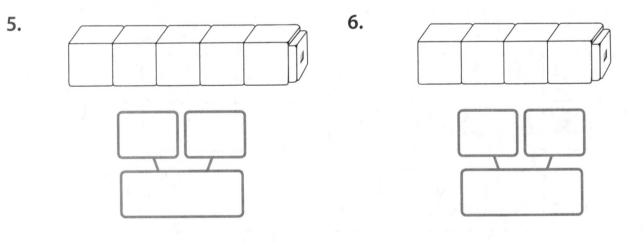

Color the shapes that are the same shape as the first one.

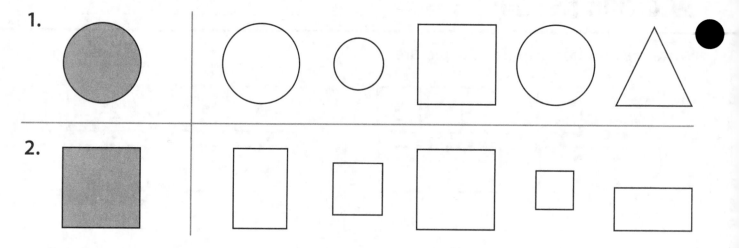

1.

2.

Draw more shapes to represent the number.
Complete the sentence.

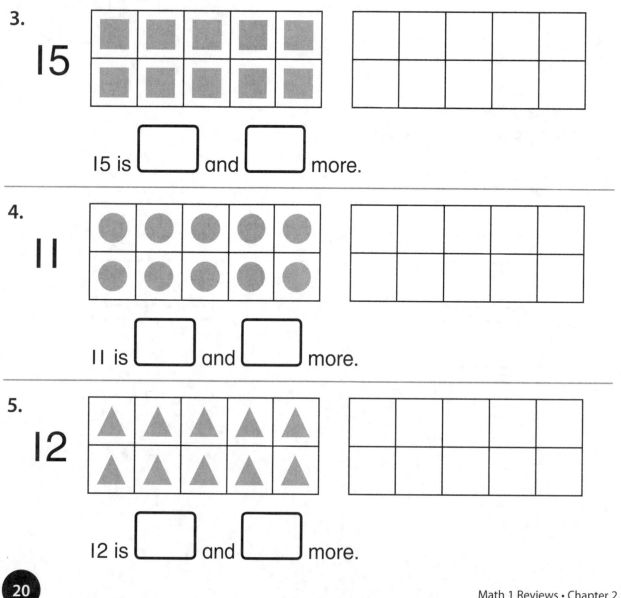

3.

15

15 is [ ] and [ ] more.

4.

11

11 is [ ] and [ ] more.

5.

12

12 is [ ] and [ ] more.

Add Zero

Write an addition sentence for the picture.
Complete the sentence.

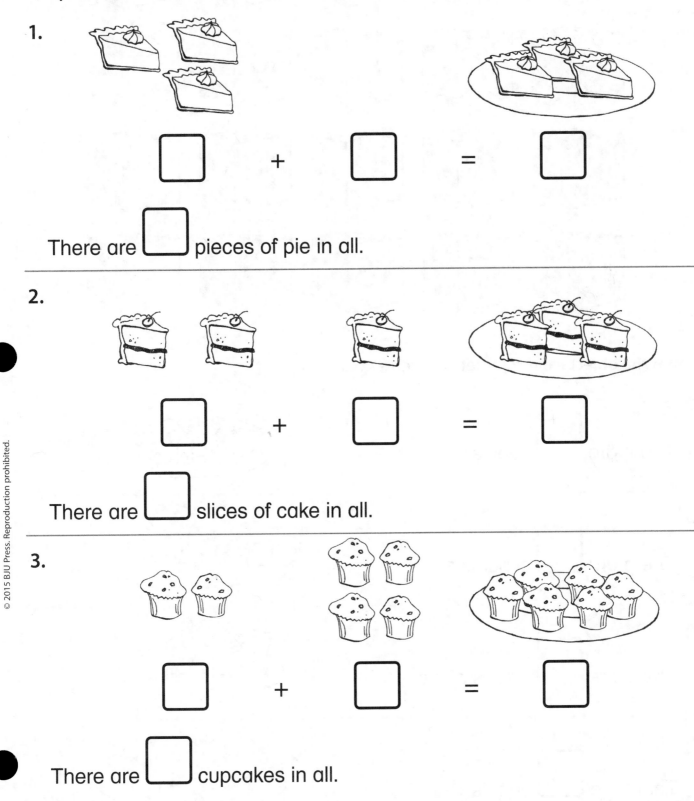

1.

☐ + ☐ = ☐

There are ☐ pieces of pie in all.

2.

☐ + ☐ = ☐

There are ☐ slices of cake in all.

3.

☐ + ☐ = ☐

There are ☐ cupcakes in all.

Write the missing numbers to show counting by 5s.

1.

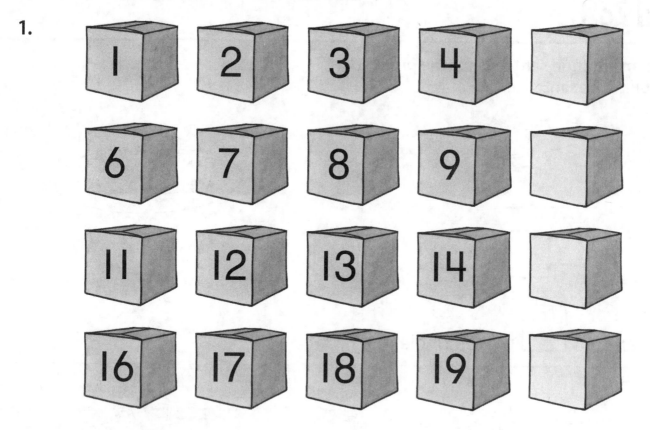

1	2	3	4	
6	7	8	9	
11	12	13	14	
16	17	18	19	

Count the objects and complete the sentences.

2. There are ☐ cookies.

3. There are ☐ cupcakes.

4. There are ☐ pieces of pie.

5. There are ☐ donuts.

Addition Sentences

Mark the picture of the joined sets.
Complete the sentence.

1.

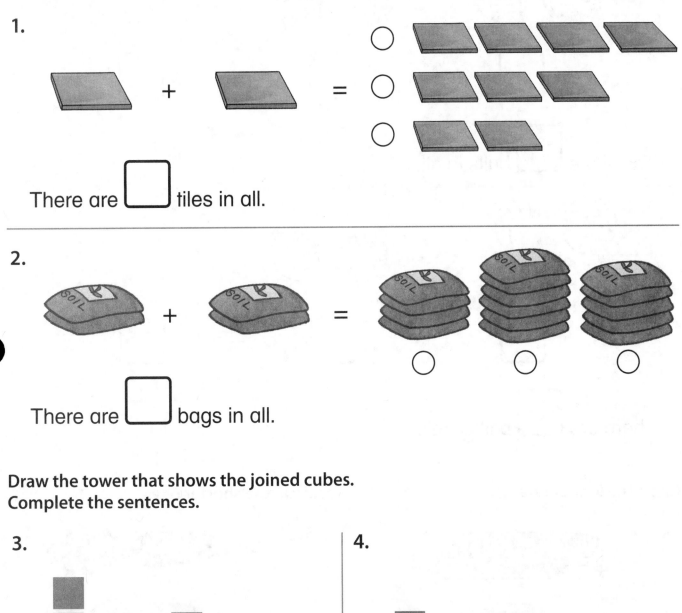

There are ☐ tiles in all.

2.

There are ☐ bags in all.

Draw the tower that shows the joined cubes.
Complete the sentences.

3.

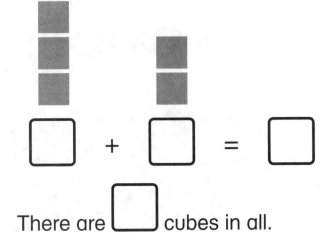

☐ + ☐ = ☐

There are ☐ cubes in all.

4.

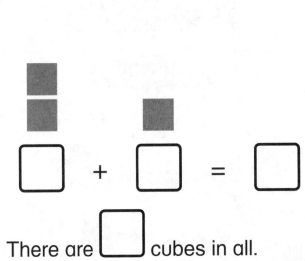

☐ + ☐ = ☐

There are ☐ cubes in all.

Write an addition sentence for the picture.
Complete the sentence.

1.

$\boxed{}$ + $\boxed{}$ = $\boxed{}$

There are $\boxed{}$ balls in all.

2.

$\boxed{}$ + $\boxed{}$ = $\boxed{}$

There are $\boxed{}$ balls in all.

Circle the longer one.

3.

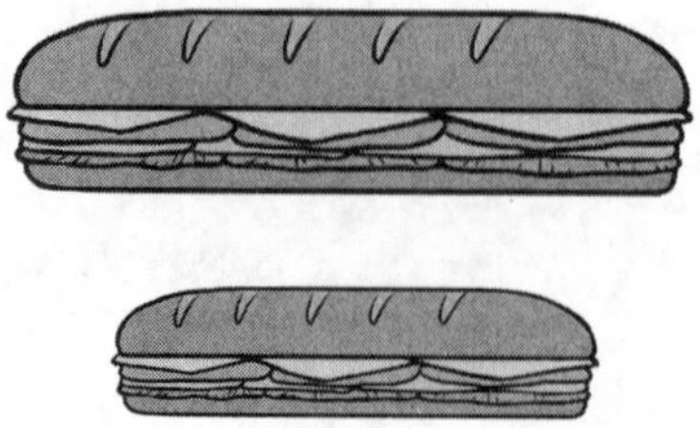

4.

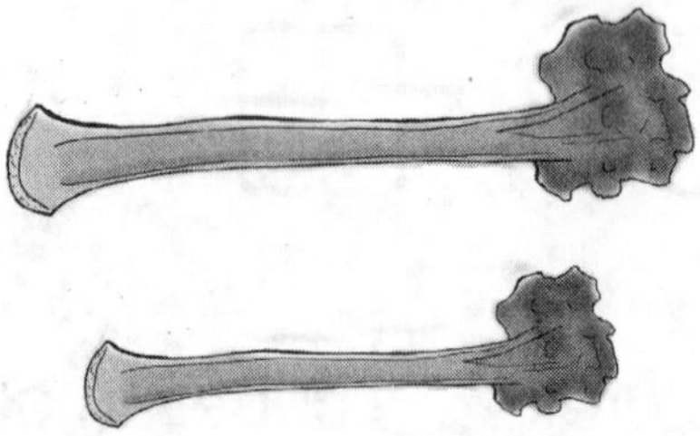

Circle the shorter one.

5.

6.

Illustrate an Addition Sentence

Write an addition sentence for the picture.
Complete the statement.

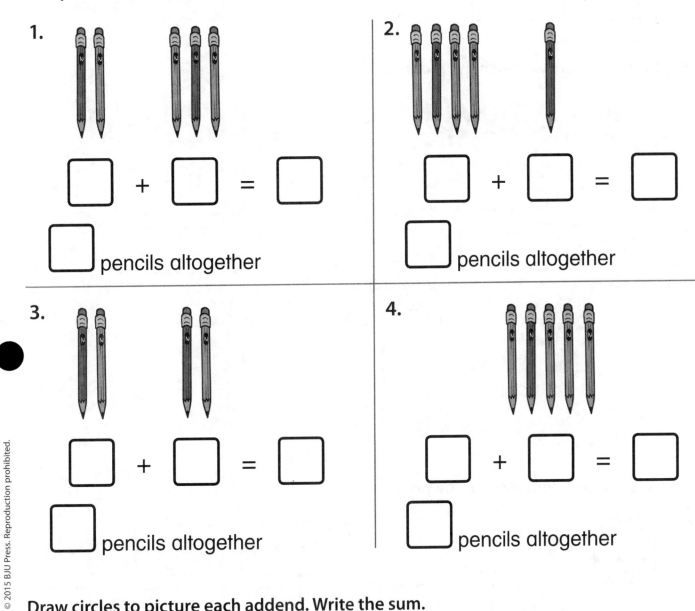

1.

☐ + ☐ = ☐

☐ pencils altogether

2.

☐ + ☐ = ☐

☐ pencils altogether

3.

☐ + ☐ = ☐

☐ pencils altogether

4.

☐ + ☐ = ☐

☐ pencils altogether

Draw circles to picture each addend. Write the sum.

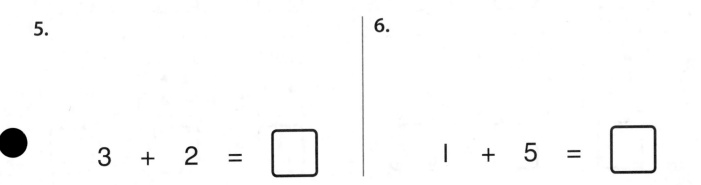

5.

3 + 2 = ☐

6.

1 + 5 = ☐

Draw circles to make 10. Complete the sentence.

1.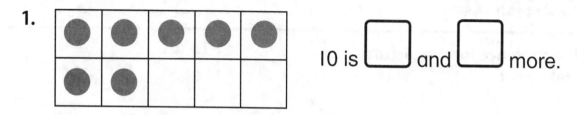

10 is ☐ and ☐ more.

Write the numbers to match the picture.

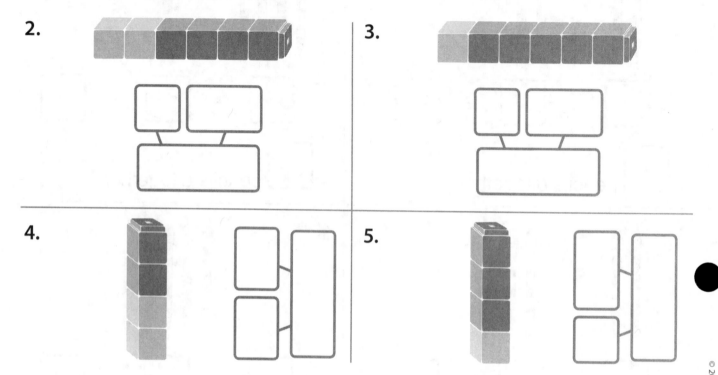

2.

3.

4.

5.

Write an addition sentence for the picture.

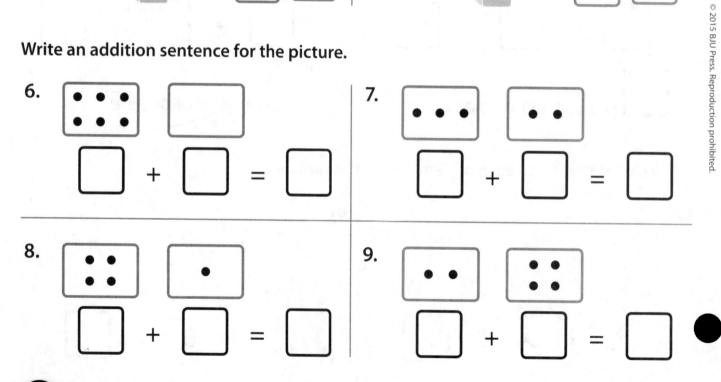

6.

☐ + ☐ = ☐

7.

☐ + ☐ = ☐

8.

☐ + ☐ = ☐

9.

☐ + ☐ = ☐

Addition in Vertical Form

Complete the addition problems. Complete the sentence.

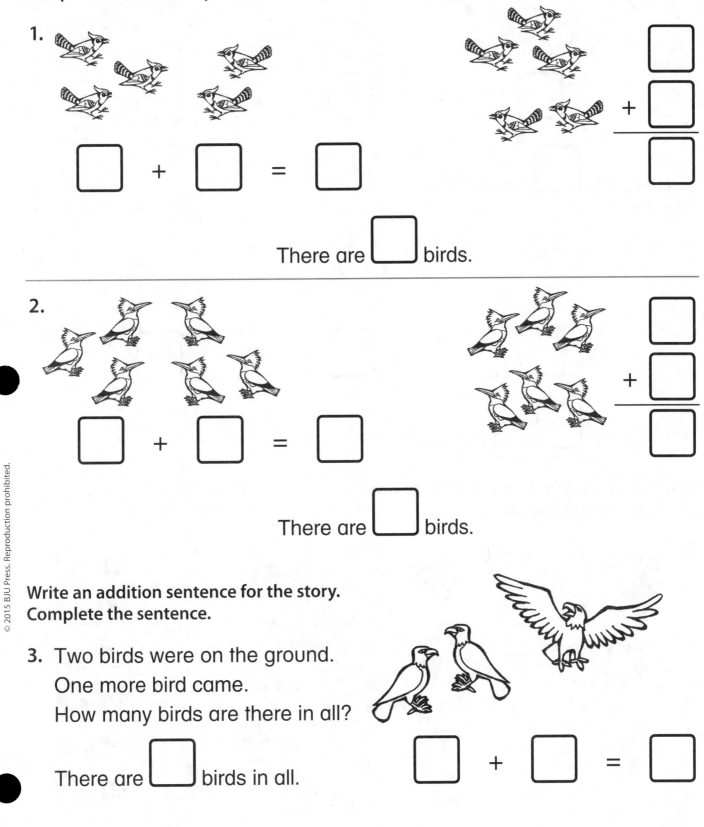

1. ☐ + ☐ = ☐

   ☐ + ☐

   There are ☐ birds.

2. ☐ + ☐ = ☐

   ☐ + ☐

   There are ☐ birds.

Write an addition sentence for the story.
Complete the sentence.

3. Two birds were on the ground.
   One more bird came.
   How many birds are there in all?

   There are ☐ birds in all.

   ☐ + ☐ = ☐

Write an addition sentence for the picture.
Complete the sentence.

1.

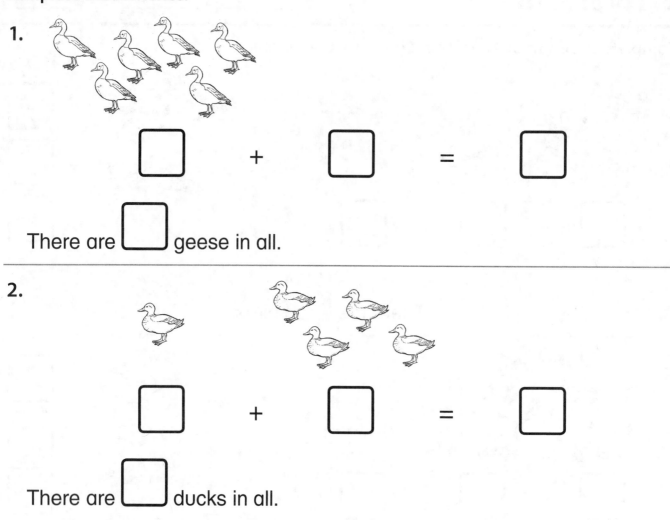

☐ + ☐ = ☐

There are ☐ geese in all.

2.

☐ + ☐ = ☐

There are ☐ ducks in all.

Draw lines to match the objects one to one.
Circle the set that has more.

3.

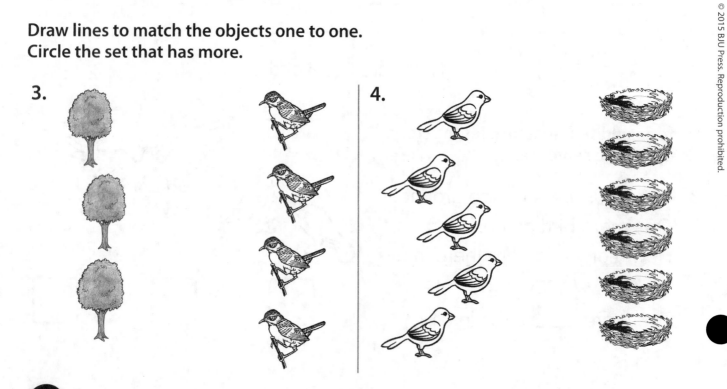

4.

Order of Addends

Use the shapes to write an addition sentence.

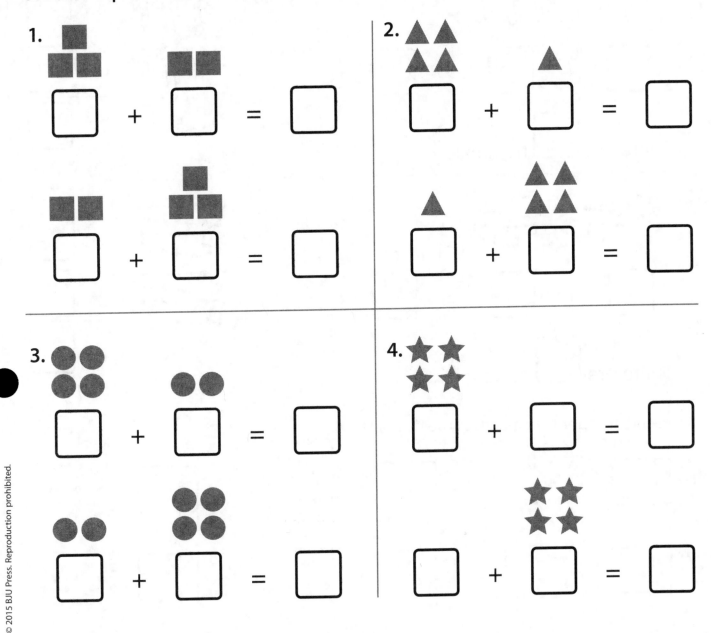

1. ☐ + ☐ = ☐

   ☐ + ☐ = ☐

2. ☐ + ☐ = ☐

   ☐ + ☐ = ☐

3. ☐ + ☐ = ☐

   ☐ + ☐ = ☐

4. ☐ + ☐ = ☐

   ☐ + ☐ = ☐

Draw dots to picture the story. Complete the sentences.

5. Anna has 1 big doll.

   She has 3 little dolls.

   How many dolls does Anna have?

   Anna has ☐ dolls.

Write an addition sentence for the picture.
Complete the sentence.

1.

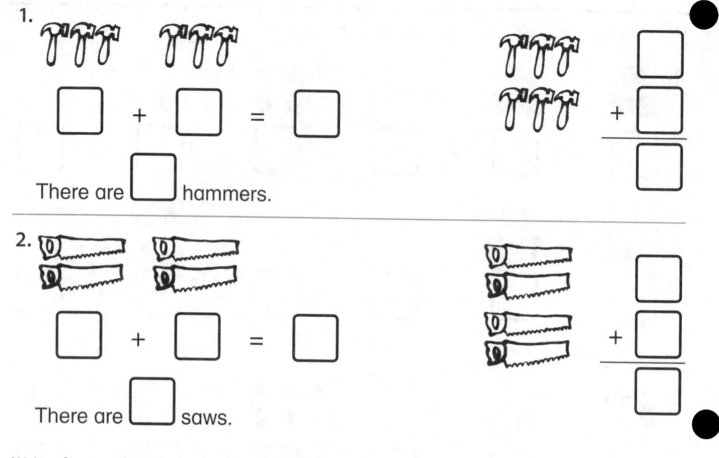

☐ + ☐ = ☐

There are ☐ hammers.

___

2.

☐ + ☐ = ☐

There are ☐ saws.

Write the number that matches the dot pattern.

3. ☐

4. ☐

5. ☐

6. ☐

7. ☐

8. ☐

Draw more boxes to represent the number. Complete the sentence.

9.

15

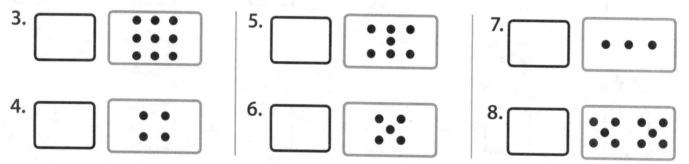

15 is ☐ and ☐ more.

Combinations for 4, 5 & 6

Use the circles to write addition combinations for 4 and 5.

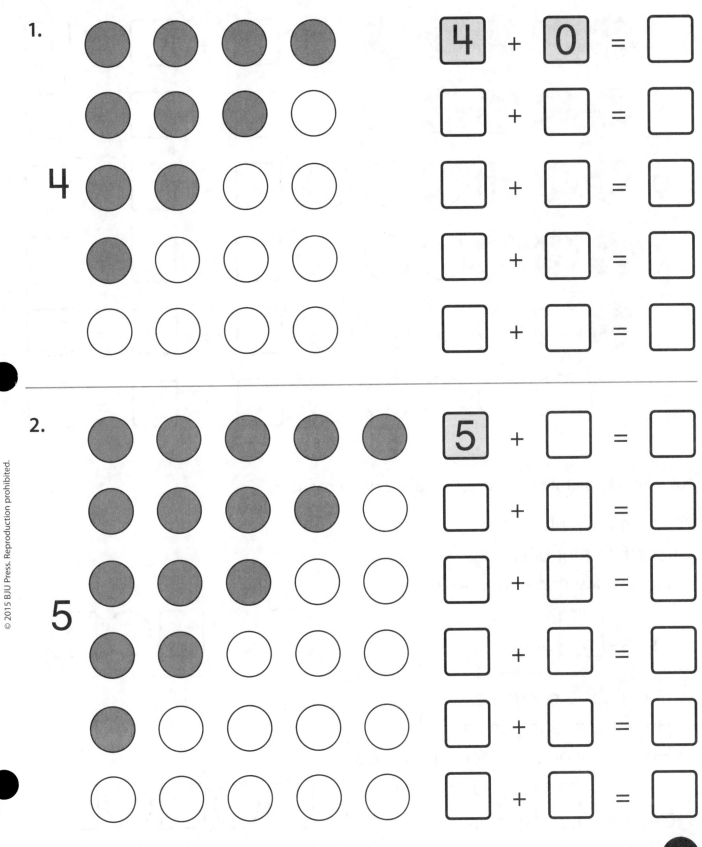

1.

4

$4 + 0 = \square$

$\square + \square = \square$

$\square + \square = \square$

$\square + \square = \square$

$\square + \square = \square$

2.

5

$5 + \square = \square$

$\square + \square = \square$

$\square + \square = \square$

$\square + \square = \square$

$\square + \square = \square$

$\square + \square = \square$

Use the circles to write addition combinations for 6.

1.

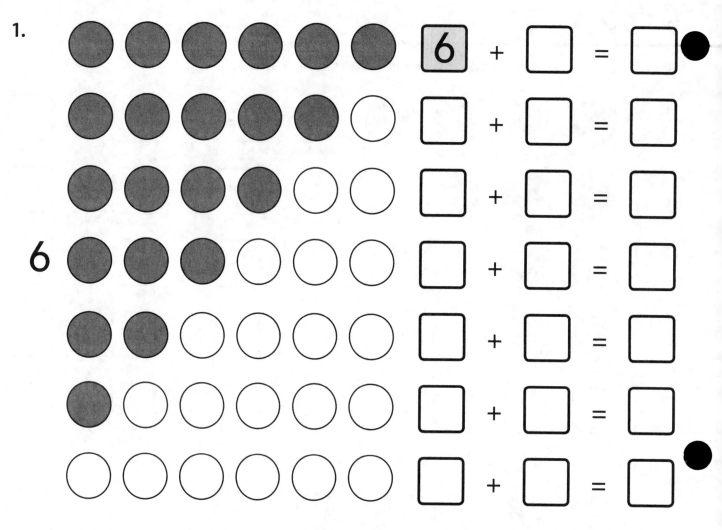

Draw dots to picture the story. Complete the sentences.

2. Ali has two blue rings.
   She has four pink rings.
   How many rings does Ali have?

   Ali has  rings.

3. Grant has 3 car games.
   He has 3 sports games.
   How many games does Grant have?

   Grant has ☐ games.

Chapter 2 Review

Write the numbers to match the picture.

1.

2.

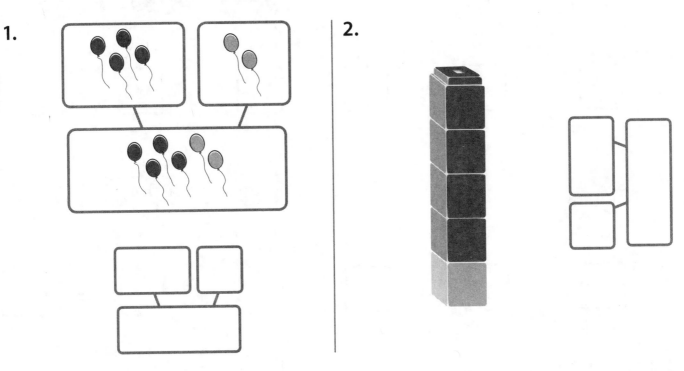

Draw dots to picture the story. Complete the sentences.

3. Noah hit 3 balls.
   He hit 2 more balls.
   How many balls did Noah hit?

   Noah hit ☐ balls.

   ☐ ◯ ☐ ◯ ☐

4. Emma made 1 card.
   She made 3 more cards.
   How many cards did Emma make?

   Emma made ☐ cards.

   ☐ ◯ ☐ ◯ ☐

Write an addition sentence for the picture.

5.
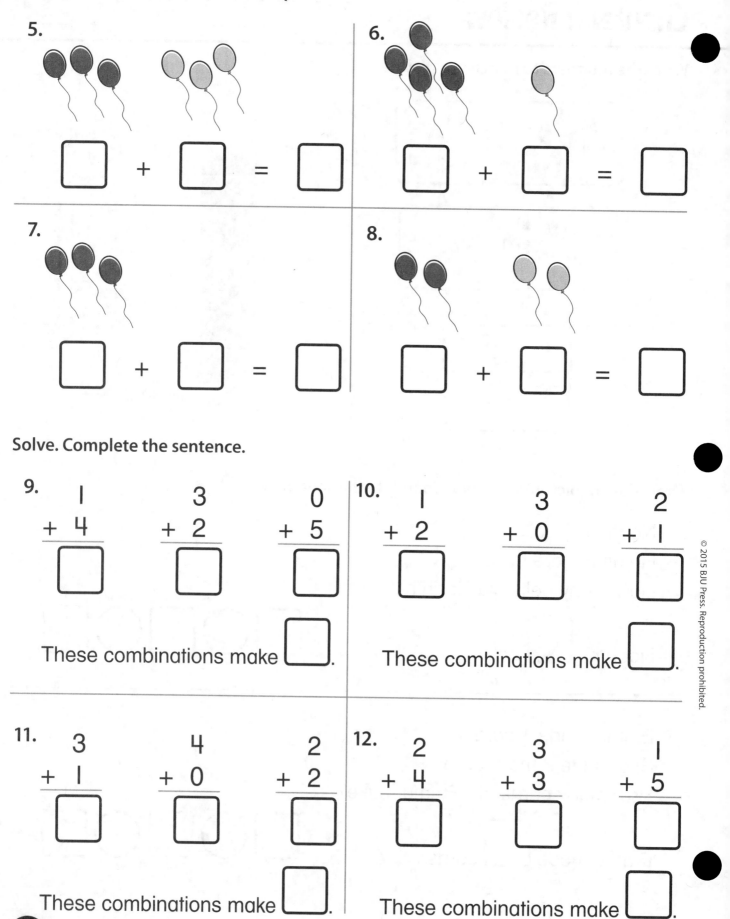

☐ + ☐ = ☐

6.

☐ + ☐ = ☐

7.

☐ + ☐ = ☐

8.

☐ + ☐ = ☐

Solve. Complete the sentence.

9.
$\begin{array}{r} 1 \\ + 4 \\ \hline \end{array}$ ☐ $\begin{array}{r} 3 \\ + 2 \\ \hline \end{array}$ ☐ $\begin{array}{r} 0 \\ + 5 \\ \hline \end{array}$ ☐

These combinations make ☐ .

10.
$\begin{array}{r} 1 \\ + 2 \\ \hline \end{array}$ ☐ $\begin{array}{r} 3 \\ + 0 \\ \hline \end{array}$ ☐ $\begin{array}{r} 2 \\ + 1 \\ \hline \end{array}$ ☐

These combinations make ☐ .

11.
$\begin{array}{r} 3 \\ + 1 \\ \hline \end{array}$ ☐ $\begin{array}{r} 4 \\ + 0 \\ \hline \end{array}$ ☐ $\begin{array}{r} 2 \\ + 2 \\ \hline \end{array}$ ☐

These combinations make ☐ .

12.
$\begin{array}{r} 2 \\ + 4 \\ \hline \end{array}$ ☐ $\begin{array}{r} 3 \\ + 3 \\ \hline \end{array}$ ☐ $\begin{array}{r} 1 \\ + 5 \\ \hline \end{array}$ ☐

These combinations make ☐ .

34

Cumulative Review

Draw more jumps to make ten.
Complete the sentence.

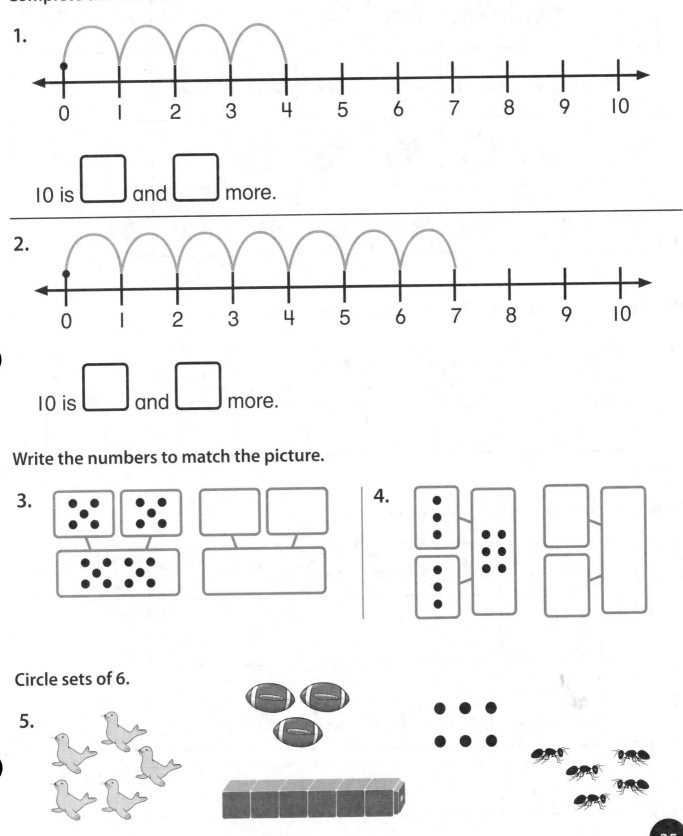

1.

0 1 2 3 4 5 6 7 8 9 10

10 is ☐ and ☐ more.

2.

0 1 2 3 4 5 6 7 8 9 10

10 is ☐ and ☐ more.

Write the numbers to match the picture.

3.

4.

Circle sets of 6.

5.

Write the total number of bugs for each row.
Circle the name of the person who collected the most.

6.

Name	Number of Bugs in Collection							Total
Joe	🐜	🐜	🐜	🐜				
Mark	🐛	🐛	🐛	🐛	🐛	🐛		
May	🦋	🦋	🦋	🦋	🦋			
Maria	🐝	🐝	🐝	🐝	🐝	🐝	🐝	

Write the number that matches the dot pattern.

7.

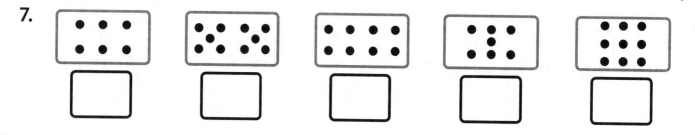

Draw more balls to represent the number.

8.

11

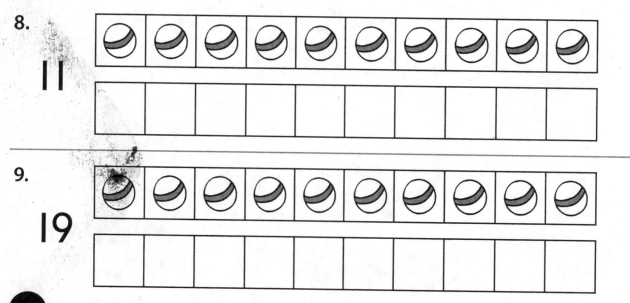

9.

19

Decade Numbers to 100

Write the number represented.

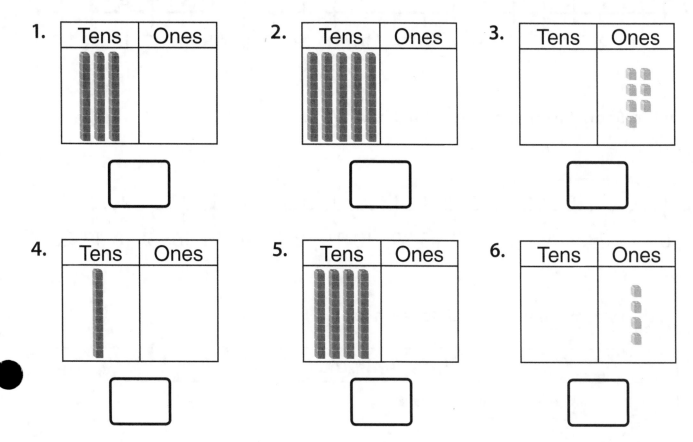

1.
Tens	Ones

2.
Tens	Ones

3.
Tens	Ones

4.
Tens	Ones

5.
Tens	Ones

6.
Tens	Ones

Write the number that matches the dot pattern.

7.
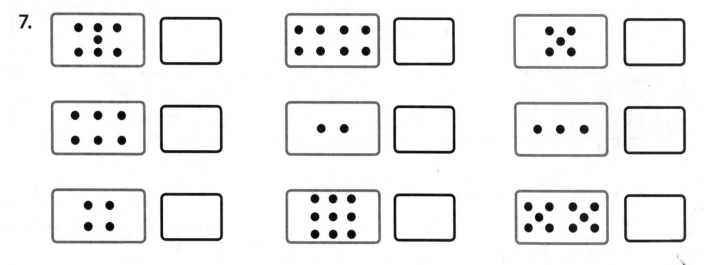

© 2015 BJU Press. Reproduction prohibited.

Math 1 Reviews • Chapter 3, Lesson 19

37

Count by 1s on the number line. Draw the jumps.

1.

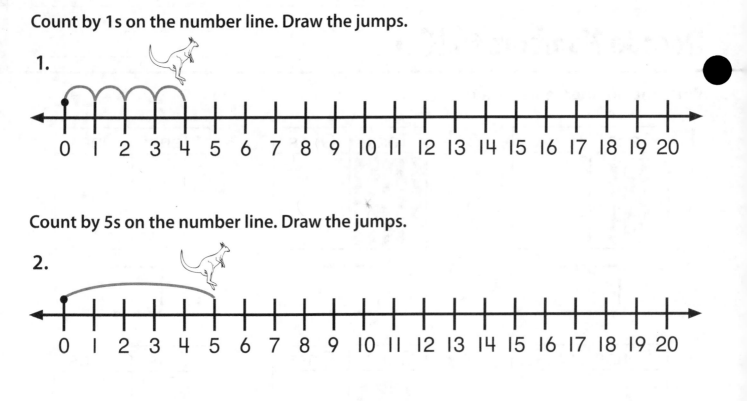

Count by 5s on the number line. Draw the jumps.

2.

Write the total number of animals for each row.

3.

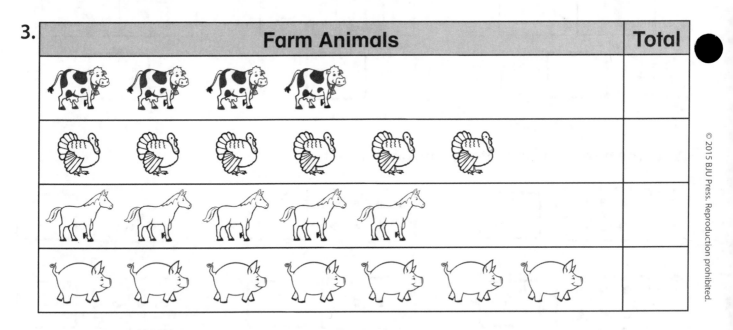

Farm Animals	Total

Put an *X* in the box of the animal represented the most.

4.

Tens & Ones; Numbers to 29

_____

Draw the ten bars and additional cubes on the Tens/Ones Frame.
Write the number represented.

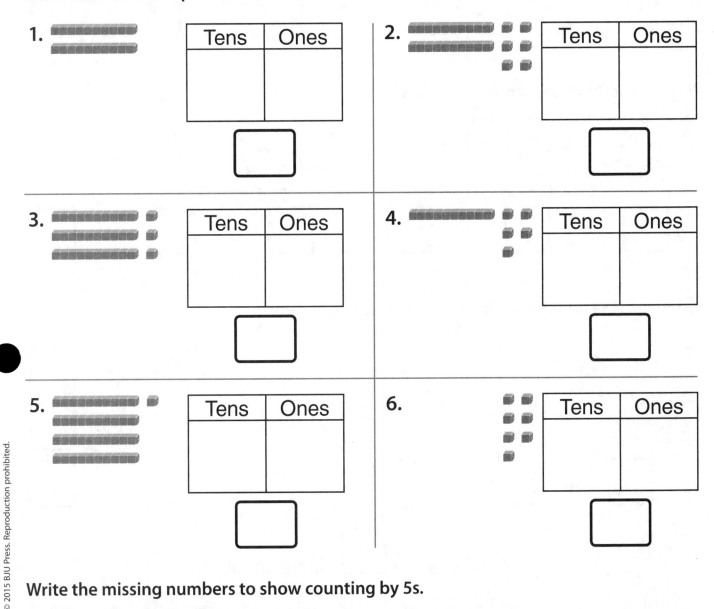

1.

Tens	Ones

2.

Tens	Ones

3.

Tens	Ones

4.

Tens	Ones

5.

Tens	Ones

6.

Tens	Ones

Write the missing numbers to show counting by 5s.

7.

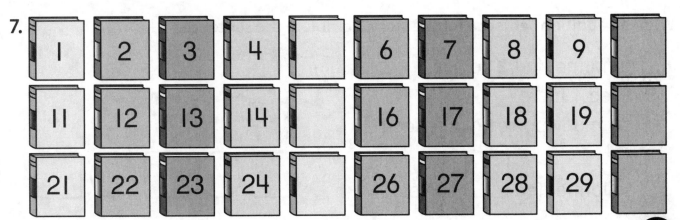

1	2	3	4		6	7	8	9	
11	12	13	14		16	17	18	19	
21	22	23	24		26	27	28	29	

Write the numbers to match the picture.

1. 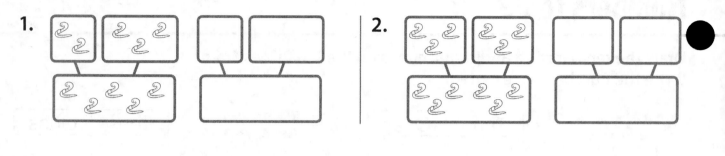 **2.**

Write an addition sentence for the picture.

3.  **4.**

☐ + ☐ = ☐   ☐ + ☐ = ☐

Complete the addition problems. Complete the sentence.

5.

☐ + ☐ = ☐

There are ☐ kittens in all.

Write an addition sentence for the story. Complete the sentence.

6. The farmer fed 2 ponies.
He fed 1 more.
How many ponies did he feed?

The farmer fed ☐ ponies.

☐ ◯ ☐ ◯ ☐

Tens & Ones;
Numbers to 39

_____

Write the number represented.
Write the expanded form.

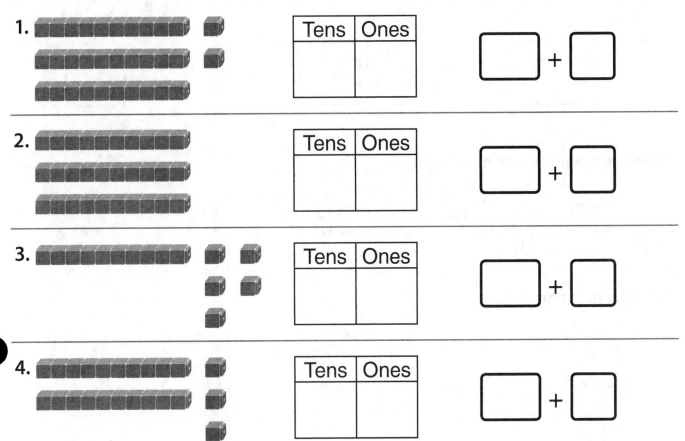

1. | Tens | Ones |
   |------|------|
   | | |

   □ + □

2. | Tens | Ones |
   |------|------|
   | | |

   □ + □

3. | Tens | Ones |
   |------|------|
   | | |

   □ + □

4. | Tens | Ones |
   |------|------|
   | | |

   □ + □

Write the number represented.
Circle the single cubes to make pairs.
Mark *even* or *odd*.

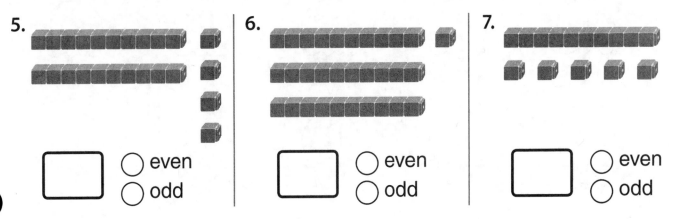

5. □   ○ even
        ○ odd

6. □   ○ even
        ○ odd

7. □   ○ even
        ○ odd

Write the number represented.

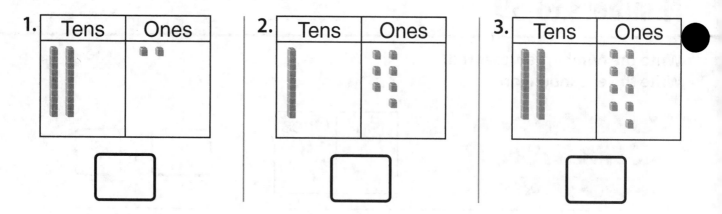

1.

Tens	Ones

2.

Tens	Ones

3.

Tens	Ones

Circle the numbers that have 3 tens.

4.   30   25   35   13   36

Write the numbers 1–20.

5.

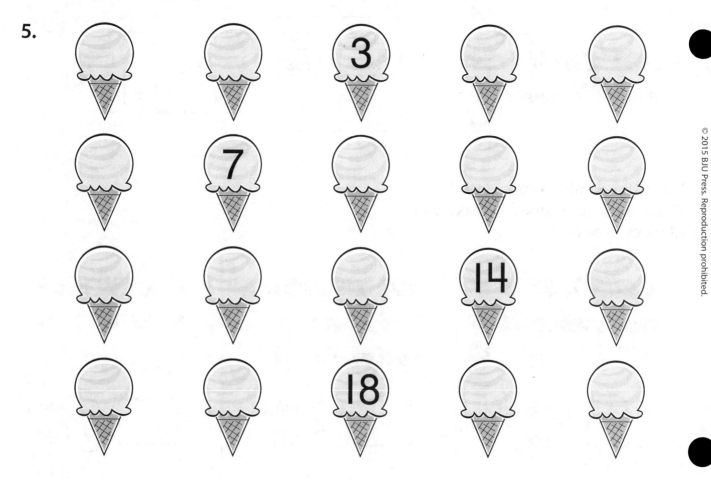

Compare Numbers; Numbers to 49

Write the numbers represented.
Read the sentence.

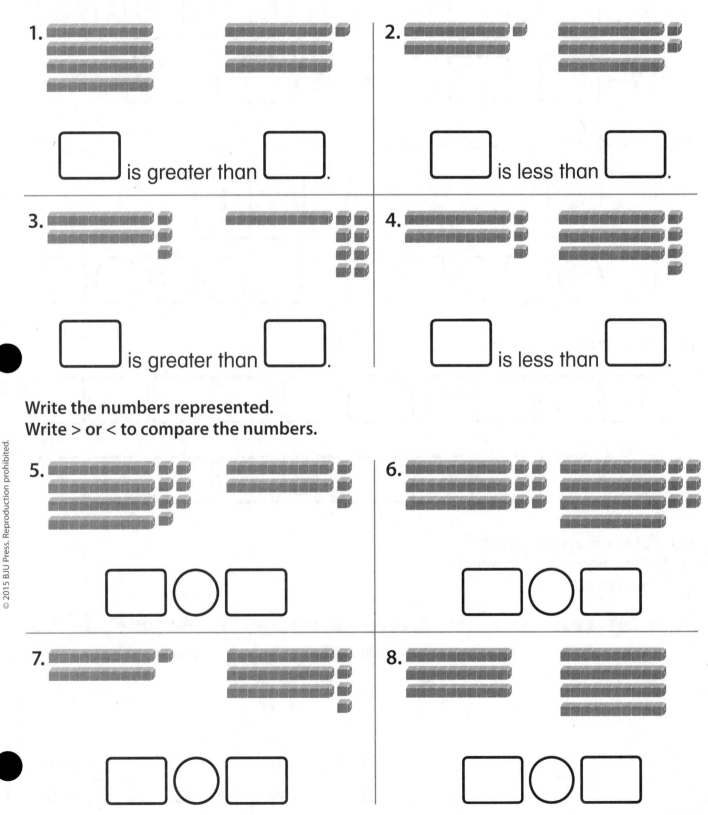

1. ☐ is greater than ☐ .

2. ☐ is less than ☐ .

3. ☐ is greater than ☐ .

4. ☐ is less than ☐ .

Write the numbers represented.
Write > or < to compare the numbers.

5. ☐ ○ ☐

6. ☐ ○ ☐

7. ☐ ○ ☐

8. ☐ ○ ☐

Complete the expanded form.

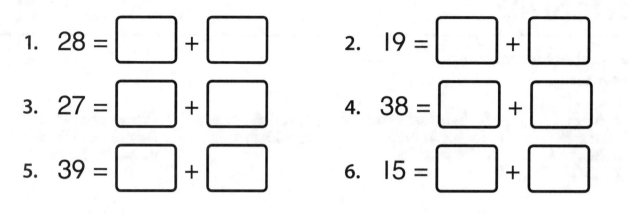

1. 28 = [ ] + [ ]

2. 19 = [ ] + [ ]

3. 27 = [ ] + [ ]

4. 38 = [ ] + [ ]

5. 39 = [ ] + [ ]

6. 15 = [ ] + [ ]

Write an addition sentence for the picture.

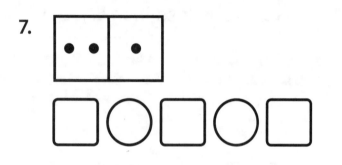

7.

[ ] ○ [ ] ○ [ ]

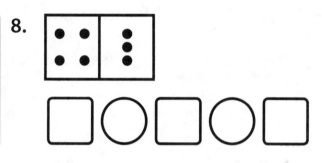

8.

[ ] ○ [ ] ○ [ ]

Write the missing numbers.

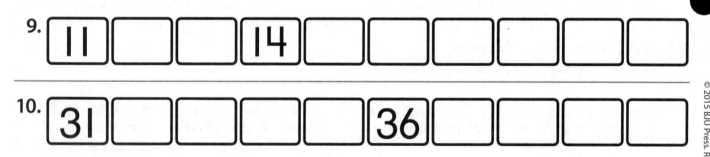

9. | 11 | | | 14 | | | | | | |

10. | 31 | | | | 36 | | | |

Write the number represented.
Circle the single cubes to make pairs.
Mark *even* or *odd*.

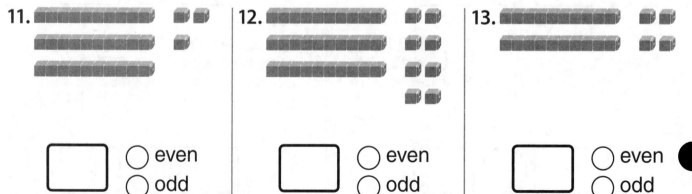

11. [ ] ○ even ○ odd

12. [ ] ○ even ○ odd

13. [ ] ○ even ○ odd

Tens & Ones;
Numbers to 59

Write the number of tens and ones.
Write the number represented.

1.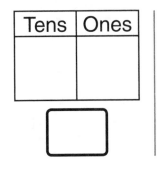

Tens	Ones

2.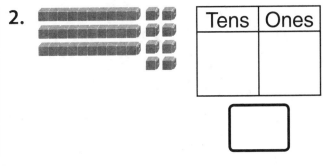

Tens	Ones

Write the number of tens and ones.
Complete the expanded form.

3.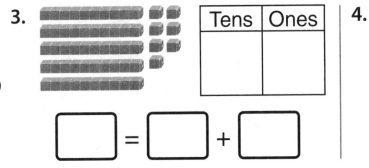

Tens	Ones

☐ = ☐ + ☐

4.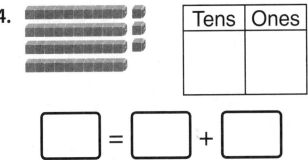

Tens	Ones

☐ = ☐ + ☐

Complete the expanded form.

5. 50 + 8 = ☐

6. 40 + 1 = ☐

7. ☐ + ☐ = 56

8. ☐ + ☐ = 32

Draw tens and ones to picture the numbers.
Complete the expanded form.

9. 30 + 4 = ☐

Write the missing numbers to show counting by 5s.

1.
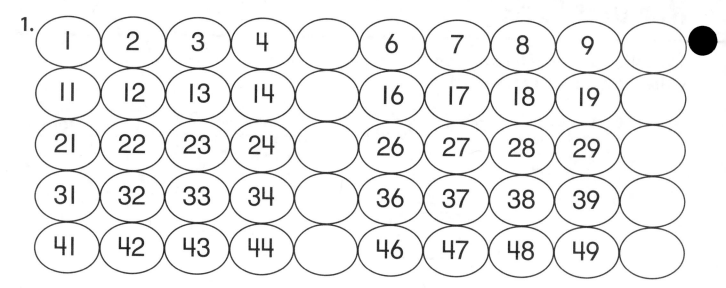

1	2	3	4		6	7	8	9	
11	12	13	14		16	17	18	19	
21	22	23	24		26	27	28	29	
31	32	33	34		36	37	38	39	
41	42	43	44		46	47	48	49	

Write the number of tens and ones.
Write the number represented.

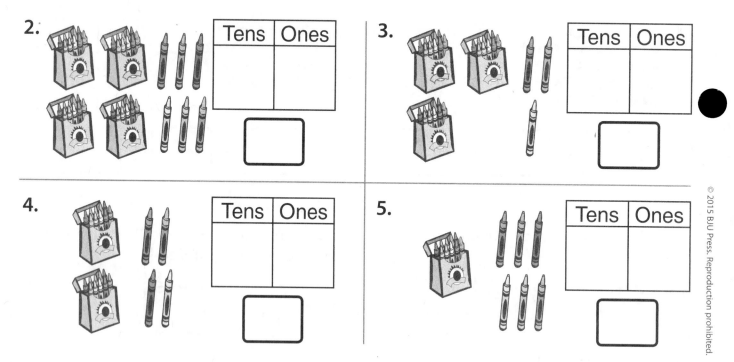

2.

Tens	Ones

3.

Tens	Ones

4.

Tens	Ones

5.

Tens	Ones

Use the colors of the cubes to write an addition sentence.

6.
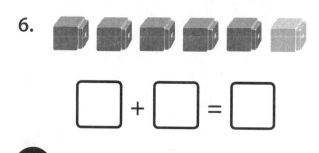

◻ + ◻ = ◻

7.
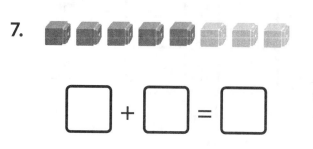

◻ + ◻ = ◻

Compare Numbers; Numbers to 79

Write the numbers represented.
Write > or < to compare.

>	<
is greater than	is less than

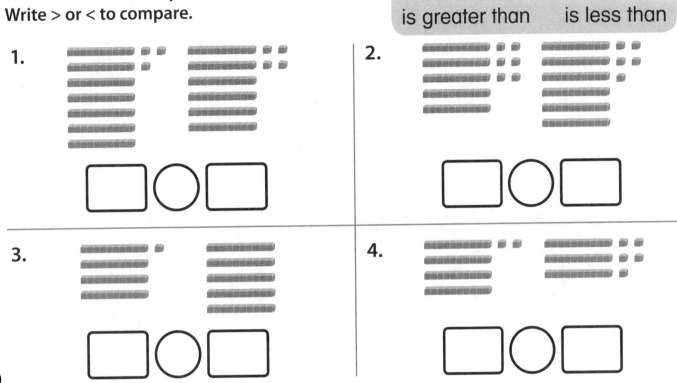

1.

☐ ◯ ☐

2.

☐ ◯ ☐

3.

☐ ◯ ☐

4.

☐ ◯ ☐

Write the number represented.
Circle the single objects to make pairs.
Circle even or odd.

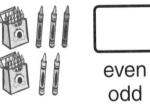

5. ☐ even odd

6. ☐ even odd

7. ☐ even odd

Write the missing numbers.

8.

31			34			37			
41	42			45				49	
	52		54		56				

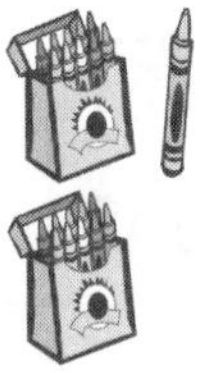

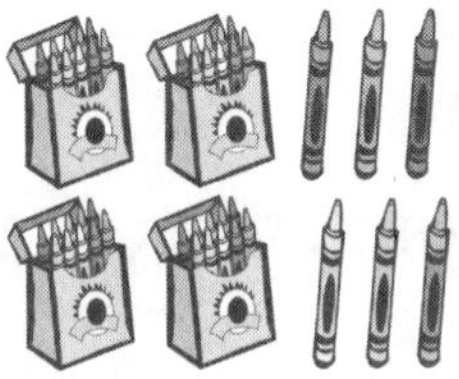

Complete the number sequence.

1. 7   8   9   ☐   2. 37   38   39   ☐

3. 25   26   27   ☐   4. 12   13   14   ☐

5. 17   18   19   ☐   6. 50   51   52   ☐

Write the total number for each row.
Answer the questions.

7.

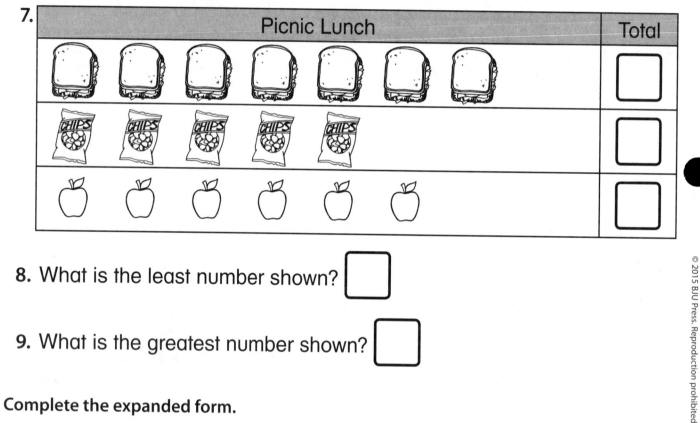

Picnic Lunch	Total
(7 sandwiches)	☐
(5 chips)	☐
(6 apples)	☐

8. What is the least number shown? ☐

9. What is the greatest number shown? ☐

Complete the expanded form.

10. 43 = ☐ + ☐   11. ☐ = 10 + 6

12. 21 = ☐ + ☐   13. ☐ = 50 + 9

14. 65 = ☐ + ☐   15. ☐ = 30 + 8

Count to 100
by 1s, by 5s & by 10s

Count to 20 by 5s on the number line.

1.

Count to 20 by 10s on the number line.

2.

Complete the number sequence.

3.	25	30	35			4.	50	60	70	
5.	85	90	95			6.	40	50	60	
7.	40	45	50			8.	20	30	40	

Write the missing numbers to show counting by 5s.

9.

51	52	53	54		56	57	58	59	
61	62	63	64		66	67	68	69	
71	72	73	74		76	77	78	79	
81	82	83	84		86	87	88	89	
91	92	93	94		96	97	98	99	

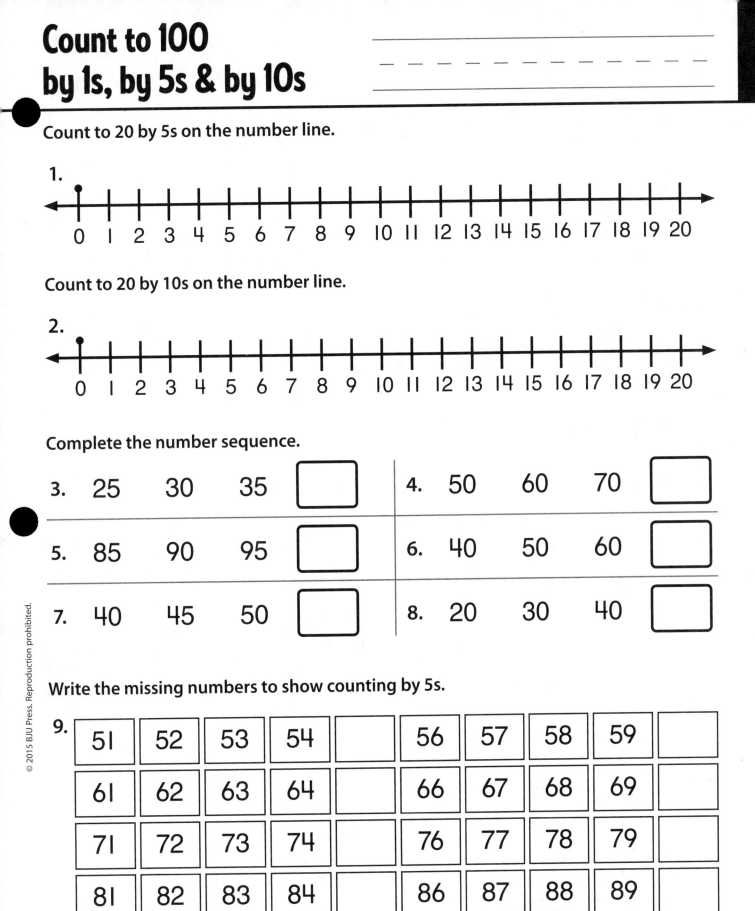

Compare the numbers.
Circle the correct sign.

1.
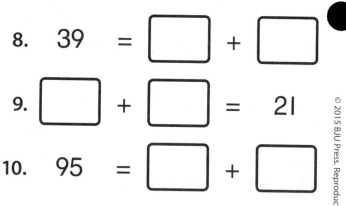

[ ] > < [ ]

2.
[ ] > < [ ]

3.
[ ] > < [ ]

4.
[ ] > < [ ]

Mark the number.

5. 30 + 7 =   35 37 73
              ○   ○   ○

6. 60 + 8 =   68 69 86
              ○   ○   ○

7. 70 + 3 =   37 72 73
              ○   ○   ○

Complete the expanded form.

8. 39 = [ ] + [ ]

9. [ ] + [ ] = 21

10. 95 = [ ] + [ ]

Write an addition sentence for the picture.

11.
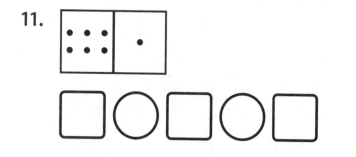

[ ] ○ [ ] ○ [ ]

12.
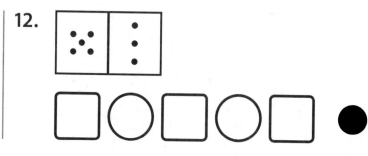

[ ] ○ [ ] ○ [ ]

Chapter 3 Review

**Write the number of tens and ones.
Write the number represented.**

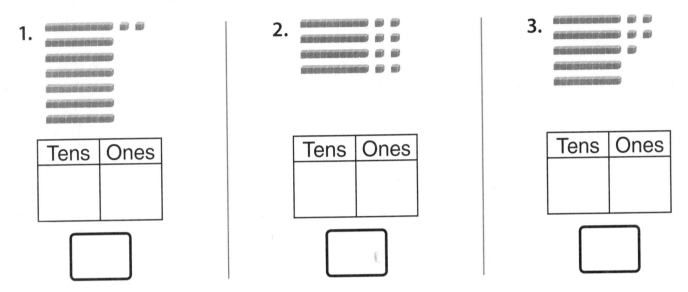

1.

Tens	Ones

2.

Tens	Ones

3.

Tens	Ones

Mark the number.

4. 80 + 9 =   37 89 98
   ○ ○ ○

5. 20 + 6 =   24 26 62
   ○ ○ ○

6. 10 + 3 =   13 15 31
   ○ ○ ○

Complete the expanded form.

7. 64 = ▢ + ▢

8. ▢ = 30 + 7

9. ▢ = 90 + 1

**Write the number represented.
Circle the single sticks to make pairs.
Mark *even* or *odd*.**

10.  ▢
   ○ even
   ○ odd

11. 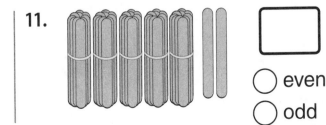 ▢
   ○ even
   ○ odd

Count to 100 by 5s. Write the missing numbers.

12.

5									
55									

Complete the number sequence.

13. 5   6   7   ☐   14. 25   30   35   ☐

15. 40   50   60   ☐   16. 85   90   95   ☐

**Compare the numbers.
Circle the correct sign.**

> **>**
> is greater than   **<** is less than

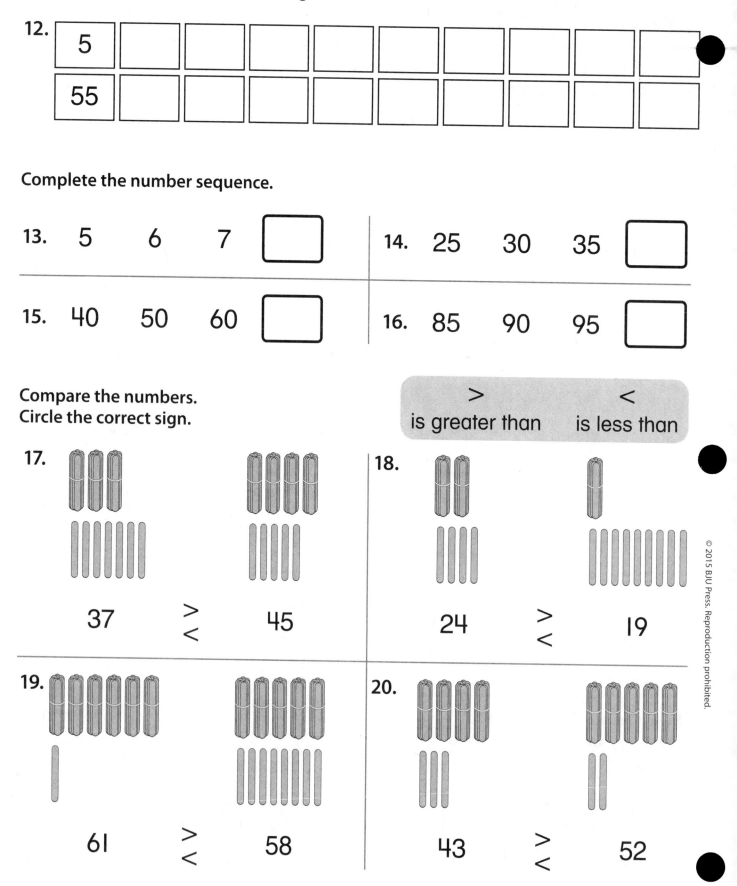

17. 37   >
         <   45

18. 24   >
         <   19

19. 61   >
         <   58

20. 43   >
         <   52

Cumulative Review

Write an addition sentence for the story.

1. Anna had 3 apples.
   She got 1 more apple.
   How many apples does she have?

2. Sam has 2 pumpkins.
   He got 2 more pumpkins.
   How many pumpkins does he have?

Write the numbers to match the picture.

3.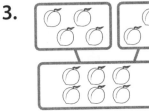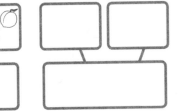

4.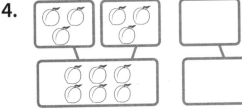

Draw more circles to make 10. Complete the sentence.

5.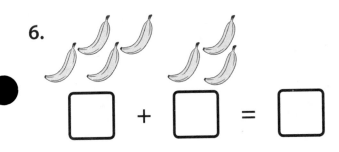

10 is ☐ and ☐ more.

Write an addition sentence for the picture.

6.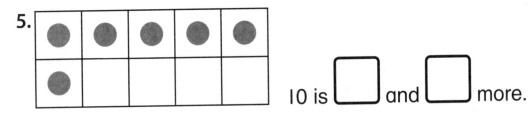

   ☐ + ☐ = ☐

7.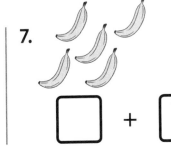

   ☐ + ☐ = ☐

Write an addition sentence for the picture.

8.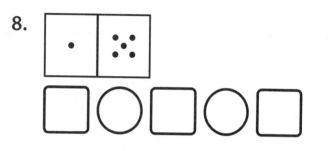

9.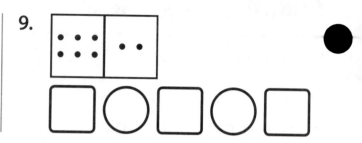

Number the baskets from smallest to largest.

10.

Put an X on the shape that is different.

11.

12.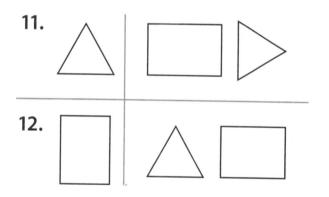

Circle the shape that is the same.

13.

14.

Circle the one that is exactly the same.

15.

Circle the longer one.

16.

Circle the shorter one.

17.

Cross Out to Subtract

Cross out to subtract. Complete the sentences.

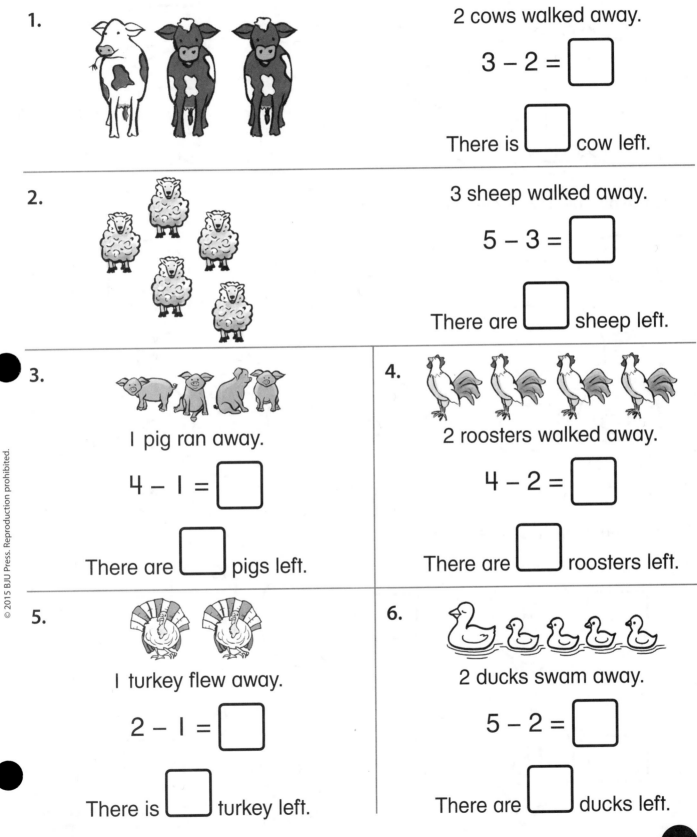

1.

2 cows walked away.

$3 - 2 =$ ☐

There is ☐ cow left.

2.

3 sheep walked away.

$5 - 3 =$ ☐

There are ☐ sheep left.

3.

1 pig ran away.

$4 - 1 =$ ☐

There are ☐ pigs left.

4.

2 roosters walked away.

$4 - 2 =$ ☐

There are ☐ roosters left.

5.

1 turkey flew away.

$2 - 1 =$ ☐

There is ☐ turkey left.

6.

2 ducks swam away.

$5 - 2 =$ ☐

There are ☐ ducks left.

Write the number that comes *between*.

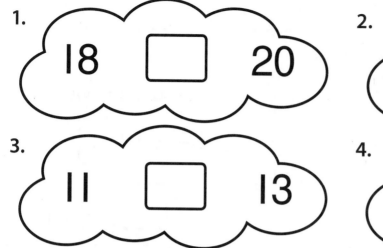

1. 18 ▢ 20

2. 6 ▢ 8

3. 11 ▢ 13

4. 16 ▢ 18

Write the number that comes *after*.

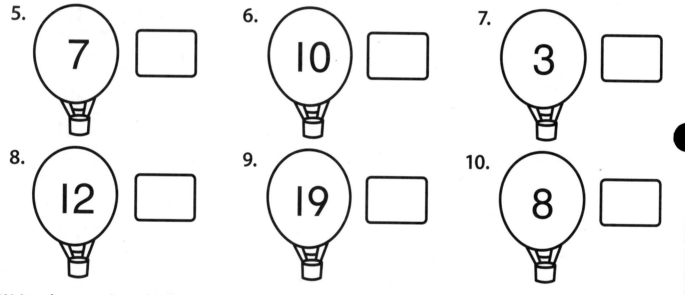

5. 7 ▢

6. 10 ▢

7. 3 ▢

8. 12 ▢

9. 19 ▢

10. 8 ▢

Write the number that comes *before*.

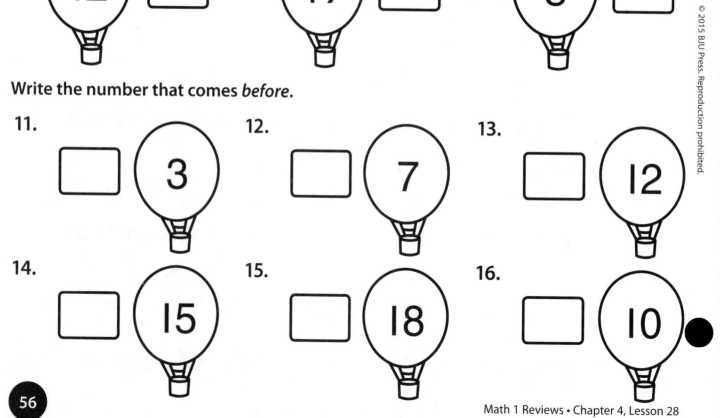

11. ▢ 3

12. ▢ 7

13. ▢ 12

14. ▢ 15

15. ▢ 18

16. ▢ 10

Subtract 0

Cross out to subtract. Complete the sentences.

1.

0 bears walked away.

$$4 - 0 = \boxed{}$$

There are $\boxed{}$ bears left.

2.

2 bears went to eat.

$$5 - 2 = \boxed{}$$

$\boxed{}$ bears stayed.

3.

3 bears were walking.

$$3 - 0 = \boxed{}$$

$\boxed{}$ bears walked.

Mark the sentence that is true.

4. ○ 3 − 0 = 2

○ 3 − 0 = 0

○ 3 − 0 = 3

Write the number represented.

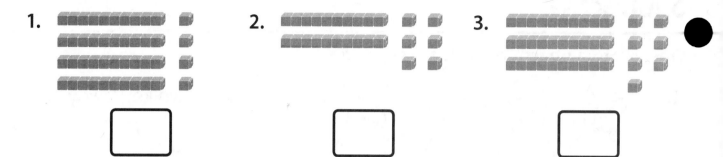

1. ☐

2. ☐

3. ☐

Complete the expanded form.

4. $20 + 4 =$ ☐

5. $10 + 5 =$ ☐

6. $40 + 9 =$ ☐

7. $58 =$ ☐ $+$ ☐

8. $37 =$ ☐ $+$ ☐

9. $81 =$ ☐ $+$ ☐

Write the number represented.
Circle the single cubes to make pairs.
Mark *even* or *odd*.

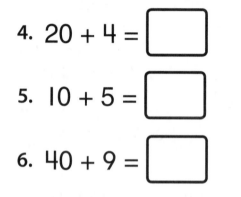

10. ☐

○ even
○ odd

11. ☐

○ even
○ odd

> **>**
> is greater than

> **<**
> is less than

Compare the numbers.
Circle the correct sign.

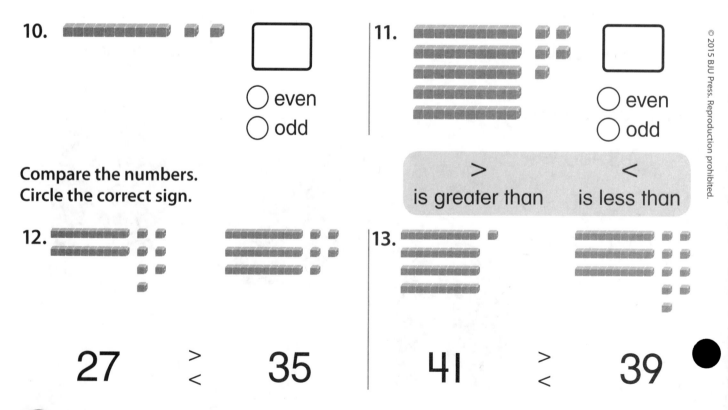

12. 27 $\genfrac{}{}{0pt}{}{>}{<}$ 35

13. 41 $\genfrac{}{}{0pt}{}{>}{<}$ 39

Draw Pictures to Subtract

Cross out to subtract. Complete the sentences.

1.

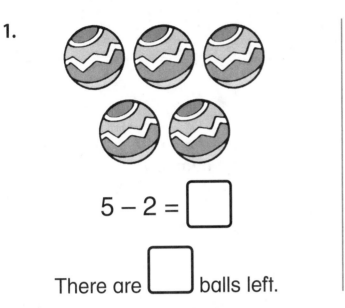

$5 - 2 = \boxed{}$

There are $\boxed{}$ balls left.

2.

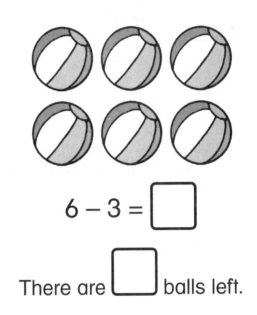

$6 - 3 = \boxed{}$

There are $\boxed{}$ balls left.

Draw a circle for each ball. Cross out to subtract. Complete the sentences.

3. Mia had 4 balls.

She gave 1 ball to Sam.

How many balls does Mia have now?

Mia has $\boxed{}$ balls now.

$\boxed{} - \boxed{} = \boxed{}$

4. Jake had 5 balls.

He lost 3 balls.

How many balls does Jake have now?

Jake has $\boxed{}$ balls now.

$\boxed{} - \boxed{} = \boxed{}$

Cross out to subtract. Complete the subtraction sentence.

1.

   $6 - 5 = \boxed{}$

2.

   $3 - 2 = \boxed{}$

3.

   $5 - 1 = \boxed{}$

Write the number of tens and ones. Complete the expanded form.

4.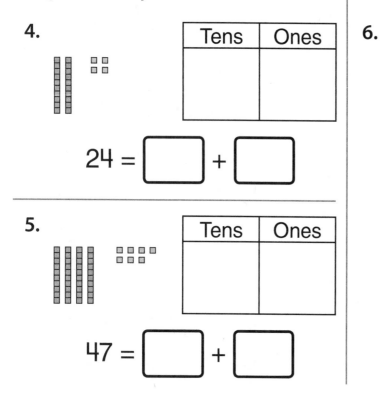

Tens	Ones

$24 = \boxed{} + \boxed{}$

5.

Tens	Ones

$47 = \boxed{} + \boxed{}$

Draw a line to match the expanded form to the correct number.

6.

$30 + 7$ 23

$50 + 9$ 14

$20 + 3$ 37

$10 + 4$ 72

$70 + 2$ 59

Write the number that comes *after*.

7. 38

8. 24

9. 43

Subtraction in Vertical Form

Cross out to subtract. Complete the subtraction problems.

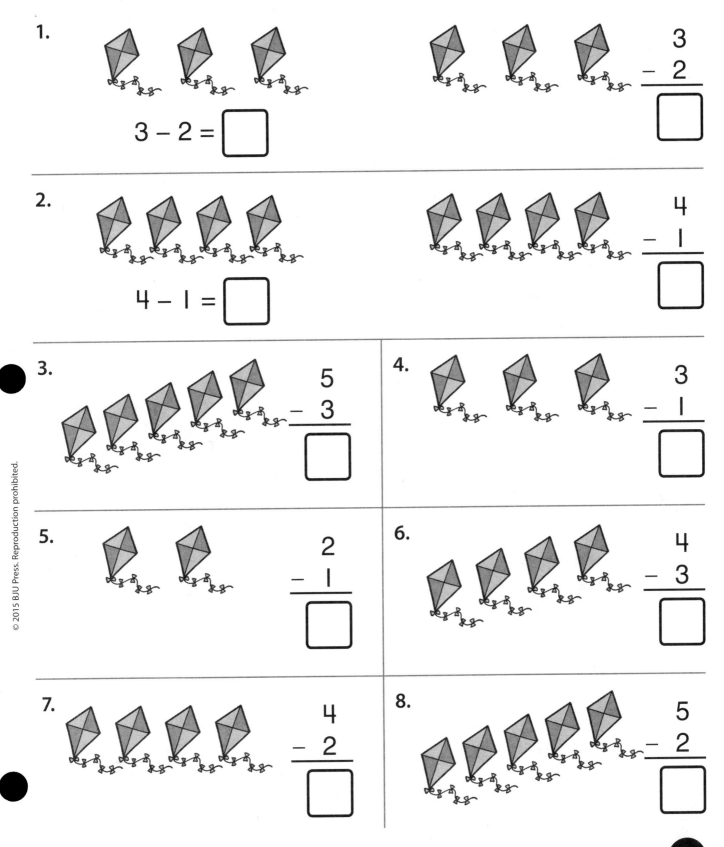

1. $3 - 2 = \boxed{}$

    $\begin{array}{r} 3 \\ -\ 2 \\ \hline \boxed{} \end{array}$

2. $4 - 1 = \boxed{}$

    $\begin{array}{r} 4 \\ -\ 1 \\ \hline \boxed{} \end{array}$

3. $\begin{array}{r} 5 \\ -\ 3 \\ \hline \boxed{} \end{array}$

4. $\begin{array}{r} 3 \\ -\ 1 \\ \hline \boxed{} \end{array}$

5. $\begin{array}{r} 2 \\ -\ 1 \\ \hline \boxed{} \end{array}$

6. $\begin{array}{r} 4 \\ -\ 3 \\ \hline \boxed{} \end{array}$

7. $\begin{array}{r} 4 \\ -\ 2 \\ \hline \boxed{} \end{array}$

8. $\begin{array}{r} 5 \\ -\ 2 \\ \hline \boxed{} \end{array}$

Draw the tower that comes next.

1.

2.

Write the number that comes *between*.

3. 15 ☐ 17

4. 29 ☐ 31

5. 58 ☐ 60

Color the triangles red and the circles blue.

6.

Write the missing numbers to show counting by 5s.

7.

1	2	3	4	☐	6	7	8	9	☐
11	12	13	14	☐	16	17	18	19	☐
21	22	23	24	☐	26	27	28	29	☐

Write the number represented.

8.

Tens	Ones

☐

9.

Tens	Ones

☐

10.

Tens	Ones

☐

Related Subtraction Facts

Complete the related subtraction facts.

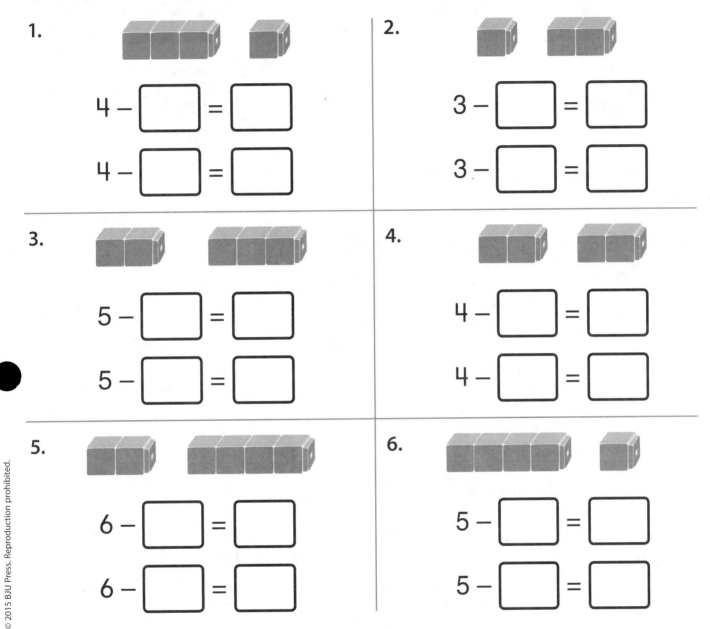

1.

$4 - \boxed{} = \boxed{}$

$4 - \boxed{} = \boxed{}$

2.

$3 - \boxed{} = \boxed{}$

$3 - \boxed{} = \boxed{}$

3.

$5 - \boxed{} = \boxed{}$

$5 - \boxed{} = \boxed{}$

4.

$4 - \boxed{} = \boxed{}$

$4 - \boxed{} = \boxed{}$

5.

$6 - \boxed{} = \boxed{}$

$6 - \boxed{} = \boxed{}$

6.

$5 - \boxed{} = \boxed{}$

$5 - \boxed{} = \boxed{}$

Draw circles to picture the story. Cross out to subtract.
Complete the sentences.

7. Amy had 5 cookies.

She ate 2 cookies.

How many cookies does Amy have?

Amy has $\boxed{}$ cookies.

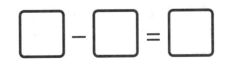

Math 1 Reviews • Chapter 4, Lesson 32

63

Circle the one that is exactly the same.

1.

2.

Write an addition sentence for the picture.
Complete the sentences.

3.

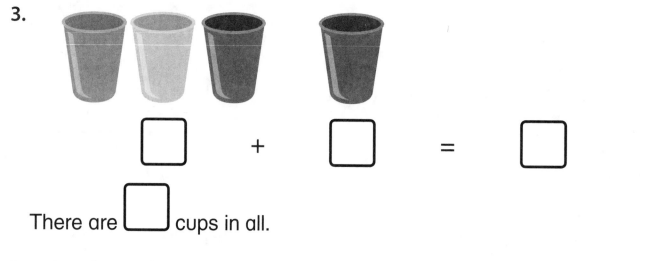

□ + □ = □

There are □ cups in all.

Complete the number sequence.

4.	9	10	11	□	5.	15	16	17	□
6.	32	33	34	□	7.	71	72	73	□

Write the number that matches the dot pattern.

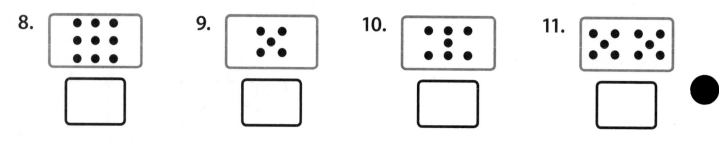

8. □   **9.** □   **10.** □   **11.** □

More Subtraction

Cross out to subtract. Complete the subtraction problems.

1.

5 − 2 = ☐

$$\begin{array}{r} 5 \\ -\ 2 \\ \hline \end{array}$$ ☐

2.

$$\begin{array}{r} 3 \\ -\ 0 \\ \hline \end{array}$$ ☐

3.

$$\begin{array}{r} 4 \\ -\ 1 \\ \hline \end{array}$$ ☐

4.

$$\begin{array}{r} 2 \\ -\ 1 \\ \hline \end{array}$$ ☐

5.

$$\begin{array}{r} 5 \\ -\ 3 \\ \hline \end{array}$$ ☐

Draw circles to picture the story. Cross out to subtract.
Complete the sentences.

6. Joy had 6 dog treats.

She gave 2 to her dog.

How many treats does Joy have left?

Joy has ☐ dog treats left.

☐ − ☐ = ☐

Complete the related subtraction facts.

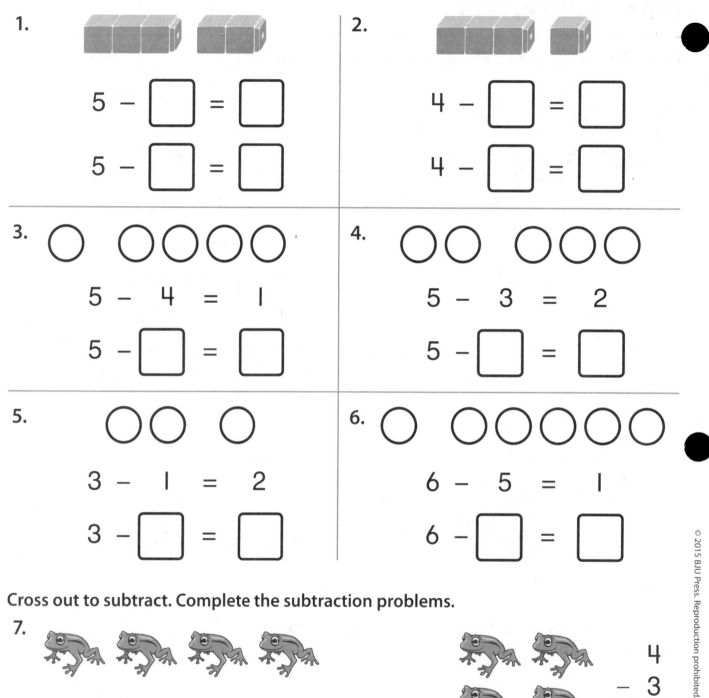

1.

5 − ☐ = ☐

5 − ☐ = ☐

2.

4 − ☐ = ☐

4 − ☐ = ☐

3.

5 − 4 = 1

5 − ☐ = ☐

4.

5 − 3 = 2

5 − ☐ = ☐

5.

3 − 1 = 2

3 − ☐ = ☐

6.

6 − 5 = 1

6 − ☐ = ☐

Cross out to subtract. Complete the subtraction problems.

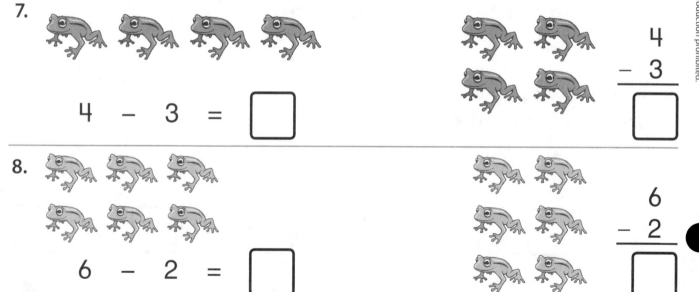

7.

4 − 3 = ☐

```
  4
− 3
───
 ☐
```

8.

6 − 2 = ☐

```
  6
− 2
───
 ☐
```

Chapter 4 Review

Cross out to subtract. Complete the sentences.

1.

6 – 4 = ☐

There are ☐ hens.

2.

4 – 3 = ☐

There is ☐ hen.

Circle the minus sign. Draw a box around the equal sign.

3.

× = + –

Cross out to subtract. Complete the subtraction problems.

4.

$\begin{array}{r} 3 \\ -\ 2 \\ \hline \boxed{} \end{array}$

5.

$\begin{array}{r} 4 \\ -\ 1 \\ \hline \boxed{} \end{array}$

6.

$\begin{array}{r} 6 \\ -\ 2 \\ \hline \boxed{} \end{array}$

7.

$\begin{array}{r} 5 \\ -\ 3 \\ \hline \boxed{} \end{array}$

Draw circles to picture the story. Cross out to subtract. Complete the sentences.

8. Aaron had 5 balls.

He gave 2 away.

How many balls does Aaron have now?

Aaron has  balls now.

Draw lines to match the related subtraction facts.

9.

$3 - 1 = 2$ $6 - 4 = 2$

$5 - 4 = 1$ $3 - 2 = 1$

$6 - 2 = 4$ $5 - 1 = 4$

Draw circles to picture the problem. Cross out to subtract. Complete the subtraction sentence.

10.

$$4 - 2 = \square$$

11.

$$5 - 3 = \square$$

Cumulative Review

Write the number represented.
Circle the single cubes to make pairs. Mark *even* or *odd*.

1.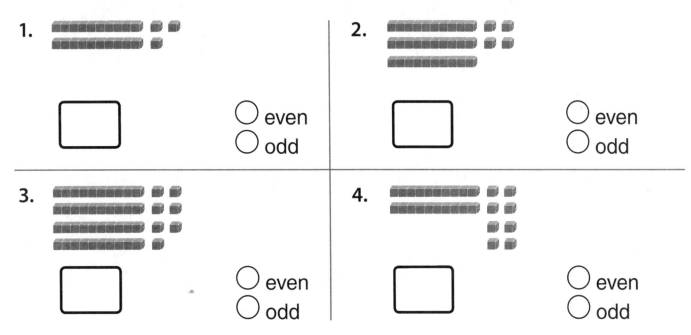

   [   ]   ◯ even
             ◯ odd

2. ◯ even
    ◯ odd

3. [   ]   ◯ even
             ◯ odd

4. [   ]   ◯ even
             ◯ odd

Write the number of tens and ones. Complete the expanded form.

5.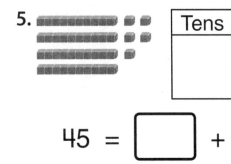

Tens	Ones

45 = [   ] + [   ]

6.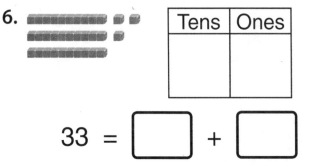

Tens	Ones

33 = [   ] + [   ]

Complete the expanded form.

7. 38 = [   ] + [   ]

8. 47 = [   ] + [   ]

9. 21 = [   ] + [   ]

Write the missing numbers.

10.

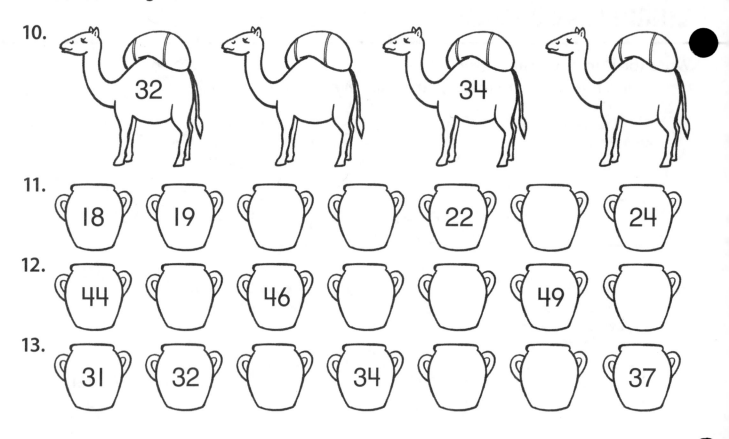

32   34

11. 18 19 ___ ___ 22 ___ 24

12. 44 ___ 46 ___ ___ 49 ___

13. 31 32 ___ 34 ___ ___ 37

Color the correct number of objects.

14. 15

15. 19

16. 17

Tally Charts

Make a tally for each object.
Write the total for each set.

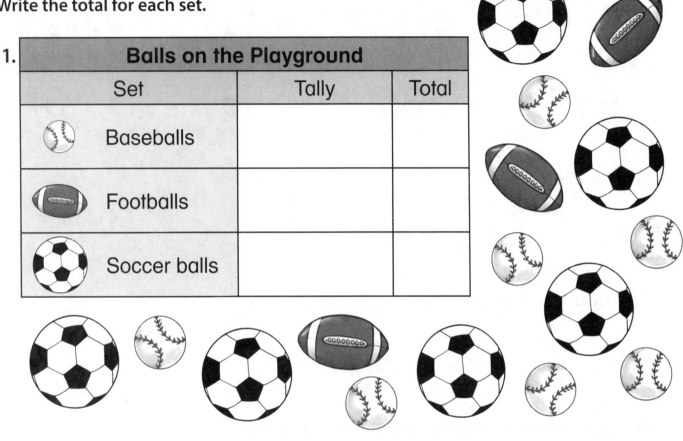

1.

Balls on the Playground		
Set	Tally	Total
🔵 Baseballs		
🏈 Footballs		
⚽ Soccer balls		

Use the tally chart to answer the question.

2. Which set has the most balls?

3. Are there more 🏈 or more ⚽ ?

4. How many more 🔵 are there than ⚽ ?

5. How many more 🔵 are there than 🏈 ?

Compare the numbers.
Circle the correct sign.

> is greater than
< is less than

1. 45 > < 36

2. 43 > < 51

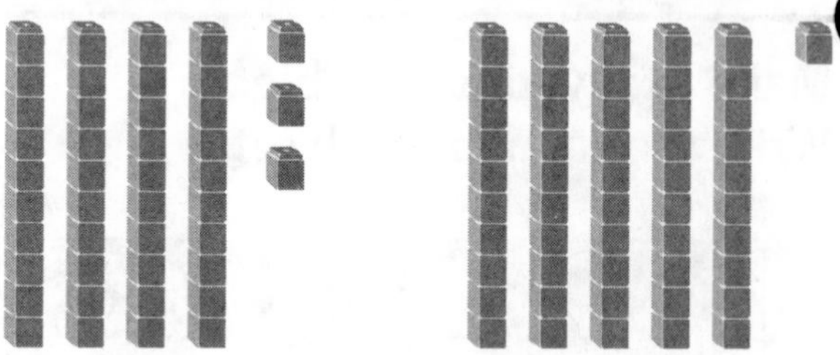

Follow the directions.

3. Draw a ▢ around the first fish.

4. Draw a ◯ around the second fish.

5. Draw a △ around the third fish.

Cross out to subtract. Complete the subtraction problems.

6. 5 − 4 = ▢

$$\begin{array}{r} 5 \\ -\ 4 \\ \hline \end{array}$$

7. 3 − 1 = ▢

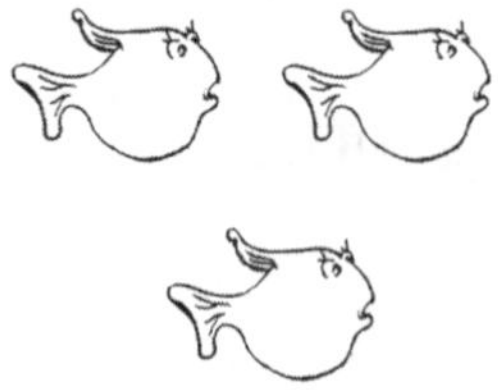

$$\begin{array}{r} 3 \\ -\ 1 \\ \hline \end{array}$$

Picture Graphs

Use the picture graph to answer the question.

Favorite Bugs						
Ladybug	🐞	🐞	🐞	🐞	🐞	
Bee	🐝	🐝	🐝	🐝	🐝	🐝	🐝
Grasshopper	🦗	🦗	🦗	🦗		

Each picture equals 1 student's choice.

1. Which bug was chosen the most?

2. Which bug was chosen the least?

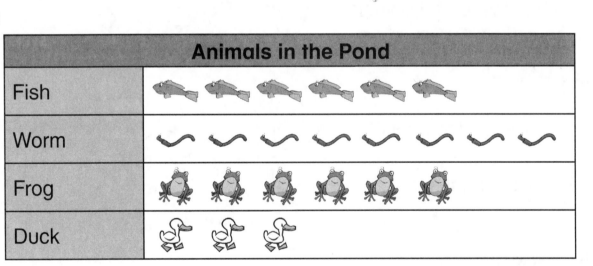

Each picture equals 1 animal.

3. How many 🐟 are in the pond?

4. Which set has the most animals?

5. Which set has the fewest animals?

Write the total for each set.

1.

Baseball Supplies		
Set	Tally	Total
Glove	|||| |||| ||	
Bat	||||	
Ball	|||| |||	

Use the tally chart to answer the question.

2. Which set has 8 objects?

3. Which set has the most objects?

4. Which set has the fewest objects?

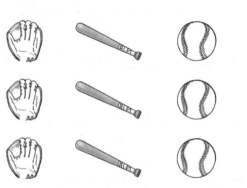

Follow the directions.

5. Circle the player on the right.

6. Color the player on the left.

Complete the related subtraction facts.

7.

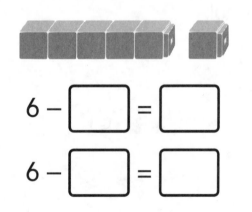

6 − ☐ = ☐

6 − ☐ = ☐

8.

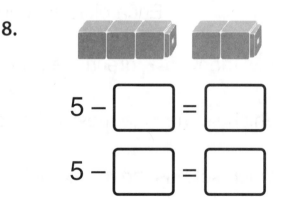

5 − ☐ = ☐

5 − ☐ = ☐

Bar Graphs

Use the bar graph to answer the question.

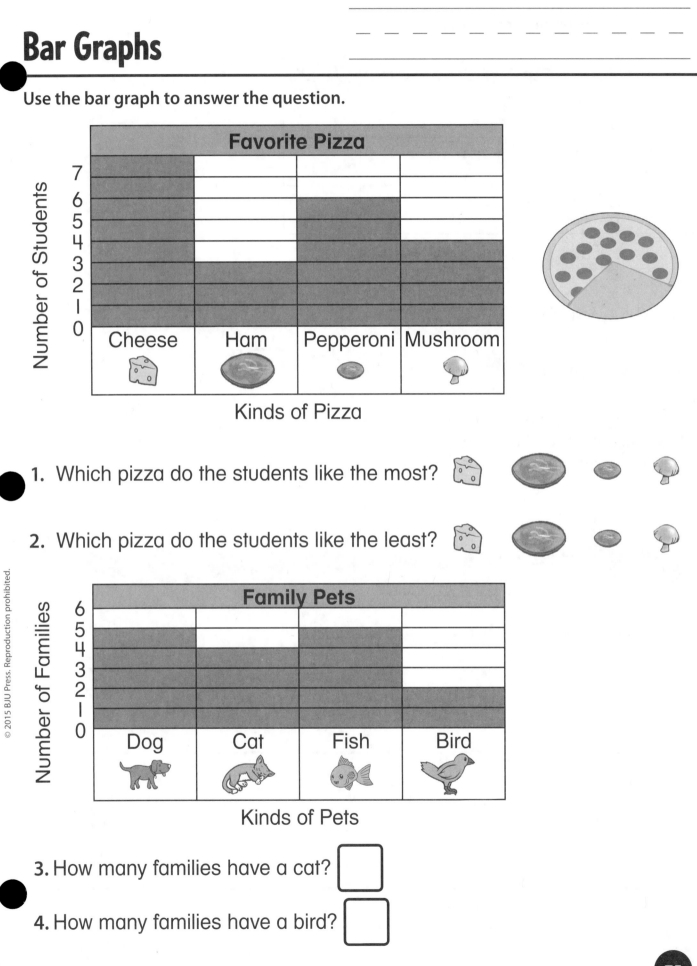

1. Which pizza do the students like the most?

2. Which pizza do the students like the least?

3. How many families have a cat?

4. How many families have a bird?

Write the number of each flower.

1.	Flowers in the Garden	Total
	🌷 🌷 🌷 🌷 🌷	
	🌻 🌻 🌻 🌻 🌻 🌻 🌻	
	🌼 🌼 🌼 🌼	

Each picture equals 1 flower.

2. Which set has the most flowers? 🌷 🌻 🌼

3. How many more 🌻 are there than 🌼 ? ☐

Draw a <u>line</u> under the third duck.
Draw a (circle) around the ninth duck.
Draw a |box| around the seventh duck.

4.

Make a tally for each number.

5.   1   2   3   4   5

_____   _____   _____   _____   _____

   6   7   8   9   10

_____   _____   _____   _____   _____

Chapter 5 Review

Write the total for each set.

1.

Lunch Count		
Set	Tally	Total
Hot lunch 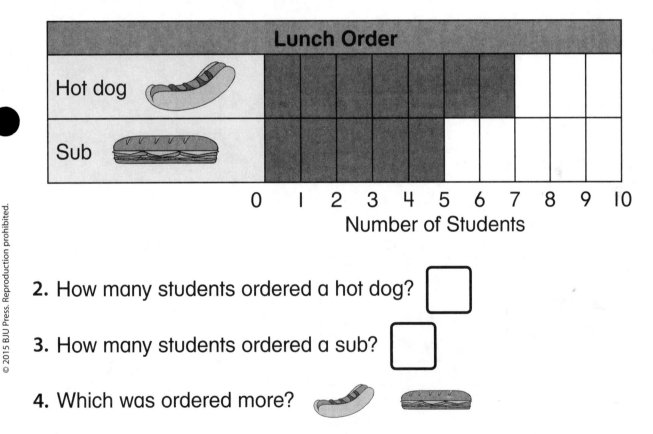	||||| ||||| ||	
Cold lunch	||||| |||	

Use the bar graph to answer the question.

Lunch Order

Hot dog

Sub

0 1 2 3 4 5 6 7 8 9 10
Number of Students

2. How many students ordered a hot dog? ☐

3. How many students ordered a sub? ☐

4. Which was ordered more?

Use the picture graph to answer the question.

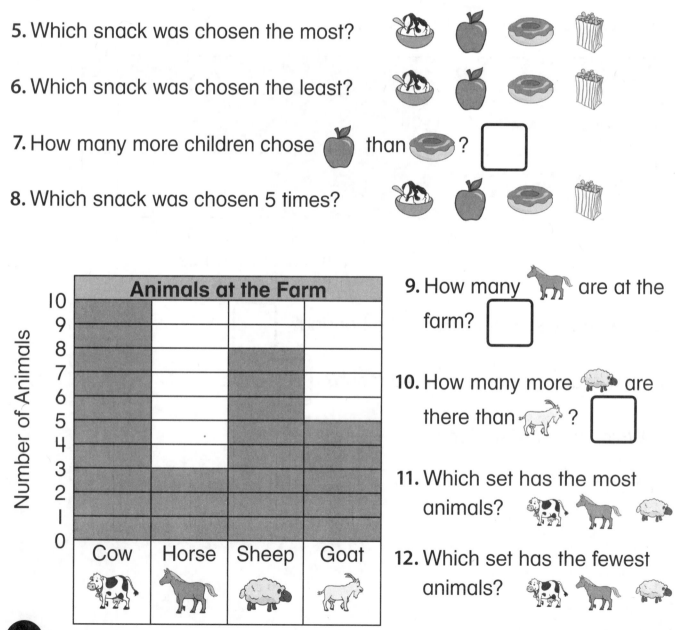

Favorite Snack							
Ice cream	🍨	🍨	🍨	🍨	🍨		
Apple	🍎	🍎	🍎	🍎	🍎	🍎	
Donut	🍩	🍩	🍩				
Nuts	🥜	🥜	🥜	🥜	🥜	🥜	🥜 🥜

Each picture equals I student's choice.

5. Which snack was chosen the most?

6. Which snack was chosen the least?

7. How many more children chose 🍎 than 🍩 ?

8. Which snack was chosen 5 times?

Animals at the Farm

Number of Animals (0–10)

	Cow	Horse	Sheep	Goat

9. How many 🐴 are at the farm?

10. How many more 🐑 are there than 🐐 ?

11. Which set has the most animals?

12. Which set has the fewest animals?

Cumulative Review

_____

Write the number that comes _before_.

1. ☐ 23

2. ☐ 46

3. ☐ 70

Write the number that comes _after_.

4. 35 ☐

5. 59 ☐

6. 98 ☐

Write the number that comes _between_.

7. 29 ☐ 31

8. 14 ☐ 16

9. 83 ☐ 85

Count each shape. Write the number of each shape.

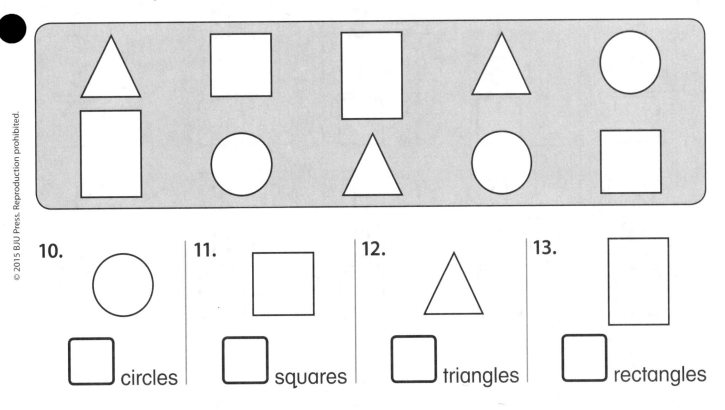

10. ☐ circles

11. ☐ squares

12. ☐ triangles

13. ☐ rectangles

Cross out to subtract. Complete the subtraction problems.

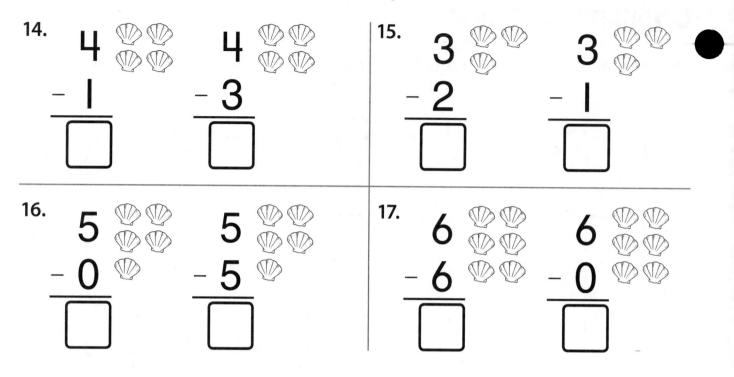

14.
$$4 - 1 = \boxed{}$$
$$4 - 3 = \boxed{}$$

15.
$$3 - 2 = \boxed{}$$
$$3 - 1 = \boxed{}$$

16.
$$5 - 0 = \boxed{}$$
$$5 - 5 = \boxed{}$$

17.
$$6 - 6 = \boxed{}$$
$$6 - 0 = \boxed{}$$

Complete the addition problems.

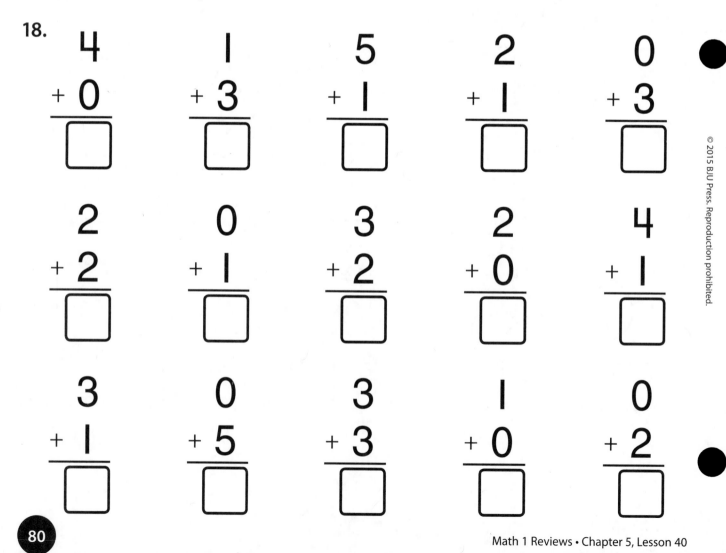

18.
$$4 + 0 = \boxed{}$$
$$1 + 3 = \boxed{}$$
$$5 + 1 = \boxed{}$$
$$2 + 1 = \boxed{}$$
$$0 + 3 = \boxed{}$$

$$2 + 2 = \boxed{}$$
$$0 + 1 = \boxed{}$$
$$3 + 2 = \boxed{}$$
$$2 + 0 = \boxed{}$$
$$4 + 1 = \boxed{}$$

$$3 + 1 = \boxed{}$$
$$0 + 5 = \boxed{}$$
$$3 + 3 = \boxed{}$$
$$1 + 0 = \boxed{}$$
$$0 + 2 = \boxed{}$$

Pennies, Nickels & Dimes

Write the value of the coin.

1.  ☐ ¢   **2.** 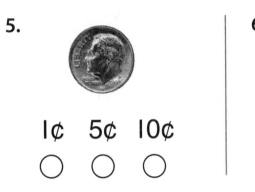 ☐ ¢   **3.** ☐ ¢

Write the value of the coin.

4.
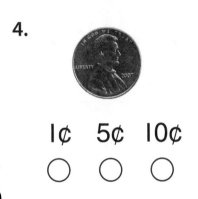

1¢   5¢   10¢
○   ○   ○

5.

1¢   5¢   10¢
○   ○   ○

6.

1¢   5¢   10¢
○   ○   ○

Put an *X* on each penny.
Draw a box around each nickel.
Circle each dime.

7.

Draw dots to picture the story. Complete the sentences.

1. Don saw 2 birds.

   He saw 3 more birds.

   How many birds did Don see?

   Don saw ☐ birds.

   ☐ ○ ☐ ○ ☐

2. Mia picked 4 flowers for Mother.

   She picked 2 more flowers for Mother.

   How many flowers did she pick?

   Mia picked ☐ flowers.

   ☐ ○ ☐ ○ ☐

Write an addition sentence for the picture.

3.

   ☐ + ☐ = ☐

4.

   ☐ + ☐ = ☐

Color the combinations for 4 blue.
Color the combinations for 5 red.

5.

2 + 2	1 + 3	4 + 1
3 + 1	4 + 0	1 + 4
5 + 0		0 + 5
2 + 3		3 + 2

Sets of Coins

Mark each set that matches the value of the picture.

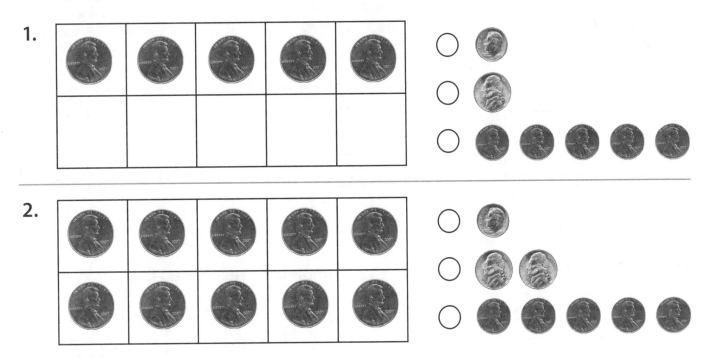

1.

2.

Circle the coin with the greatest value.
Draw a box around the coin with the least value.

3.

Draw lines to match the sets that have the same value.

4.

5.

Draw pennies to match the value of the coin.

6.

Write the number of tens and ones.
Write the number represented.

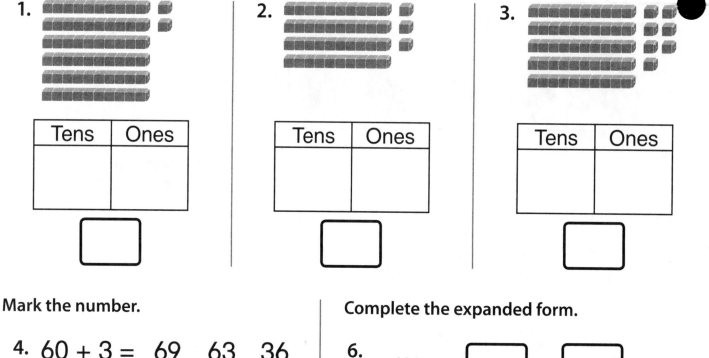

1.

Tens	Ones

2.

Tens	Ones

3.

Tens	Ones

Mark the number.

4. $60 + 3 =$ 69   63   36
       ○   ○   ○

5. $20 + 7 =$ 12   21   27
       ○   ○   ○

Complete the expanded form.

6. $49 = \boxed{} + \boxed{}$

7. $\boxed{} = 50 + 8$

Write the number represented.
Circle the single cubes to make pairs.
Mark *even* or *odd*.

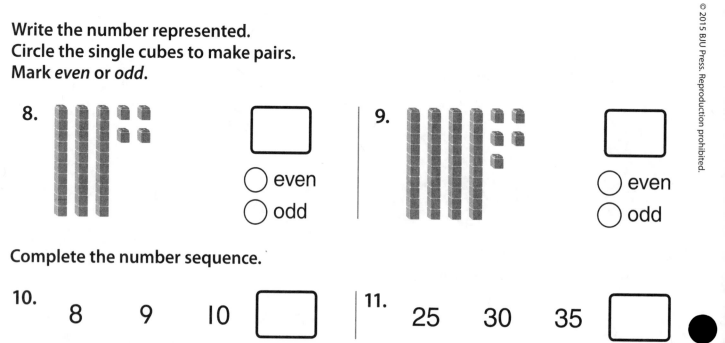

8. $\boxed{}$
   ○ even
   ○ odd

9. $\boxed{}$
   ○ even
   ○ odd

Complete the number sequence.

10.   8   9   10 $\boxed{}$

11.   25   30   35 $\boxed{}$

Count by 1s, by 5s & by 10s

_____
_ _ _ _ _ _ _ _ _
_____

Mark the coin that matches the value.

1.   1¢   ○ 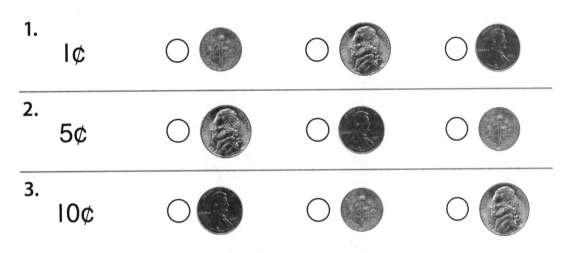 ○ ○

2.   5¢   ○ ○ ○

3.   10¢   ○ ○ ○

Count by 1s, by 5s, or by 10s. Write the value of each set.

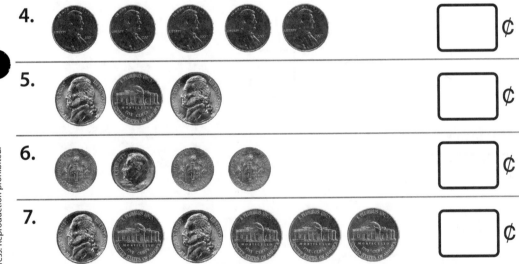

4.   [ ] ¢

5.   [ ] ¢

6.   [ ] ¢

7.   [ ] ¢

Count by 1s, by 5s, or by 10s. Write the total value.
Do you have enough money to buy the item? Circle _yes_ or _no_.

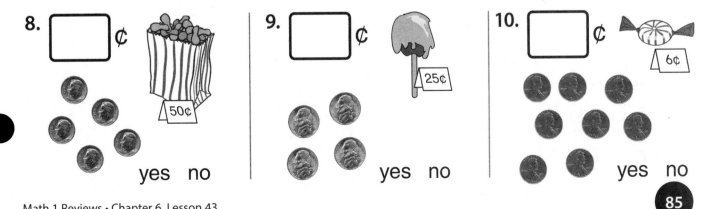

8. [ ] ¢   50¢   yes   no

9. [ ] ¢   25¢   yes   no

10. [ ] ¢   6¢   yes   no

Cross out to subtract. Complete the sentences.

1.

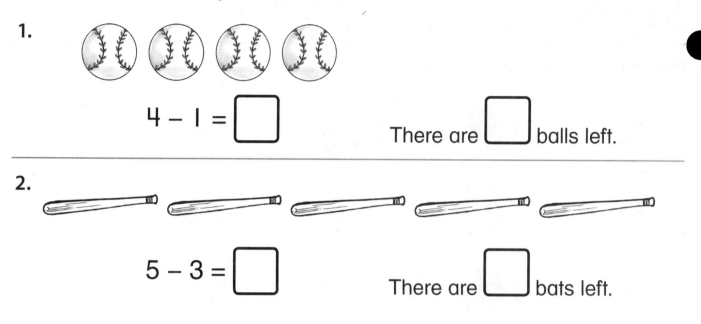

$4 - 1 = \boxed{}$

There are $\boxed{}$ balls left.

2.

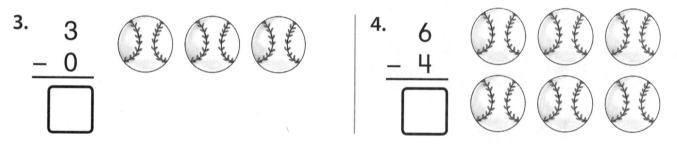

$5 - 3 = \boxed{}$

There are $\boxed{}$ bats left.

Cross out to subtract. Complete the subtraction problem.

3.
$$\begin{array}{r} 3 \\ - \ 0 \\ \hline \boxed{} \end{array}$$

4.
$$\begin{array}{r} 6 \\ - \ 4 \\ \hline \boxed{} \end{array}$$
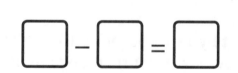

Draw circles to picture the story.
Cross out to subtract. Complete the sentences.

5. Wes had 6 balls.

He gave 2 balls to Kim.

How many balls does Wes have now?

Wes has $\boxed{}$ balls.

$\boxed{} - \boxed{} = \boxed{}$

Draw lines to match the related subtraction facts.

6.

$3 - 2 = 1$	$5 - 2 = 3$
$5 - 3 = 2$	$3 - 1 = 2$
$6 - 1 = 5$	$6 - 5 = 1$

Count Dimes & Pennies

Write the total value as you *count on*.
Do you have enough money to buy the item? Circle *yes* or *no*.

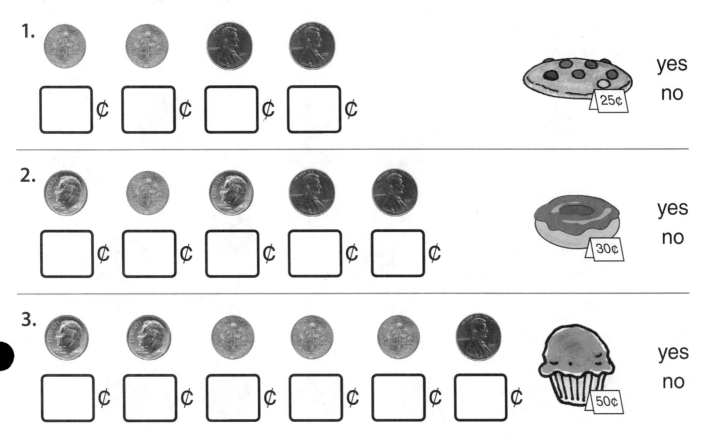

1. ☐¢ ☐¢ ☐¢ ☐¢   25¢   yes   no

2. ☐¢ ☐¢ ☐¢ ☐¢ ☐¢   30¢   yes   no

3. ☐¢ ☐¢ ☐¢ ☐¢ ☐¢ ☐¢   50¢   yes   no

Write the number of dimes and pennies.
Write the values. Complete the addition sentence.

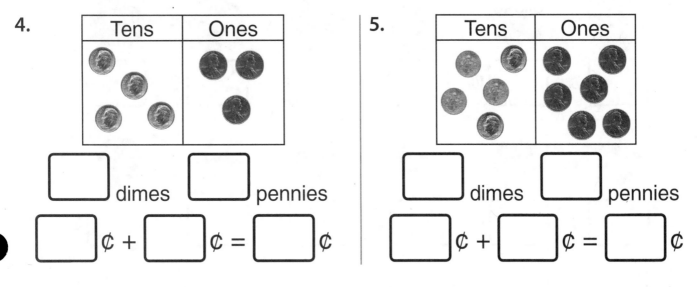

4.

Tens	Ones

☐ dimes   ☐ pennies

☐¢ + ☐¢ = ☐¢

5.

Tens	Ones

☐ dimes   ☐ pennies

☐¢ + ☐¢ = ☐¢

Write the value of the coin.

1. 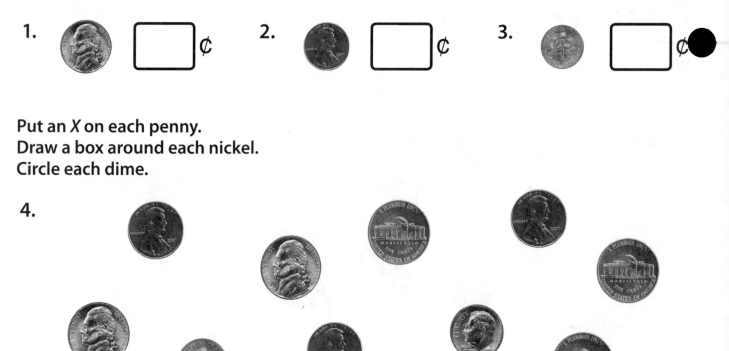 ☐ ¢

2. ☐ ¢

3. ☐ ¢

Put an X on each penny.
Draw a box around each nickel.
Circle each dime.

4.

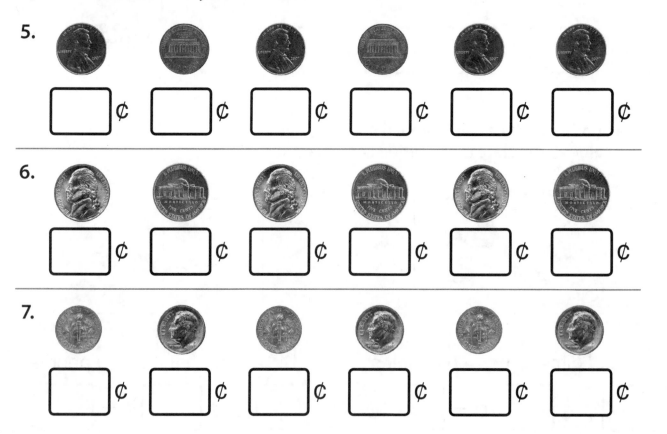

Write the total value as you *count on*.

5. ☐ ¢   ☐ ¢   ☐ ¢   ☐ ¢   ☐ ¢   ☐ ¢

6. ☐ ¢   ☐ ¢   ☐ ¢   ☐ ¢   ☐ ¢   ☐ ¢

7. ☐ ¢   ☐ ¢   ☐ ¢   ☐ ¢   ☐ ¢   ☐ ¢

Count Dimes, Nickels & Pennies

Write the total value as you *count on*.

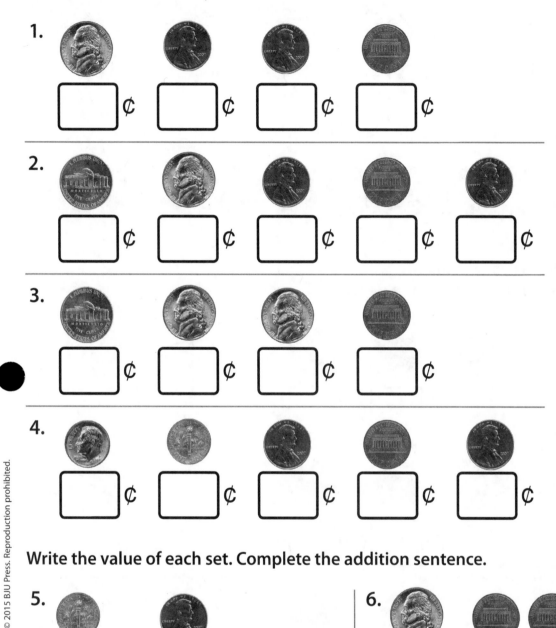

1.

  □ ¢   □ ¢   □ ¢   □ ¢

2.

  □ ¢   □ ¢   □ ¢   □ ¢   □ ¢

3.

  □ ¢   □ ¢   □ ¢   □ ¢

4.

  □ ¢   □ ¢   □ ¢   □ ¢   □ ¢

Write the value of each set. Complete the addition sentence.

5. □ ¢ + □ ¢ = □ ¢   **6.** □ ¢ + □ ¢ = □ ¢

Circle the coins needed to make 10 cents.

7.

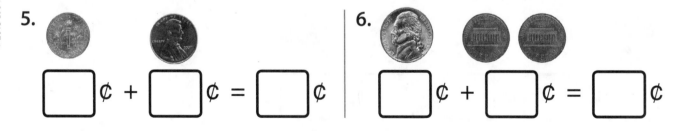

Color green the apples with the value of a penny.
Color red the apples with the value of a nickel.
Color yellow the apples with the value of a dime.

1.
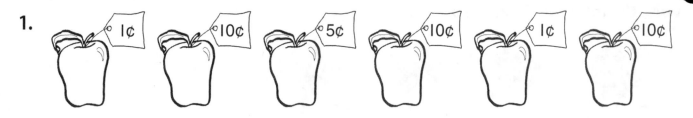

Count by 1s. Circle the coins needed to make 10 cents.

2.

Write the total value as you *count on*.
Do you have enough money to buy the item? Circle *yes* or *no*.

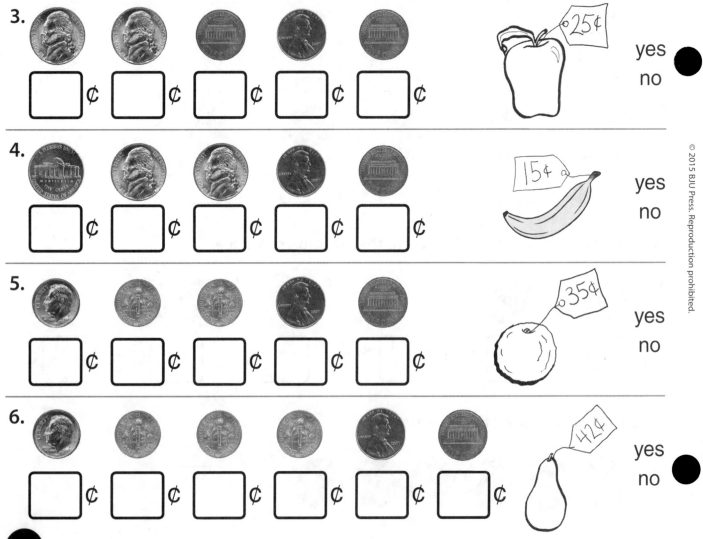

3.
[ ]¢ [ ]¢ [ ]¢ [ ]¢ [ ]¢   yes
                             no

4.
[ ]¢ [ ]¢ [ ]¢ [ ]¢ [ ]¢   yes
                             no

5.
[ ]¢ [ ]¢ [ ]¢ [ ]¢ [ ]¢   yes
                             no

6.
[ ]¢ [ ]¢ [ ]¢ [ ]¢ [ ]¢   yes
                             no

Chapter 6 Review

Write the value of the coin.

1. [ ] ¢   2. [ ] ¢   3. [ ] ¢

Count by 1s, by 5s, or by 10s. Write the total value.

4. [ ] ¢

5. [ ] ¢

6. [ ] ¢

Write the total value as you *count on*.

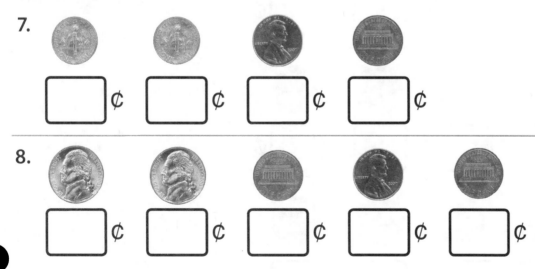

7. [ ] ¢   [ ] ¢   [ ] ¢   [ ] ¢

8. [ ] ¢   [ ] ¢   [ ] ¢   [ ] ¢   [ ] ¢

Write the number of dimes and pennies.
Write the values. Complete the addition sentence.

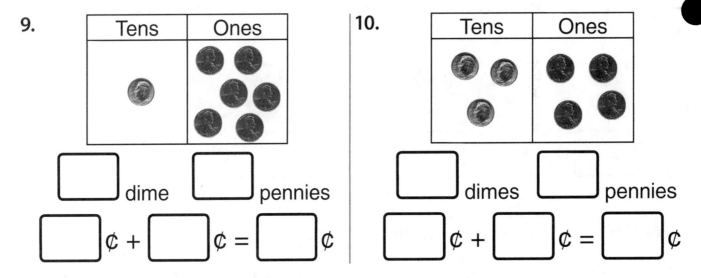

9.

Tens	Ones

[ ] dime   [ ] pennies

[ ] ¢ + [ ] ¢ = [ ] ¢

10.

Tens	Ones

[ ] dimes   [ ] pennies

[ ] ¢ + [ ] ¢ = [ ] ¢

Write the total value as you *count on*.
Do you have enough money to buy the item? Circle *yes* or *no*.

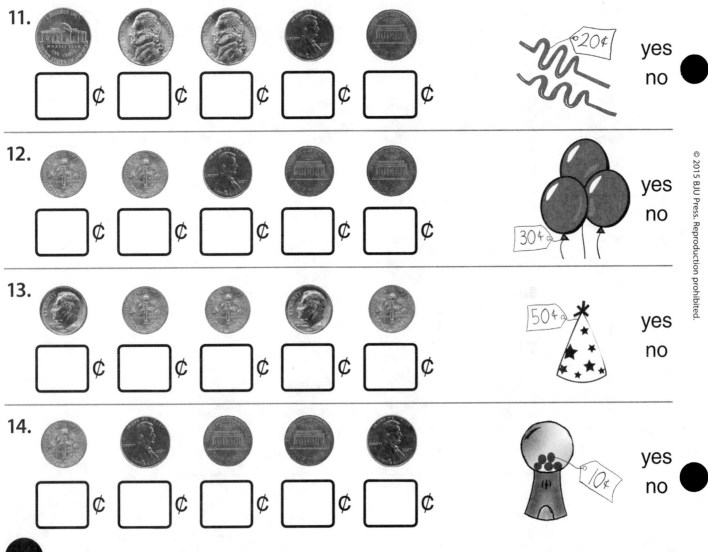

11. [ ] ¢ [ ] ¢ [ ] ¢ [ ] ¢ [ ] ¢   20¢   yes   no

12. [ ] ¢ [ ] ¢ [ ] ¢ [ ] ¢ [ ] ¢   30¢   yes   no

13. [ ] ¢ [ ] ¢ [ ] ¢ [ ] ¢ [ ] ¢   50¢   yes   no

14. [ ] ¢ [ ] ¢ [ ] ¢ [ ] ¢ [ ] ¢   10¢   yes   no

Cumulative Review

Count by 10s. Write the missing numbers.

1. 10 ☐ ☐ 40 ☐ 60 ☐ 80 ☐ 100

Write the number of tens and ones.
Write the number represented.

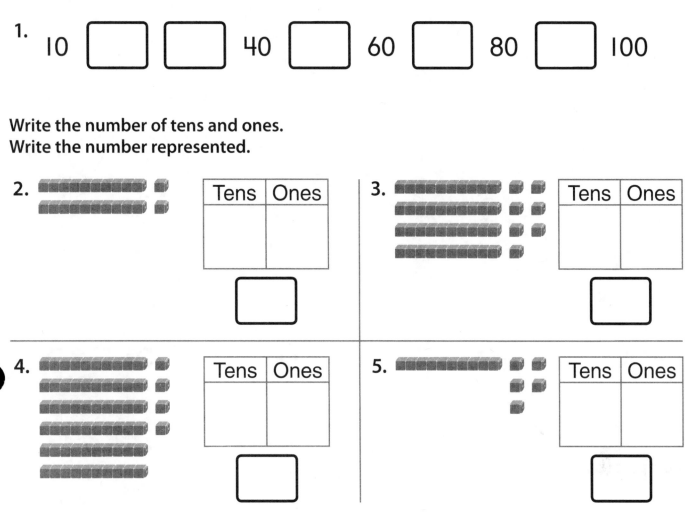

2.

Tens	Ones

☐

3.

Tens	Ones

☐

4.

Tens	Ones

☐

5.

Tens	Ones

☐

Draw a line to match the number to the expanded form.

6.

43   20 + 5

78   40 + 3

25   60 + 2

62   70 + 8

Circle the one that extends the pattern.

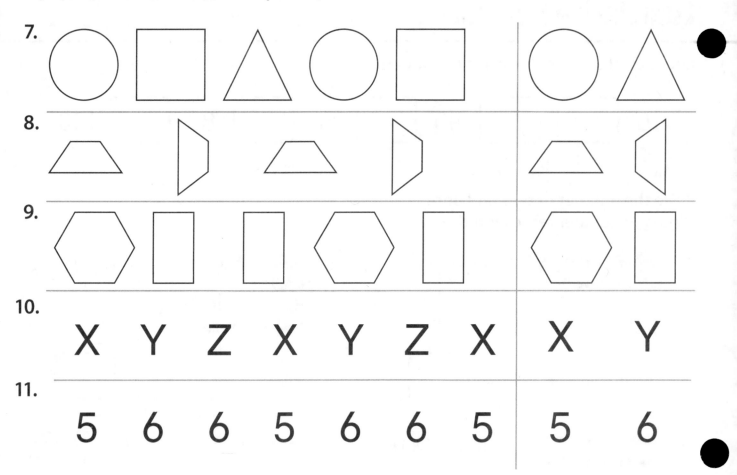

7.

8.

9.

10. X   Y   Z   X   Y   Z   X | X   Y

11. 5   6   6   5   6   6   5 | 5   6

Complete the addition problems.

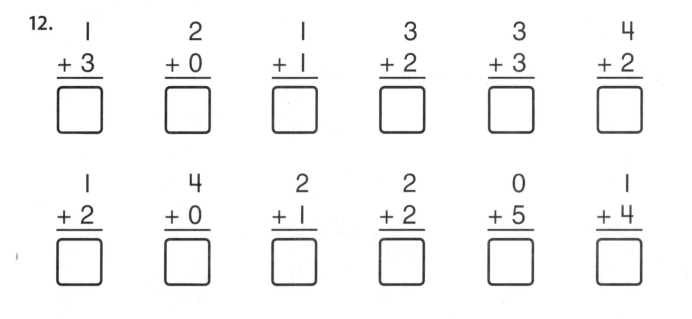

12.

$$\begin{array}{r} 1 \\ + 3 \\ \hline \square \end{array} \quad \begin{array}{r} 2 \\ + 0 \\ \hline \square \end{array} \quad \begin{array}{r} 1 \\ + 1 \\ \hline \square \end{array} \quad \begin{array}{r} 3 \\ + 2 \\ \hline \square \end{array} \quad \begin{array}{r} 3 \\ + 3 \\ \hline \square \end{array} \quad \begin{array}{r} 4 \\ + 2 \\ \hline \square \end{array}$$

$$\begin{array}{r} 1 \\ + 2 \\ \hline \square \end{array} \quad \begin{array}{r} 4 \\ + 0 \\ \hline \square \end{array} \quad \begin{array}{r} 2 \\ + 1 \\ \hline \square \end{array} \quad \begin{array}{r} 2 \\ + 2 \\ \hline \square \end{array} \quad \begin{array}{r} 0 \\ + 5 \\ \hline \square \end{array} \quad \begin{array}{r} 1 \\ + 4 \\ \hline \square \end{array}$$

Addends & Sum

Complete the sentences.

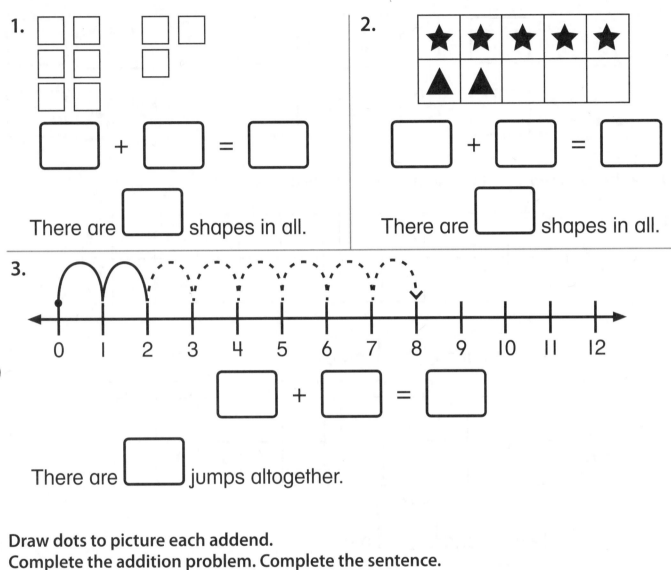

1.

☐ + ☐ = ☐

There are ☐ shapes in all.

2.

☐ + ☐ = ☐

There are ☐ shapes in all.

3.

0 1 2 3 4 5 6 7 8 9 10 11 12

☐ + ☐ = ☐

There are ☐ jumps altogether.

Draw dots to picture each addend.
Complete the addition problem. Complete the sentence.

4.

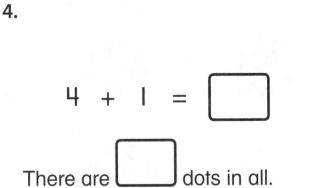

4 + 1 = ☐

There are ☐ dots in all.

5.

$$\begin{array}{r} 7 \\ + \ 3 \\ \hline \end{array}$$

☐

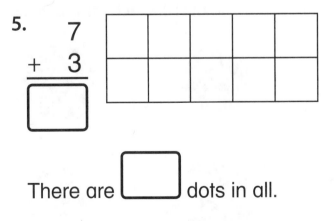

There are ☐ dots in all.

Write the number that matches the dot pattern.

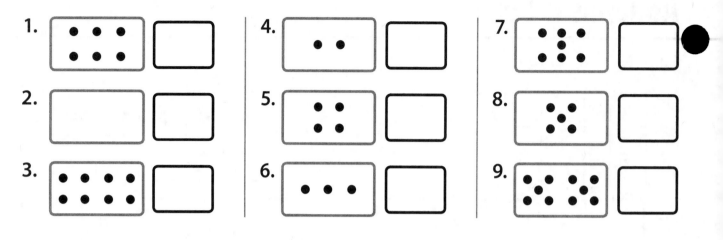

1. [ ]   4. [ ]   7. [ ]

2. [ ]   5. [ ]   8. [ ]

3. [ ]   6. [ ]   9. [ ]

Draw circles to represent the number. Complete the sentence.

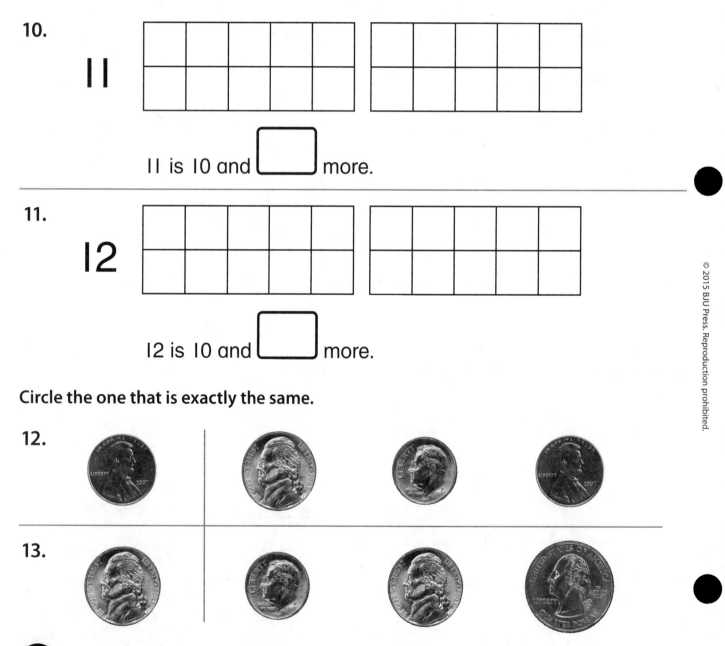

10. 11

11 is 10 and [ ] more.

11. 12

12 is 10 and [ ] more.

Circle the one that is exactly the same.

12.

13.

Addition Rules

When zero is an addend, the sum is the same as the other addend.

$$6 + 0 = \boxed{6}$$
$$0 + 6 = \boxed{6}$$

addend   addend   sum

The order of the addends can be changed without changing the sum.

$$2 + 4 = \boxed{6}$$
$$4 + 2 = \boxed{6}$$

addend   addend   sum

Complete the addition sentences.

1. $5 + 0 = \boxed{}$

   $0 + 5 = \boxed{}$

2. $2 + 0 = \boxed{}$

   $0 + 2 = \boxed{}$

Complete the addition problem.
Reorder the addends to write the related addition fact.

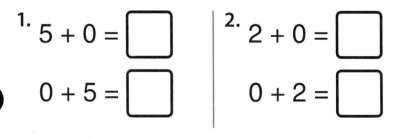

3.
$$\begin{array}{r} 3 \\ + 2 \\ \hline \end{array}$$

4.
$$\begin{array}{r} 1 \\ + 7 \\ \hline \end{array}$$

5.
$$\begin{array}{r} 3 \\ + 4 \\ \hline \end{array}$$

Circle the larger number. *Count on* to add.

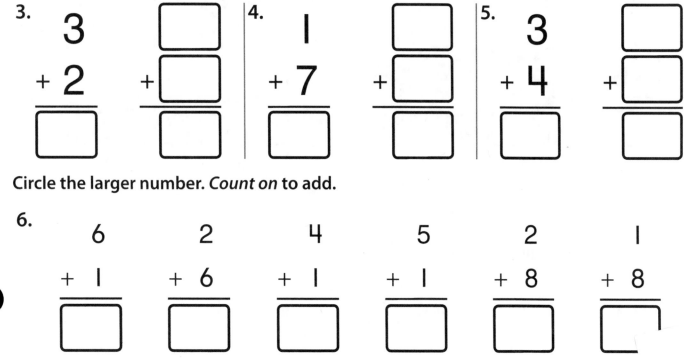

6.
$$\begin{array}{r} 6 \\ + 1 \\ \hline \end{array} \qquad \begin{array}{r} 2 \\ + 6 \\ \hline \end{array} \qquad \begin{array}{r} 4 \\ + 1 \\ \hline \end{array} \qquad \begin{array}{r} 5 \\ + 1 \\ \hline \end{array} \qquad \begin{array}{r} 2 \\ + 8 \\ \hline \end{array} \qquad \begin{array}{r} 1 \\ + 8 \\ \hline \end{array}$$

Number the balls from smallest to largest.

1.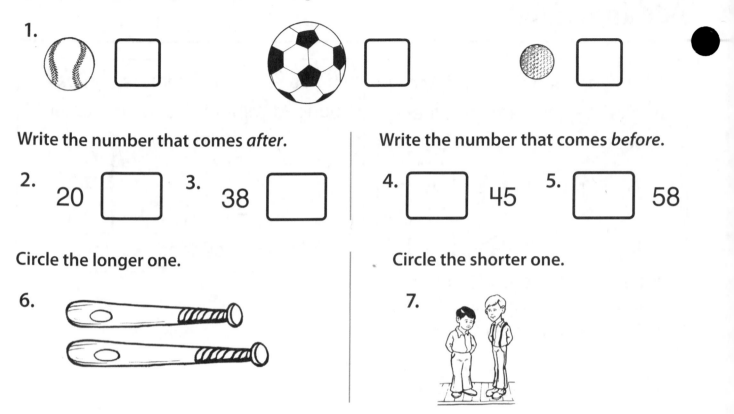

Write the number that comes *after*.

2. 20 ☐   3. 38 ☐

Write the number that comes *before*.

4. ☐ 45   5. ☐ 58

Circle the longer one.

6.

Circle the shorter one.

7.

Use the graph to answer the question.

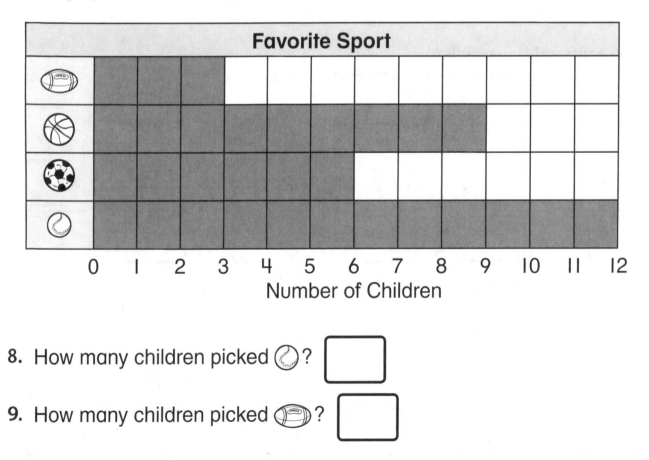

8. How many children picked 🎾? ☐

9. How many children picked 🏈? ☐

Add on a Number Line; Add Doubles

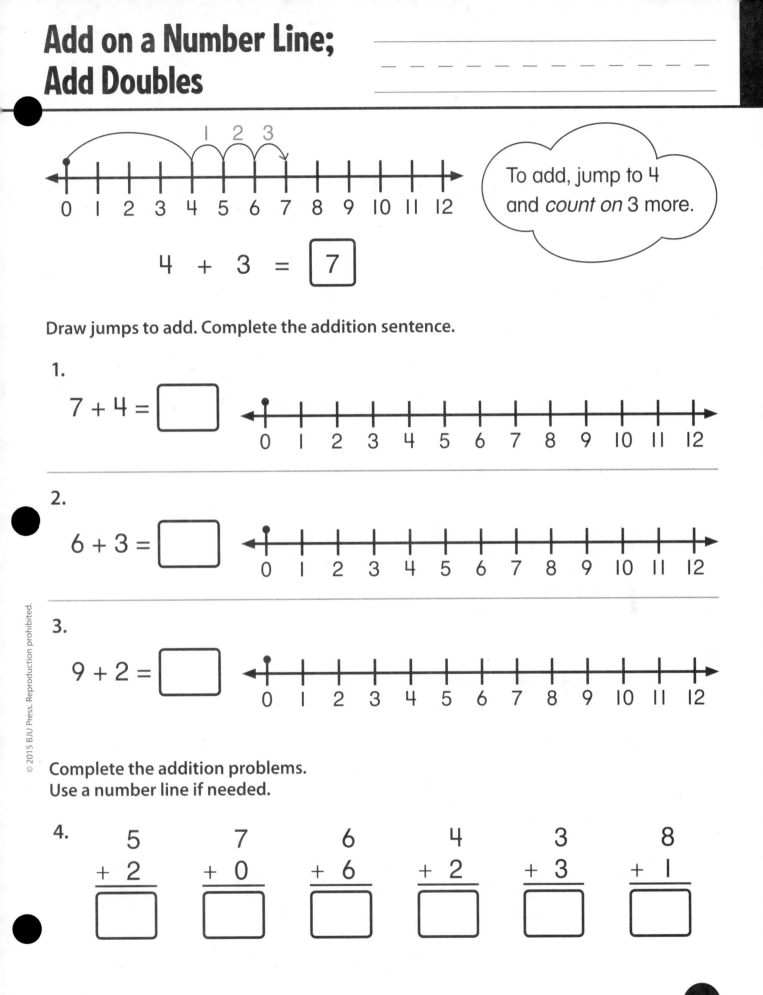

0 1 2 3 4 5 6 7 8 9 10 11 12

To add, jump to 4 and *count on* 3 more.

4 + 3 = 7

Draw jumps to add. Complete the addition sentence.

1.

7 + 4 = ☐

0 1 2 3 4 5 6 7 8 9 10 11 12

2.

6 + 3 = ☐

0 1 2 3 4 5 6 7 8 9 10 11 12

3.

9 + 2 = ☐

0 1 2 3 4 5 6 7 8 9 10 11 12

**Complete the addition problems.
Use a number line if needed.**

4.

$$\begin{array}{r} 5 \\ + 2 \\ \hline \end{array}$$
$$\begin{array}{r} 7 \\ + 0 \\ \hline \end{array}$$
$$\begin{array}{r} 6 \\ + 6 \\ \hline \end{array}$$
$$\begin{array}{r} 4 \\ + 2 \\ \hline \end{array}$$
$$\begin{array}{r} 3 \\ + 3 \\ \hline \end{array}$$
$$\begin{array}{r} 8 \\ + 1 \\ \hline \end{array}$$

Write an addition sentence for the picture.
Complete the sentence.

1.

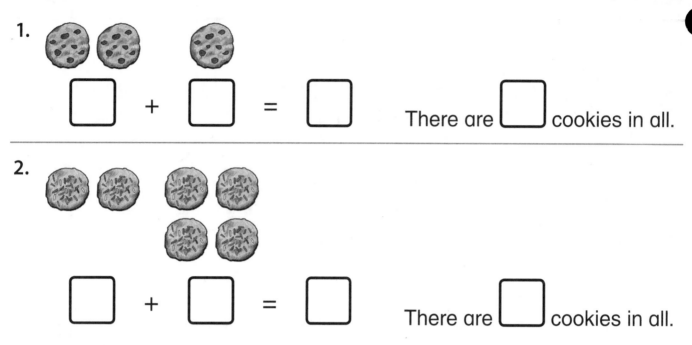

☐ + ☐ = ☐   There are ☐ cookies in all.

2.

☐ + ☐ = ☐   There are ☐ cookies in all.

Cross out to subtract. Complete the subtraction problems.

3.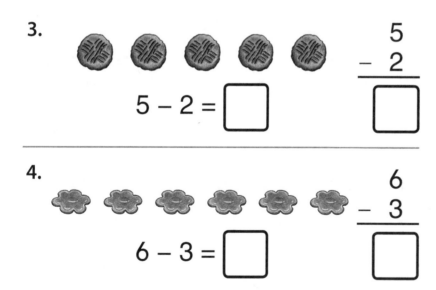

5 − 2 = ☐

$$\begin{array}{r} 5 \\ -\ 2 \\ \hline \square \end{array}$$

4.

6 − 3 = ☐

$$\begin{array}{r} 6 \\ -\ 3 \\ \hline \square \end{array}$$

Write the total value as you *count on*.

5.

☐ ¢   ☐ ¢   ☐ ¢   ☐ ¢   ☐ ¢

Add to 5

Use 2 colors to picture the addends.
Count on from 5 to add. Complete the addition sentence.

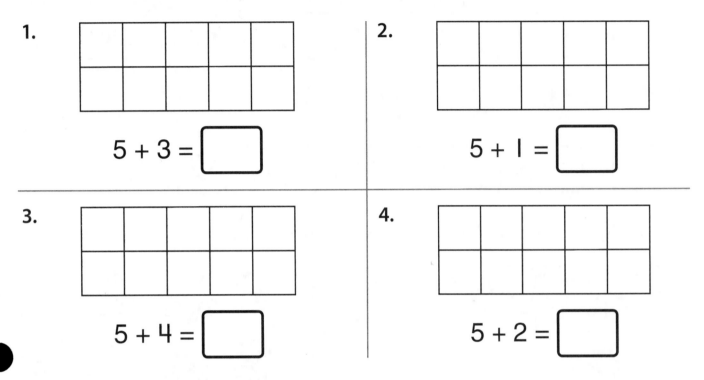

1.

$5 + 3 = \boxed{}$

2.

$5 + 1 = \boxed{}$

3.

$5 + 4 = \boxed{}$

4.

$5 + 2 = \boxed{}$

Use 2 colors to picture the addends.
Count on from 10 to add.
Complete the addition sentence.

5.

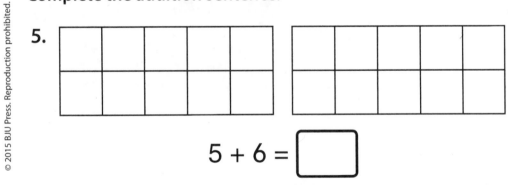

$5 + 6 = \boxed{}$

Complete the sentences.

6. Leo had 6 cookies.

He gave 2 cookies to Cion.

How many cookies does Leo have?

Leo has  cookies.

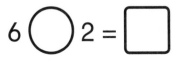

$6 \bigcirc 2 = \boxed{}$

Write the total value as you *count on*.
Do you have enough money to buy the item? Circle *yes* or *no*.

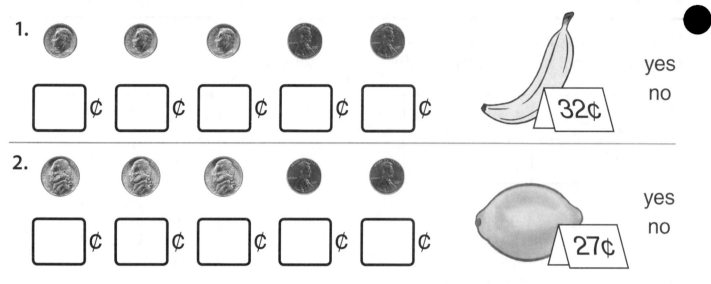

1. [ ]¢ [ ]¢ [ ]¢ [ ]¢ [ ]¢   32¢   yes
                                              no

2. [ ]¢ [ ]¢ [ ]¢ [ ]¢ [ ]¢   27¢   yes
                                              no

Make a tally for each coin. Write the total value for each set.

3.

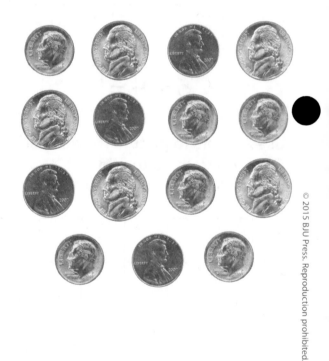

Coin Collection		
Set	Tally	Total
		¢
		¢
		¢

Draw dots to picture the story. Complete the sentences.

4. Matt had 3 trucks.
   He found 2 more trucks on the shelf.
   How many trucks does Matt have?

   Matt has [ ] trucks.

Combinations for 10

Complete the addition combinations for 10.

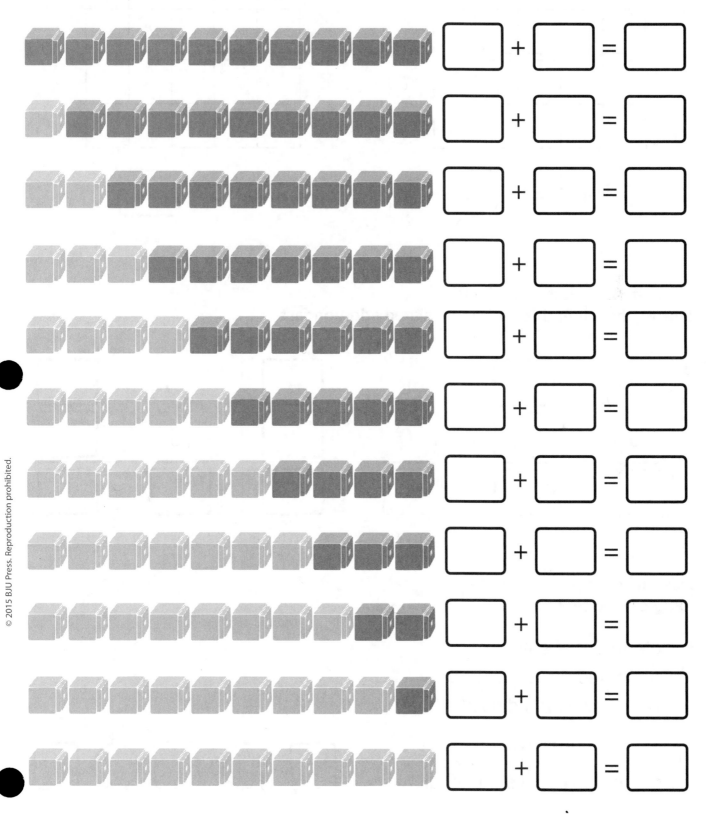

Use 2 colors to picture the addends.
Complete the addition sentence.

1.

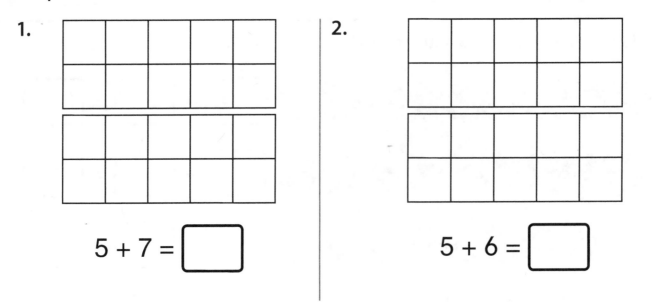

$5 + 7 = \boxed{}$

2.

$5 + 6 = \boxed{}$

Complete the addition problem.
Reorder the addends to write the related addition fact.

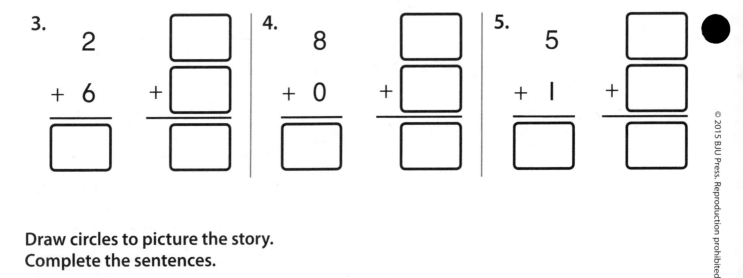

3.
$$\begin{array}{r} 2 \\ + 6 \\ \hline \boxed{} \end{array}$$
$$\begin{array}{r} \boxed{} \\ + \boxed{} \\ \hline \boxed{} \end{array}$$

4.
$$\begin{array}{r} 8 \\ + 0 \\ \hline \boxed{} \end{array}$$
$$\begin{array}{r} \boxed{} \\ + \boxed{} \\ \hline \boxed{} \end{array}$$

5.
$$\begin{array}{r} 5 \\ + 1 \\ \hline \boxed{} \end{array}$$
$$\begin{array}{r} \boxed{} \\ + \boxed{} \\ \hline \boxed{} \end{array}$$

Draw circles to picture the story.
Complete the sentences.

6. Kate folded 4 shirts.

    She folded 2 more shirts.

    How many shirts did Kate fold?

    Kate folded $\boxed{}$ shirts in all.

3 Addends

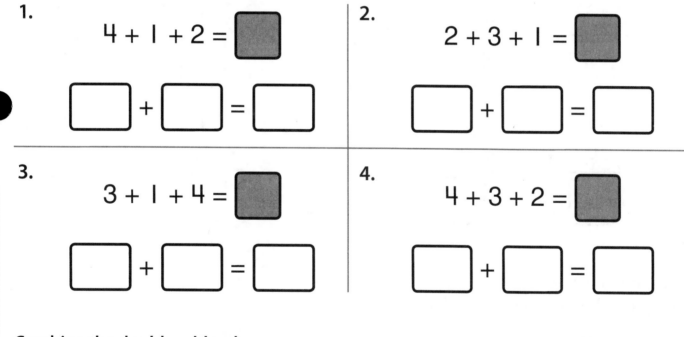

Combine addends to make 5 or make 10.

$$2 + 3 + 3 = \boxed{}$$
$$\boxed{5} + \boxed{3} = \boxed{8}$$

Combine double addends.

$$2 + 3 + 3 = \boxed{}$$
$$\boxed{2} + \boxed{6} = \boxed{8}$$

Combine addends to make 5.
Write the new addition sentence.

1.

$$4 + 1 + 2 = \boxed{}$$

$\boxed{} + \boxed{} = \boxed{}$

2.

$$2 + 3 + 1 = \boxed{}$$

$\boxed{} + \boxed{} = \boxed{}$

3.

$$3 + 1 + 4 = \boxed{}$$

$\boxed{} + \boxed{} = \boxed{}$

4.

$$4 + 3 + 2 = \boxed{}$$

$\boxed{} + \boxed{} = \boxed{}$

Combine the double addends.
Write the new addition sentence.

5.

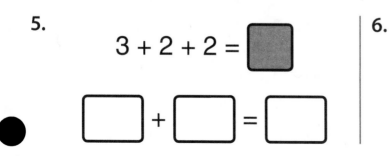

$$3 + 2 + 2 = \boxed{}$$

$\boxed{} + \boxed{} = \boxed{}$

6.

$$3 + 3 + 5 = \boxed{}$$

$\boxed{} + \boxed{} = \boxed{}$

Write an addition sentence for the story.
Complete the sentence.

1. Anna made 2 pictures.
   Leah made 3 pictures.
   How many pictures did the girls make?

   The girls made ⬜ pictures.

   ⬜ + ⬜ = ⬜

Complete the addition problems.

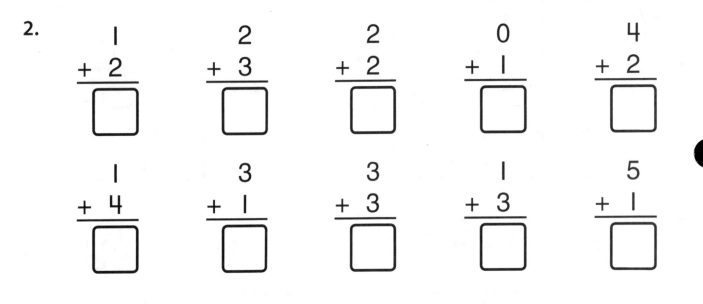

2.
$$\begin{array}{r} 1 \\ + 2 \\ \hline \square \end{array} \qquad \begin{array}{r} 2 \\ + 3 \\ \hline \square \end{array} \qquad \begin{array}{r} 2 \\ + 2 \\ \hline \square \end{array} \qquad \begin{array}{r} 0 \\ + 1 \\ \hline \square \end{array} \qquad \begin{array}{r} 4 \\ + 2 \\ \hline \square \end{array}$$

$$\begin{array}{r} 1 \\ + 4 \\ \hline \square \end{array} \qquad \begin{array}{r} 3 \\ + 1 \\ \hline \square \end{array} \qquad \begin{array}{r} 3 \\ + 3 \\ \hline \square \end{array} \qquad \begin{array}{r} 1 \\ + 3 \\ \hline \square \end{array} \qquad \begin{array}{r} 5 \\ + 1 \\ \hline \square \end{array}$$

Cross out to subtract.
Complete the subtraction problems.

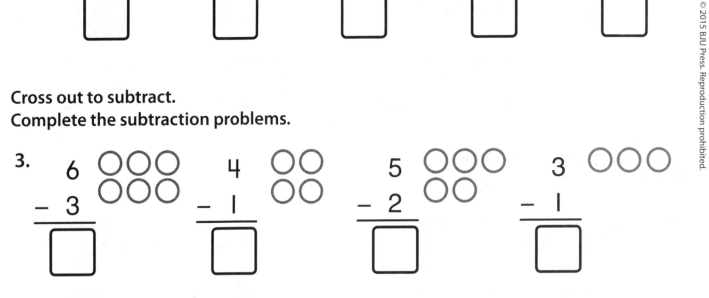

3.
$$\begin{array}{r} 6 \\ - 3 \\ \hline \square \end{array} \qquad \begin{array}{r} 4 \\ - 1 \\ \hline \square \end{array} \qquad \begin{array}{r} 5 \\ - 2 \\ \hline \square \end{array} \qquad \begin{array}{r} 3 \\ - 1 \\ \hline \square \end{array}$$

Chapter 7 Review

Complete the addition problems.
Use the number line if needed.

1.

$\begin{array}{r} 5 \\ + 4 \\ \hline \end{array}$ $\begin{array}{r} 3 \\ + 3 \\ \hline \end{array}$ $\begin{array}{r} 4 \\ + 2 \\ \hline \end{array}$ $\begin{array}{r} 6 \\ + 1 \\ \hline \end{array}$

$\begin{array}{r} 7 \\ + 0 \\ \hline \end{array}$ $\begin{array}{r} 5 \\ + 3 \\ \hline \end{array}$ $\begin{array}{r} 4 \\ + 4 \\ \hline \end{array}$ $\begin{array}{r} 4 \\ + 3 \\ \hline \end{array}$

$6 + 2 = \boxed{}$ $8 + 1 = \boxed{}$ $4 + 0 = \boxed{}$

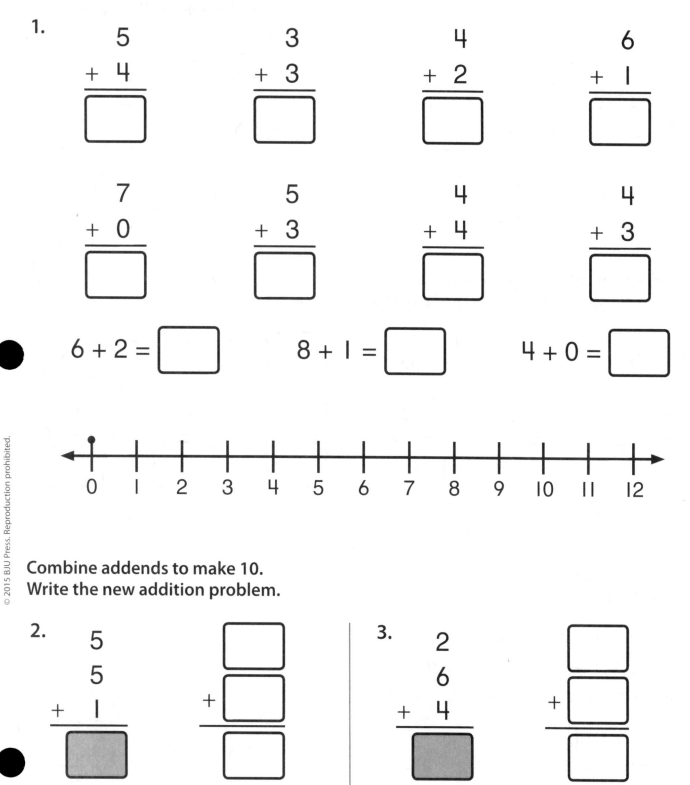

Combine addends to make 10.
Write the new addition problem.

2.
$\begin{array}{r} 5 \\ 5 \\ + 1 \\ \hline \end{array}$

3.
$\begin{array}{r} 2 \\ 6 \\ + 4 \\ \hline \end{array}$

Use 2 colors to picture the addends.
Complete the addition sentence.

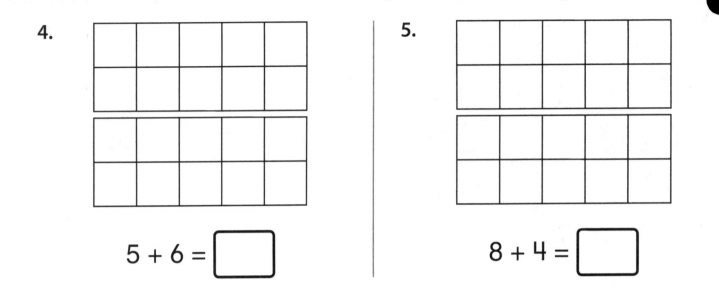

4.

5 + 6 = ☐

5.

8 + 4 = ☐

Complete the addition problem.
Reorder the addends to write the related addition fact.

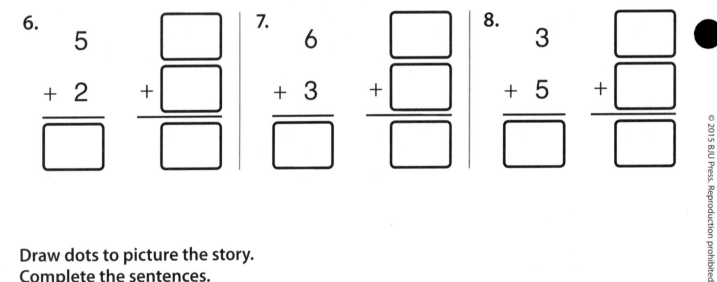

6.
5
+ 2
☐

+ ☐
☐
☐

7.
6
+ 3
☐

+ ☐
☐
☐

8.
3
+ 5
☐

+ ☐
☐
☐

Draw dots to picture the story.
Complete the sentences.

9. Lee made 3 paper planes.
   He made 4 more paper planes.
   How many planes did Lee make?

Lee made ☐ paper planes.

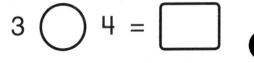

3 ◯ 4 = ☐

Cumulative Review

Write the number of tens and ones.
Write the number represented.

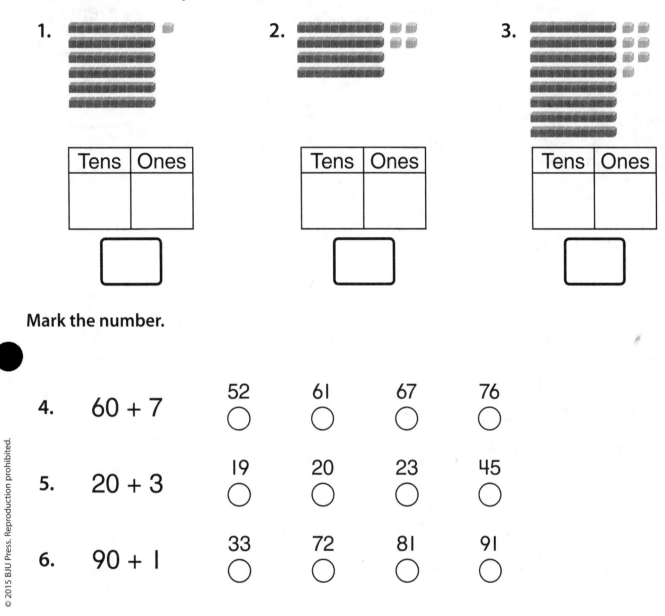

1.

Tens	Ones

2.

Tens	Ones

3.

Tens	Ones

Mark the number.

4. 60 + 7

52	61	67	76
○	○	○	○

5. 20 + 3

19	20	23	45
○	○	○	○

6. 90 + 1

33	72	81	91
○	○	○	○

Complete the expanded form.

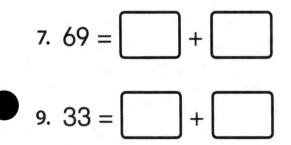

7. 69 = ☐ + ☐

8. 84 = ☐ + ☐

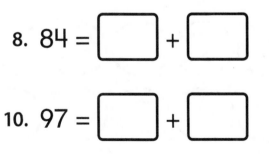

9. 33 = ☐ + ☐

10. 97 = ☐ + ☐

Write the number represented.
Circle the shoes to make pairs. Circle even or odd.

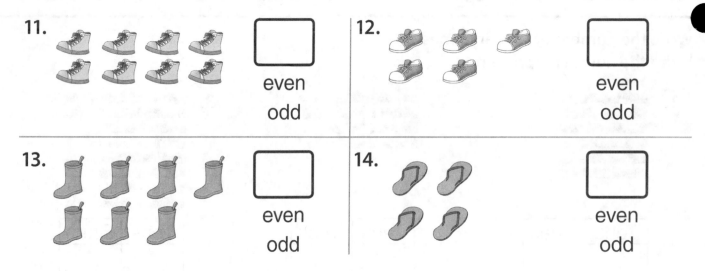

11. [ ] even odd

12. [ ] even odd

13. [ ] even odd

14. [ ] even odd

Complete the addition problems.

15.

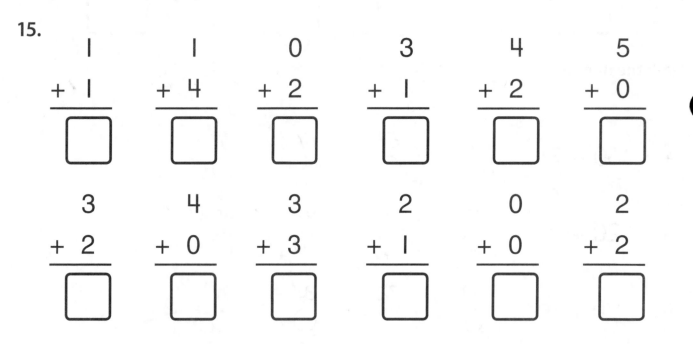

1	1	0	3	4	5
+ 1	+ 4	+ 2	+ 1	+ 2	+ 0
[ ]	[ ]	[ ]	[ ]	[ ]	[ ]

3	4	3	2	0	2
+ 2	+ 0	+ 3	+ 1	+ 0	+ 2
[ ]	[ ]	[ ]	[ ]	[ ]	[ ]

Count to 100 by 5s. Write the missing numbers.

16.

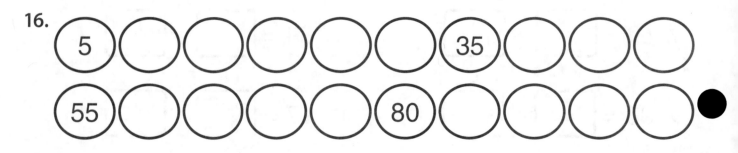

(5) ( ) ( ) ( ) ( ) ( ) (35) ( ) ( ) ( )

(55) ( ) ( ) ( ) ( ) (80) ( ) ( ) ( ) ( )

Tell Time

Mark the correct time.

1.
○ 1 o'clock
○ 2 o'clock
○ 3 o'clock

2.
○ 3 o'clock
○ 5 o'clock
○ 7 o'clock

3.
○ 12 o'clock
○ 1 o'clock
○ 10 o'clock

4.
○ 9 o'clock
○ 10 o'clock
○ 11 o'clock

Write the time.

5. ☐ o'clock

6. ☐ o'clock

7. ☐ o'clock

8. ☐ o'clock

Draw the hour and minute hands to show the time.

9.

1 o'clock

10.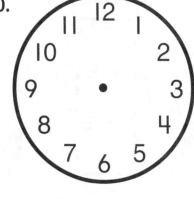

8 o'clock

Complete the addition problems.
Use the number line if needed.

0 1 2 3 4 5 6 7 8 9 10 11 12

1.

3	6	6	5	4	5
+ 3	+ 3	+ 4	+ 5	+ 4	+ 4
☐	☐	☐	☐	☐	☐

7	6	5	9	8	7
+ 2	+ 1	+ 0	+ 1	+ 2	+ 0
☐	☐	☐	☐	☐	☐

Combine addends to make 10.
Write the new addition problem.

2.
```
  0
  8
+ 2
▓▓▓
```
```
      ☐
+     ☐
    ─────
      ☐
```

3.
```
  5
  5
+ 2
▓▓▓
```
```
      ☐
+     ☐
    ─────
      ☐
```

4.
```
  3
  7
+ 1
▓▓▓
```
```
      ☐
+     ☐
    ─────
      ☐
```

Time to the Hour

Match each clock to the correct time.

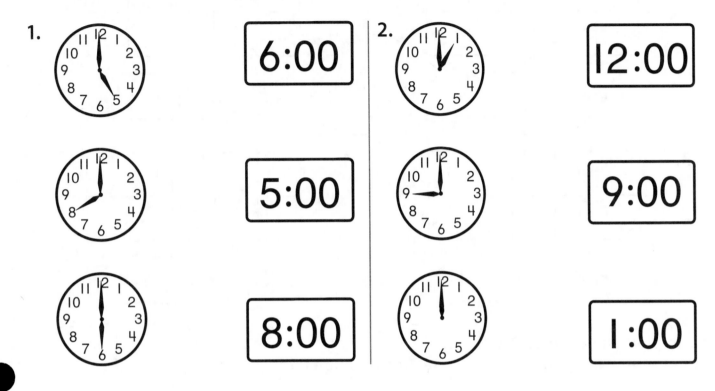

1.

6:00

2.

12:00

5:00

9:00

8:00

1:00

Write the time.

3.

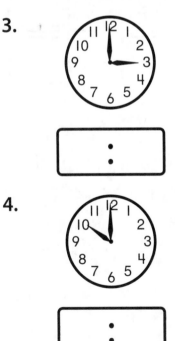

4.

Write the missing numbers on the clock.

5.

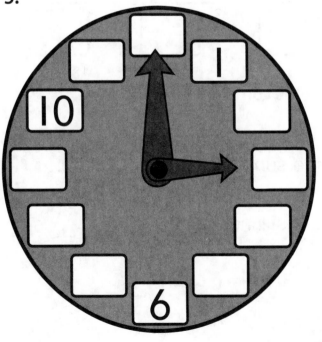

**Use 2 colors to picture the addends.
Complete the addition sentence.**

1.

5 + 2 = ☐

2.

5 + 3 = ☐

3.

5 + 4 = ☐

4.

5 + 5 = ☐

**Complete the addition problems.
Reorder the addends to write the related addition fact.**

5.
```
    6        ☐
  + 2      + ☐
  ───      ───
   ☐        ☐
```

6.
```
    7        ☐
  + 1      + ☐
  ───      ───
   ☐        ☐
```

7.
```
    8        ☐
  + 2      + ☐
  ───      ───
   ☐        ☐
```

Mark the correct number sentence.

8. There were 4 bears napping in the sun. Then 2 bears got up. How many bears are still napping?

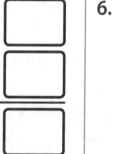

○ 4 + 2 = 6 bears

○ 4 − 2 = 2 bears

9. The 3 little bears sat on a hill. The 3 big bears sat on a hill. How many bears sat on a hill?

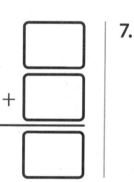

○ 3 + 3 = 6 bears

○ 3 − 3 = 0 bears

Tell Hours Passed

Write the time under each clock.
Write the hours passed.

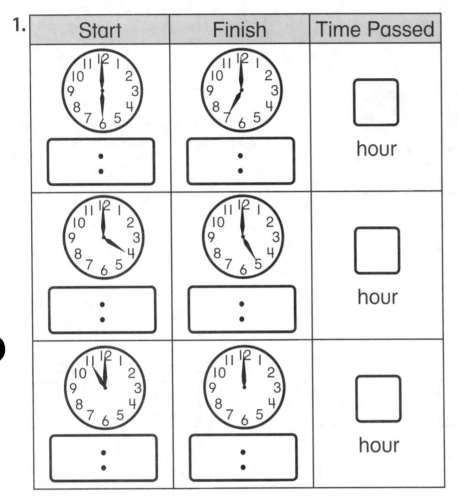

1.

Start	Finish	Time Passed
		▢ hour
		▢ hour
		▢ hour

Draw an hour hand to show 1 hour later.

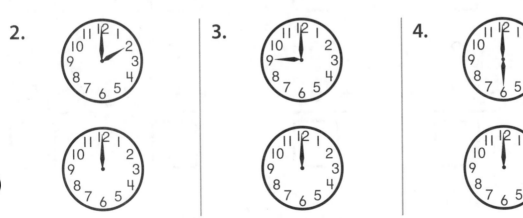

2.

3.

4.

Write the total value as you *count on*.
Do you have enough money to buy the item? Circle *yes* or *no*.

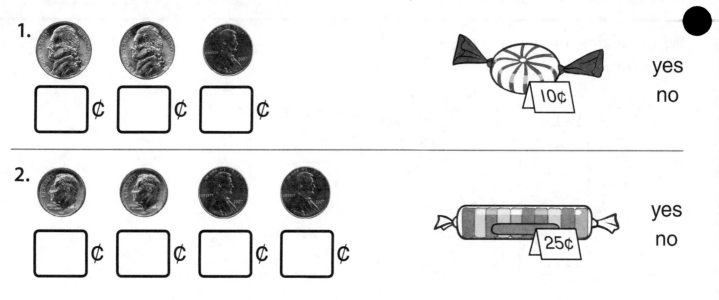

1. [ ]¢ [ ]¢ [ ]¢   10¢   yes
no

2. [ ]¢ [ ]¢ [ ]¢ [ ]¢   25¢   yes
no

Complete the addition problems.

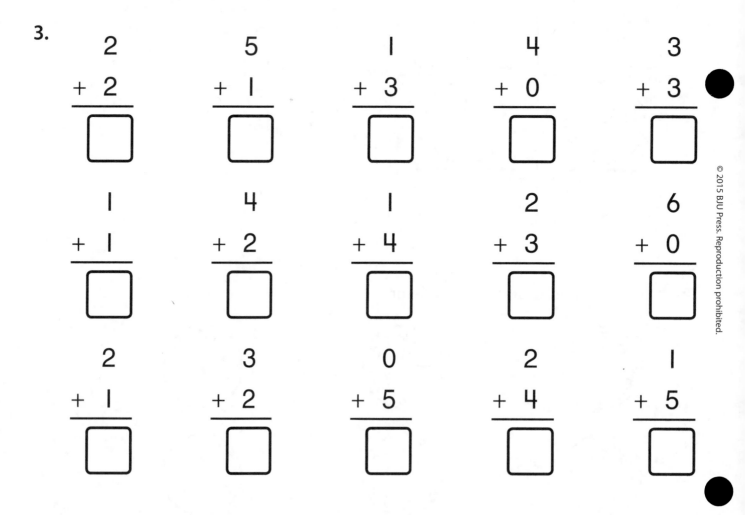

3.

2	5	1	4	3
+ 2	+ 1	+ 3	+ 0	+ 3
[ ]	[ ]	[ ]	[ ]	[ ]

1	4	1	2	6
+ 1	+ 2	+ 4	+ 3	+ 0
[ ]	[ ]	[ ]	[ ]	[ ]

2	3	0	2	1
+ 1	+ 2	+ 5	+ 4	+ 5
[ ]	[ ]	[ ]	[ ]	[ ]

Time to the Half-Hour

Write the missing numbers to show counting the minutes by 5s.

1.

Write the times.

2.

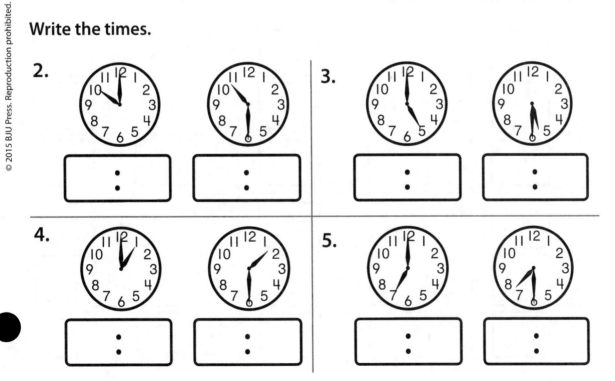

3.

4.

5.

Complete the number sequence.

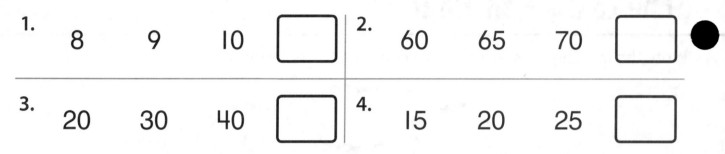

1.
8   9   10   [ ]

2.
60   65   70   [ ] ●

3.
20   30   40   [ ]

4.
15   20   25   [ ]

Write the number of dimes and pennies.
Write the values. Complete the addition sentence.

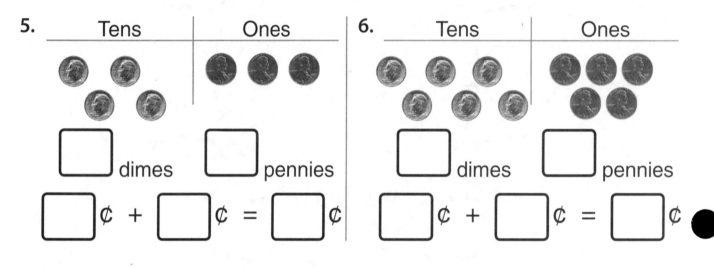

5.

Tens	Ones

[ ] dimes   [ ] pennies

[ ] ¢ + [ ] ¢ = [ ] ¢

6.

Tens	Ones

[ ] dimes   [ ] pennies

[ ] ¢ + [ ] ¢ = [ ] ¢ ●

Complete the addition problem.
Reorder the addends to write the related addition fact.

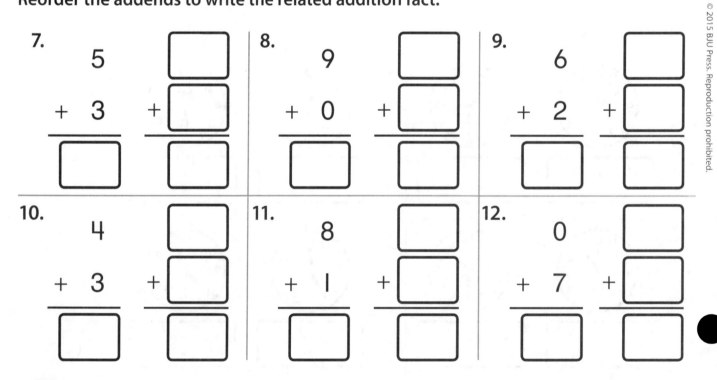

7.
```
    5        [ ]
+   3     + [ ]
─────    ─────
  [ ]      [ ]
```

8.
```
    9        [ ]
+   0     + [ ]
─────    ─────
  [ ]      [ ]
```

9.
```
    6        [ ]
+   2     + [ ]
─────    ─────
  [ ]      [ ]
```

10.
```
    4        [ ]
+   3     + [ ]
─────    ─────
  [ ]      [ ]
```

11.
```
    8        [ ]
+   1     + [ ]
─────    ─────
  [ ]      [ ]
```

12.
```
    0        [ ]
+   7     + [ ]
─────    ─────
  [ ]      [ ]
```
●

Order Events

Number the pictures in order.

1.
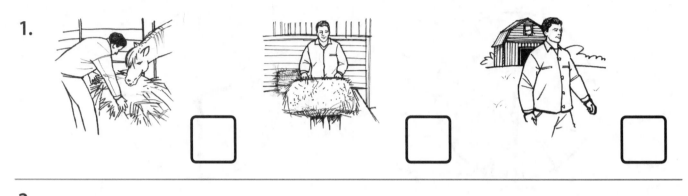

2.
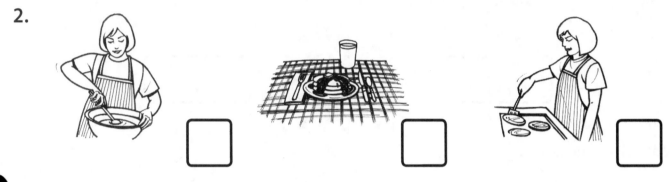

Write the time under each clock.
Circle the time passed.

3.

Weekday Schedule			
Activity	Start	Finish	Time Passed
(child reading)	*(clock)* [:]	*(clock)* [:]	30 minutes I hour
(child on swing)	*(clock)* [:]	*(clock)* [:]	30 minutes I hour

Write the missing numbers to show counting the minutes by 5s.
Write the time.

Write the time.

1.

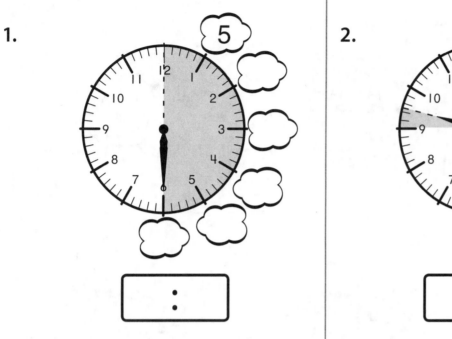

2.

Write the times.

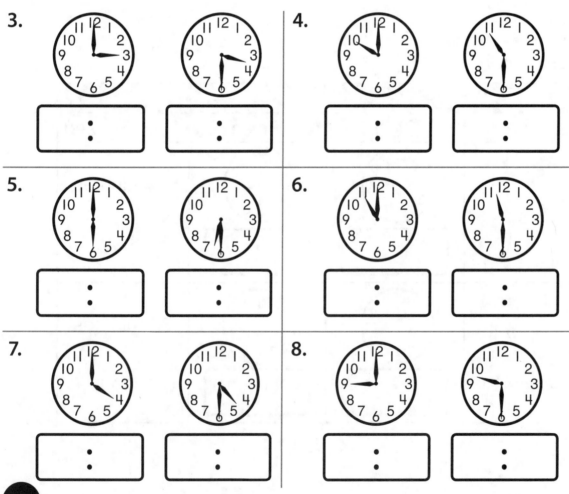

3.

4.

5.

6.

7.

8.

Calendars

	July					
Sunday	Monday	Tuesday	Wednesday	Thursday	Friday	Saturday
			1	2	3	4
5	6	7	8	9	10	11
12	13	14	15	16	17	18
19	20	21	22	23	24	25
26	27	28	29	30	31	

Use the calendar to answer the question.

1. What day is July 4?

◯ Monday   ◯ Thursday   ◯ Saturday

2. How many Wednesdays are in the month?

◯ 3   ◯ 4   ◯ 5

3. What is the date of the last Friday?

◯ 17   ◯ 24   ◯ 31

Number the days of the week in order.

4.

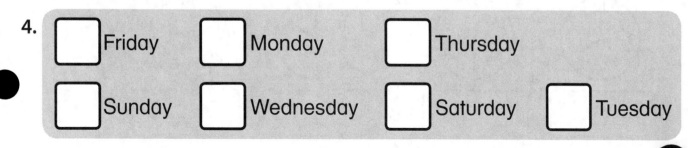

☐ Friday   ☐ Monday   ☐ Thursday

☐ Sunday   ☐ Wednesday   ☐ Saturday   ☐ Tuesday

Number the pictures in order.

1.

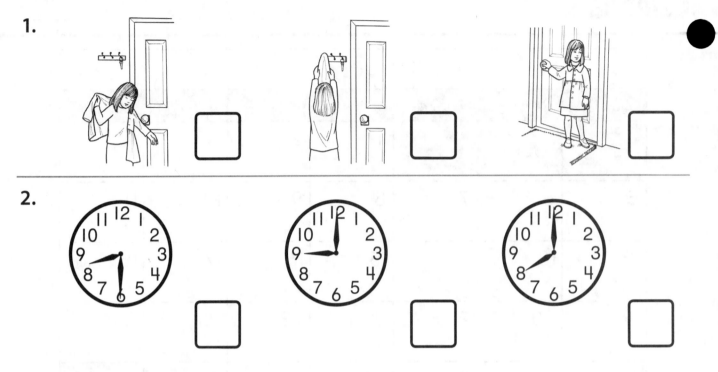

2.

Circle the time passed.

3.

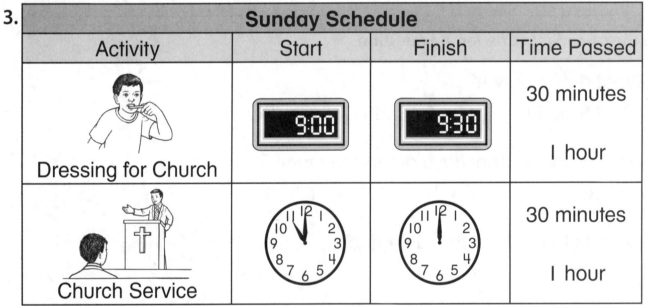

Sunday Schedule			
Activity	Start	Finish	Time Passed
Dressing for Church	9:00	9:30	30 minutes 1 hour
Church Service			30 minutes 1 hour

Write the times.

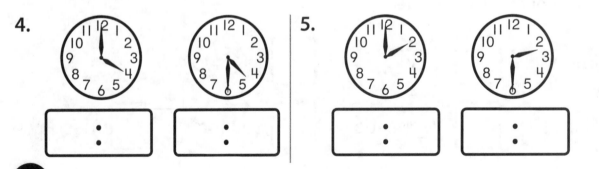

4.

5.

Chapter 8 Review

Complete the statement.

1.

I hour = ☐ minutes

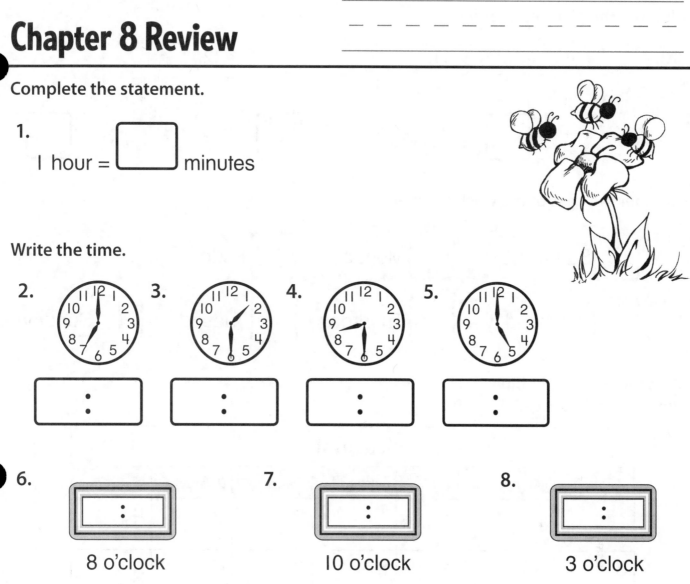

Write the time.

2.

[:]

3.

[:]

4.

[:]

5.

[:]

6.

[:]

8 o'clock

7.

[:]

10 o'clock

8.

[:]

3 o'clock

Circle the time passed.

9.

Job	Start	Finish	Time Passed
			30 minutes I hour
	6:00	7:00	30 minutes I hour

Number the pictures in order.

10. 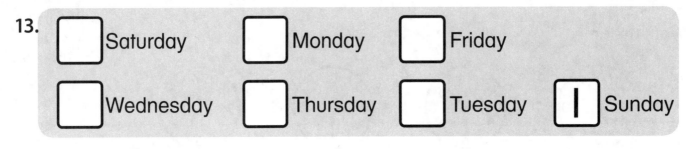 ☐

11. ☐

12. ☐

Number the days of the week in order.

13.
☐ Saturday   ☐ Monday   ☐ Friday

☐ Wednesday   ☐ Thursday   ☐ Tuesday   ☐ 1 Sunday

Color all the Fridays blue.
Put an *X* on August 22.

14.

August						
Sunday	Monday	Tuesday	Wednesday	Thursday	Friday	Saturday
			1	2	3	4
5	6	7	8	9	10	11
12	13	14	15	16	17	18
19	20	21	22	23	24	25
26	27	28	29	30	31	

Use the calendar to answer the question.

15. How many Mondays are in the month?   ◯ 4   ◯ 5   ◯ 6

16. What day is August 31?

◯ Wednesday   ◯ Thursday   ◯ Friday

Cumulative Review

Write the total value as you *count on*.

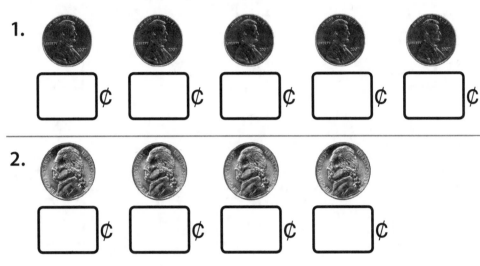

1. ☐ ¢ ☐ ¢ ☐ ¢ ☐ ¢ ☐ ¢

2. ☐ ¢ ☐ ¢ ☐ ¢ ☐ ¢

Write the number represented.
Circle the single cubes to make pairs.
Circle *even* or *odd*.

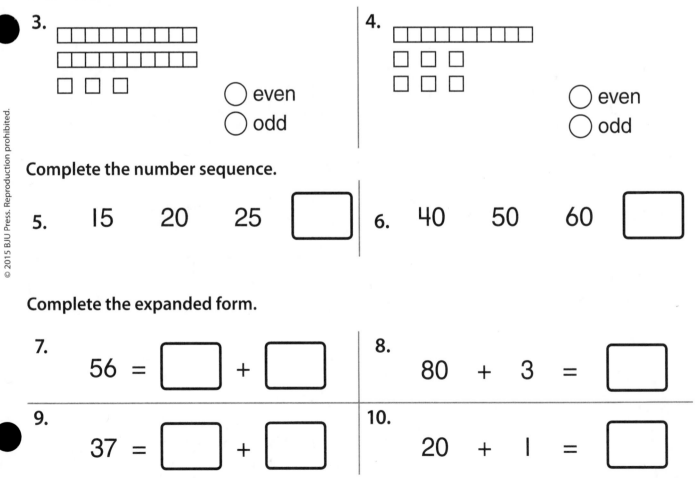

3. ○ even
   ○ odd

4. ○ even
   ○ odd

Complete the number sequence.

5. 15   20   25   ☐

6. 40   50   60   ☐

Complete the expanded form.

7. 56 = ☐ + ☐

8. 80 + 3 = ☐

9. 37 = ☐ + ☐

10. 20 + 1 = ☐

Complete the addition problems.

11.

1
$+\ 3$
☐

2
$+\ 0$
☐

1
$+\ 1$
☐

3
$+\ 2$
☐

1
$+\ 2$
☐

4
$+\ 0$
☐

2
$+\ 1$
☐

2
$+\ 2$
☐

Write an addition sentence for the picture.

12.

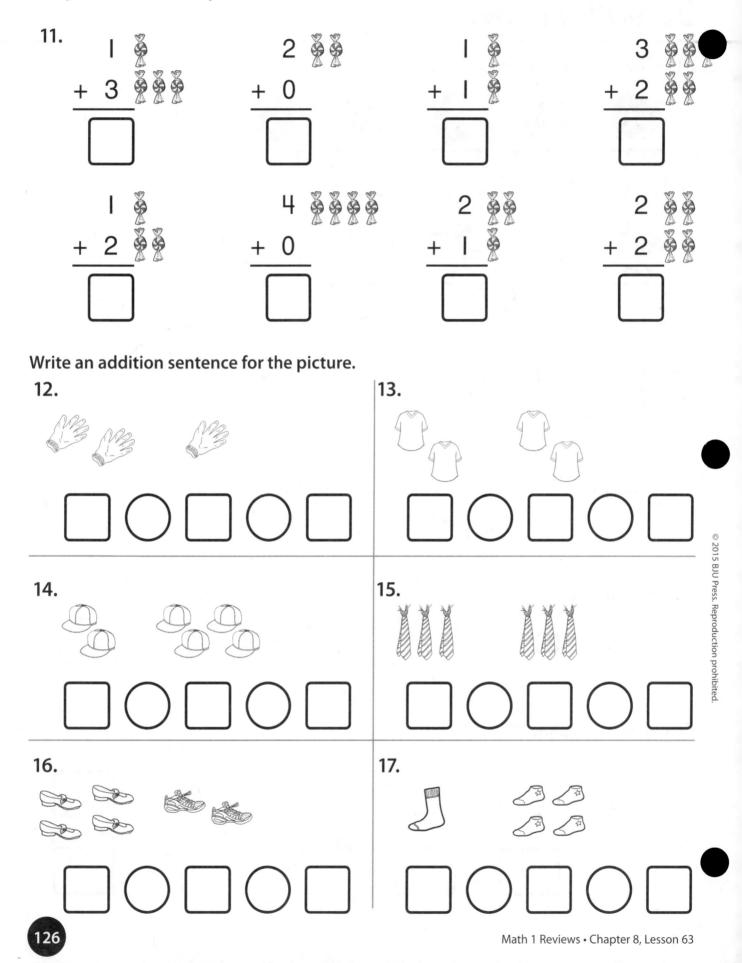

☐ ◯ ☐ ◯ ☐

13.

☐ ◯ ☐ ◯ ☐

14.

☐ ◯ ☐ ◯ ☐

15.

☐ ◯ ☐ ◯ ☐

16.

☐ ◯ ☐ ◯ ☐

17.

☐ ◯ ☐ ◯ ☐

Equal Parts

Circle the number of equal parts.

1.

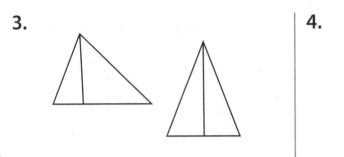

2

3

4

2.

2

3

4

Color the shape that has equal parts.

3.

4.

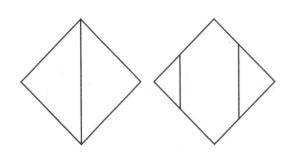

Put an *X* on each shape that does not have 2 equal parts.

5.

Complete the sentence.

6.

7.

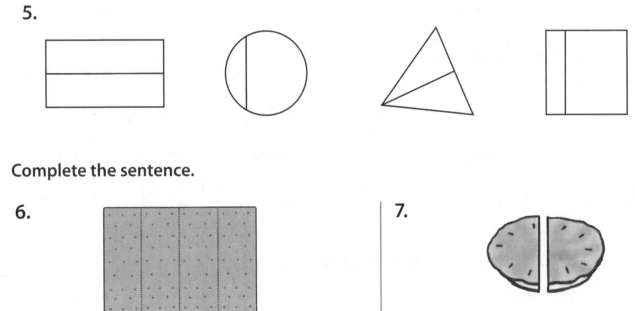

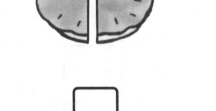

The cracker has ☐ equal parts.

The pie has ☐ equal parts.

Write the time.

1.

2.

3.

Use 2 colors to picture the addends.
Complete the addition sentence.

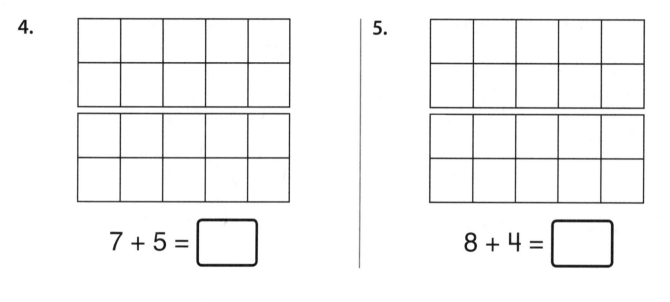

4.

5.

$7 + 5 = \boxed{}$

$8 + 4 = \boxed{}$

Complete the addition problems.

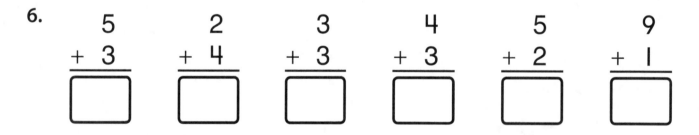

6.

$$\begin{array}{r} 5 \\ + 3 \\ \hline \boxed{} \end{array} \qquad \begin{array}{r} 2 \\ + 4 \\ \hline \boxed{} \end{array} \qquad \begin{array}{r} 3 \\ + 3 \\ \hline \boxed{} \end{array} \qquad \begin{array}{r} 4 \\ + 3 \\ \hline \boxed{} \end{array} \qquad \begin{array}{r} 5 \\ + 2 \\ \hline \boxed{} \end{array} \qquad \begin{array}{r} 9 \\ + 1 \\ \hline \boxed{} \end{array}$$

Count to 150 by 10s. Write the missing numbers.

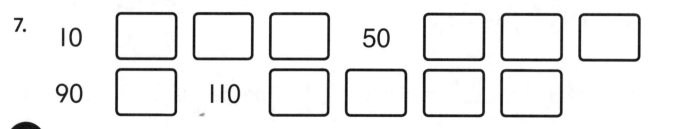

7.

10 ☐ ☐ ☐ 50 ☐ ☐ ☐

90 ☐ 110 ☐ ☐ ☐ ☐

Halves

Halves are 2 equal parts of a whole. Each part is 1 half ($\frac{1}{2}$).

The pizza has 2 equal parts.

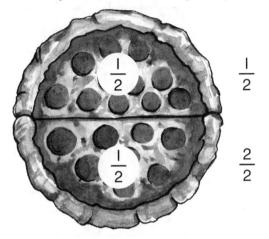

$\frac{1}{2}$

$\frac{2}{2}$

Circle the object that has 2 equal parts.

1. 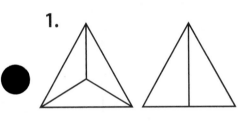   **2.** 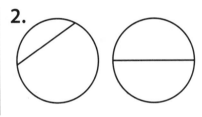   **3.**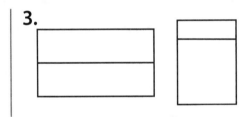

Draw a line from one dot to the other to show halves.

4.   **5.**   **6.**

Color $\frac{1}{2}$ of the shape blue.

7.   **8.**   **9.**   **10.**

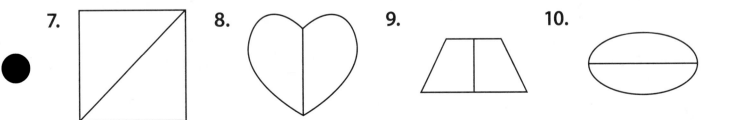

Use 2 colors to picture the addends.
Complete the addition sentence.

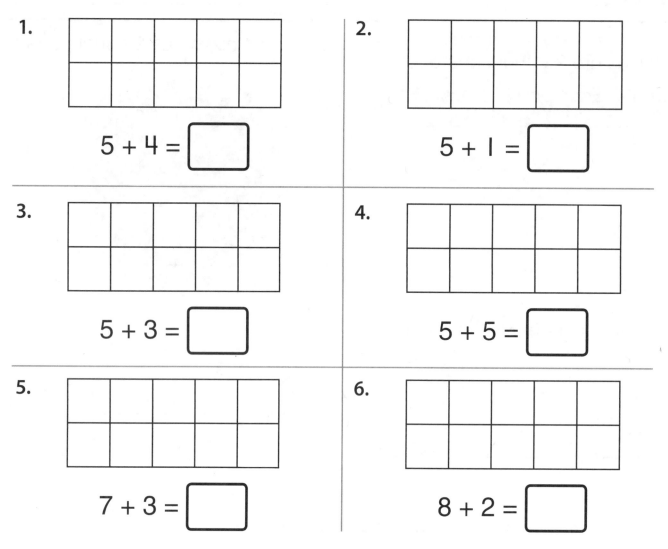

1.

5 + 4 = ☐

2.

5 + 1 = ☐

3.

5 + 3 = ☐

4.

5 + 5 = ☐

5.

7 + 3 = ☐

6.

8 + 2 = ☐

Complete the sentences.

7. Will ran 4 laps. He rested.
   Then he ran 2 more laps.
   How many laps did Will run?

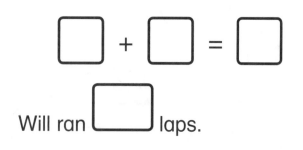

   ☐ + ☐ = ☐

   Will ran ☐ laps.

8. Liz had 6 gumdrops.
   She gave 4 gumdrops to Meg.
   How many gumdrops does Liz
   have left?

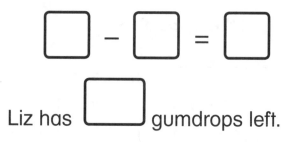

   ☐ – ☐ = ☐

   Liz has ☐ gumdrops left.

Fourths

Fourths are 4 equal parts of a whole. Each part is 1 fourth ($\frac{1}{4}$).

The cake has 4 equal parts.

$\frac{1}{4}$ $\frac{1}{4}$ $\frac{1}{4}$ $\frac{1}{4}$

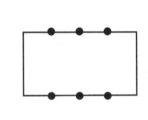

$\frac{1}{4}$ $\frac{2}{4}$ $\frac{3}{4}$ $\frac{4}{4}$

Draw lines to show fourths.

1.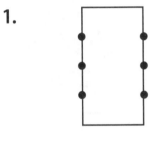

2.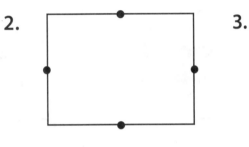

3.

Color $\frac{1}{4}$ of the shape.

4.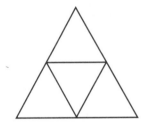

5.

6.

Count the number of shaded parts.
Mark the fraction that names the shaded part.

7.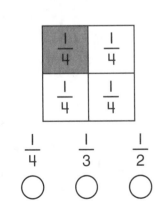

$\frac{1}{4}$ $\frac{1}{3}$ $\frac{1}{2}$

◯   ◯   ◯

8.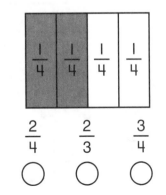

$\frac{2}{4}$ $\frac{2}{3}$ $\frac{3}{4}$

◯   ◯   ◯

9.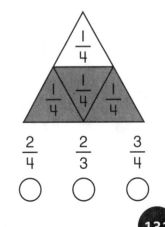

$\frac{2}{4}$ $\frac{2}{3}$ $\frac{3}{4}$

◯   ◯   ◯

Write the number of dimes and pennies.
Write the values. Complete the addition sentence.

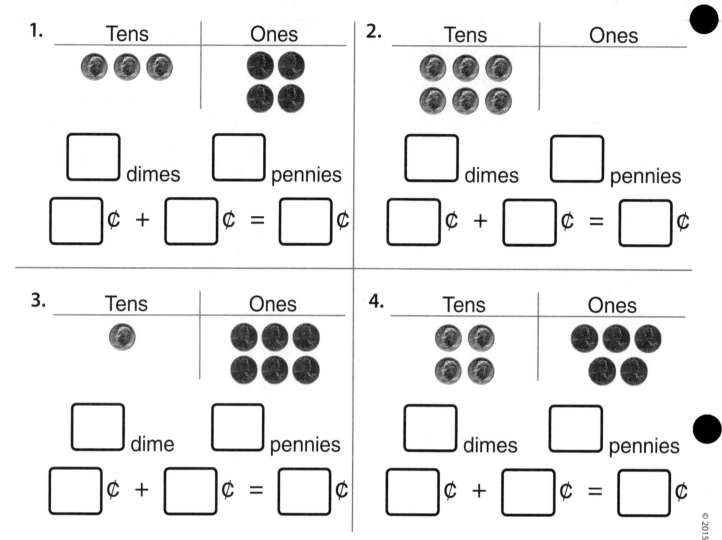

1.

Tens	Ones

☐ dimes   ☐ pennies

☐ ¢ + ☐ ¢ = ☐ ¢

2.

Tens	Ones

☐ dimes   ☐ pennies

☐ ¢ + ☐ ¢ = ☐ ¢

3.

Tens	Ones

☐ dime   ☐ pennies

☐ ¢ + ☐ ¢ = ☐ ¢

4.

Tens	Ones

☐ dimes   ☐ pennies

☐ ¢ + ☐ ¢ = ☐ ¢

Cross out to subtract. Complete the subtraction sentence.

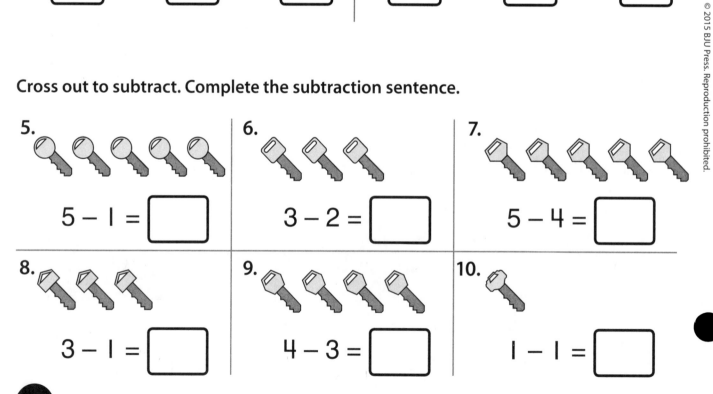

5.   5 − 1 = ☐

6.   3 − 2 = ☐

7.   5 − 4 = ☐

8.   3 − 1 = ☐

9.   4 − 3 = ☐

10.   1 − 1 = ☐

Fourths & Quarters

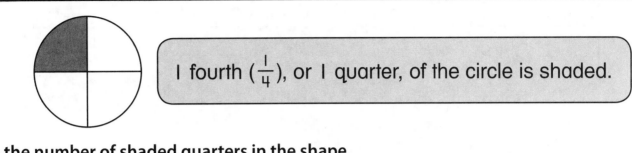

1 fourth ($\frac{1}{4}$), or 1 quarter, of the circle is shaded.

Write the number of shaded quarters in the shape.

1. [ ] quarters   2. [ ] quarters   3. [ ] quarter

Circle the part that completes the shape.

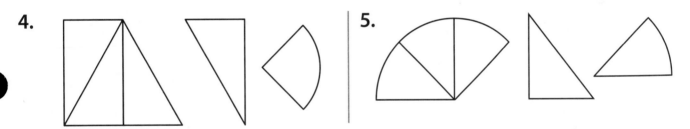

4.   5.

Color to show the named part of the object.

6.
$\frac{1}{2}$ of the pear

7.
$\frac{1}{4}$ of the melon

8.
$\frac{2}{4}$ of the donut

9.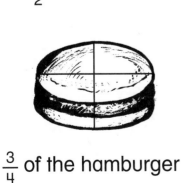
$\frac{3}{4}$ of the hamburger

10.
$\frac{1}{2}$ of the sub

11.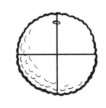
$\frac{2}{4}$ of the orange

Use the bar graph to answer the question.
Circle the answer.

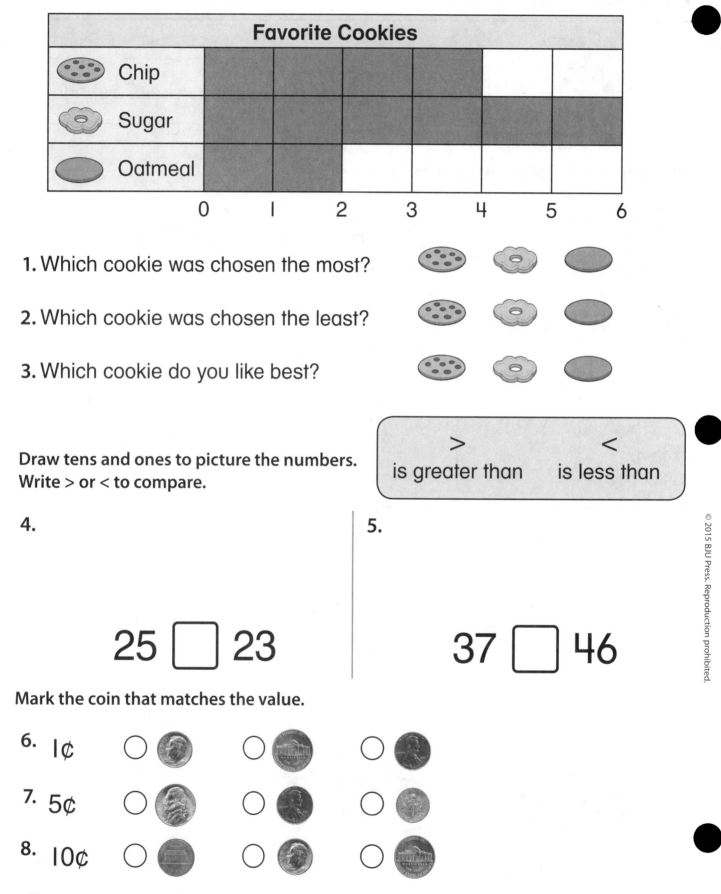

Favorite Cookies

		0	1	2	3	4	5	6
🍪	Chip							
🍩	Sugar							
🥮	Oatmeal							

1. Which cookie was chosen the most?

2. Which cookie was chosen the least?

3. Which cookie do you like best?

> is greater than   < is less than

Draw tens and ones to picture the numbers.
Write > or < to compare.

4.

25 ☐ 23

5.

37 ☐ 46

Mark the coin that matches the value.

6. 1¢ ◯ ◯ ◯

7. 5¢ ◯ ◯ ◯

8. 10¢ ◯ ◯ ◯

Part of a Set

There are 2 bags of flour and 1 of them is shaded.
You can say that $\frac{1}{2}$ of the bags are shaded.

Flour Flour

Mark the fraction that names the shaded part of the set.

1.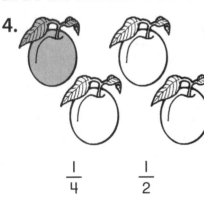

$\frac{3}{4}$ ○ $\frac{4}{4}$ ○

2.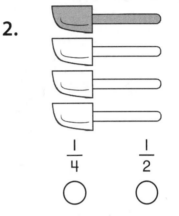

$\frac{1}{4}$ ○ $\frac{1}{2}$ ○

3.

$\frac{1}{4}$ ○ $\frac{1}{2}$ ○

Circle the fraction that names the shaded part of the set.

4.

$\frac{1}{4}$ $\frac{1}{2}$

5.

$\frac{1}{4}$ $\frac{1}{2}$

6.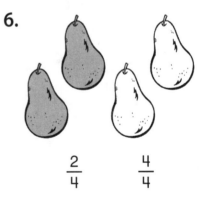

$\frac{2}{4}$ $\frac{4}{4}$

Color to show the named part of the set.

7.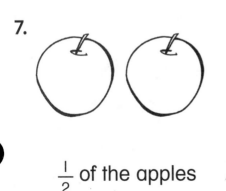

$\frac{1}{2}$ of the apples

8.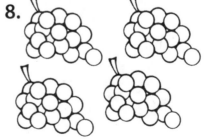

$\frac{3}{4}$ of the grapes

9.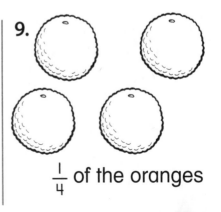

$\frac{1}{4}$ of the oranges

Does the object have fourths? Mark *yes* or *no*.

1. ○ yes ○ no
2. ○ yes ○ no
3. ○ yes ○ no

Color 1 part.
Circle the fraction that names the colored part.

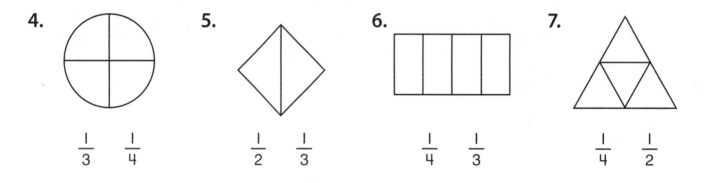

4. $\frac{1}{3}$ $\frac{1}{4}$
5. $\frac{1}{2}$ $\frac{1}{3}$
6. $\frac{1}{4}$ $\frac{1}{3}$
7. $\frac{1}{4}$ $\frac{1}{2}$

Count the parts in the whole.
Color the shape to match the fraction.

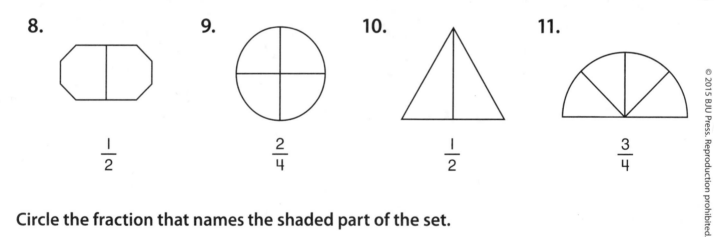

8. $\frac{1}{2}$
9. $\frac{2}{4}$
10. $\frac{1}{2}$
11. $\frac{3}{4}$

Circle the fraction that names the shaded part of the set.

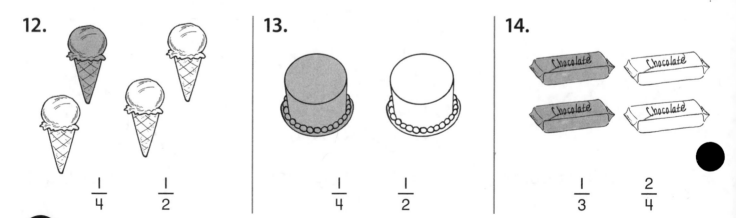

12. $\frac{1}{4}$ $\frac{1}{2}$
13. $\frac{1}{4}$ $\frac{1}{2}$
14. $\frac{1}{3}$ $\frac{2}{4}$

Equal Shares

The gingerbread men equally shared 4 balloons. Each gingerbread man got 2 balloons.

Circle the equal share for each child.
Complete the sentence.

1.

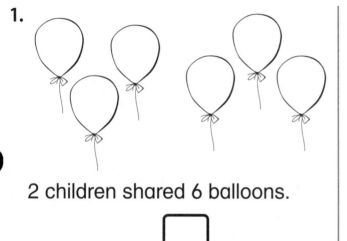

2 children shared 6 balloons.

Each child got ☐ balloons.

2.

2 children shared 4 balloons.

Each child got ☐ balloons.

Read the story. Mark the answer.

3. Ashlynn and 3 friends shared a cake. Ashlynn cut the cake into equal shares. Which picture shows the cake?

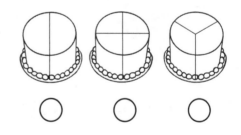

4. Josh and Aaron shared an apple. They cut the apple into equal shares. Which picture shows their apple?

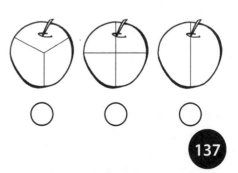

Circle the equal share for each child.
Complete the sentence.

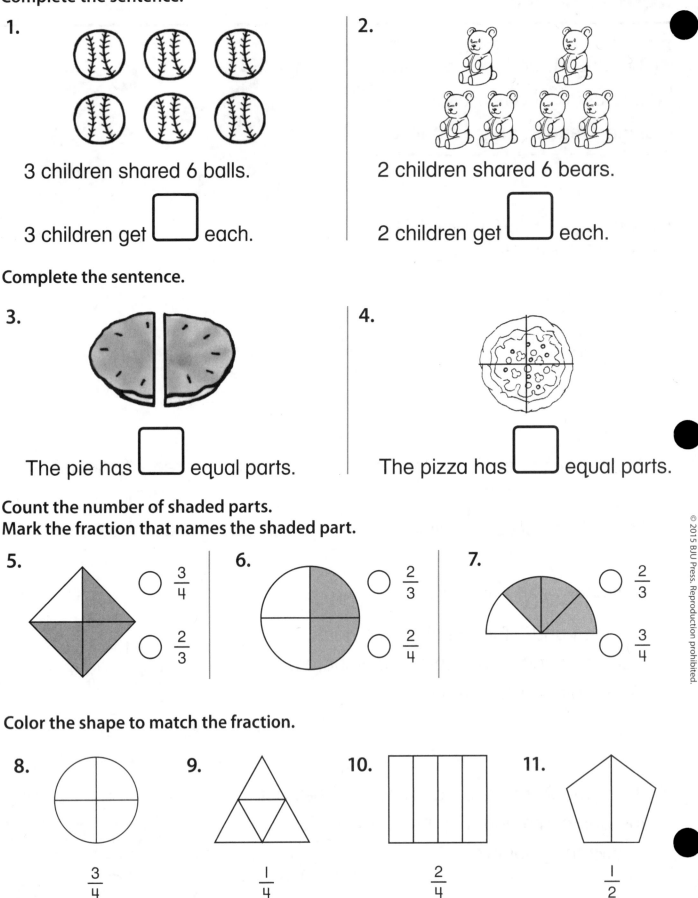

1.

3 children shared 6 balls.

3 children get ☐ each.

2.

2 children shared 6 bears.

2 children get ☐ each.

Complete the sentence.

3.

The pie has ☐ equal parts.

4.

The pizza has ☐ equal parts.

Count the number of shaded parts.
Mark the fraction that names the shaded part.

5.
○ $\frac{3}{4}$
○ $\frac{2}{3}$

6.
○ $\frac{2}{3}$
○ $\frac{2}{4}$

7.
○ $\frac{2}{3}$
○ $\frac{3}{4}$

Color the shape to match the fraction.

8.
$\frac{3}{4}$

9.
$\frac{1}{4}$

10.
$\frac{2}{4}$

11.
$\frac{1}{2}$

Chapter 9 Review

Circle the shape that has equal parts.
Write the number of equal parts.

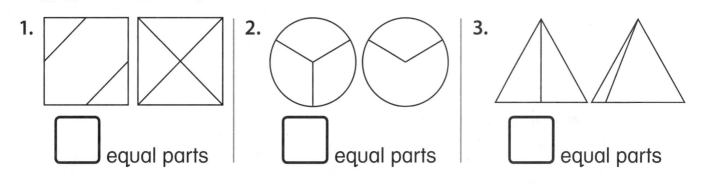

1. [ ] equal parts

2. [ ] equal parts

3. [ ] equal parts

Count the number of shaded parts.
Circle the fraction that names the shaded part.

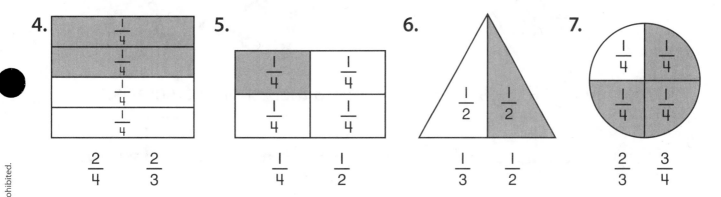

4. $\frac{2}{4}$ $\frac{2}{3}$

5. $\frac{1}{4}$ $\frac{1}{2}$

6. $\frac{1}{3}$ $\frac{1}{2}$

7. $\frac{2}{3}$ $\frac{3}{4}$

Color the shape to match the fraction.

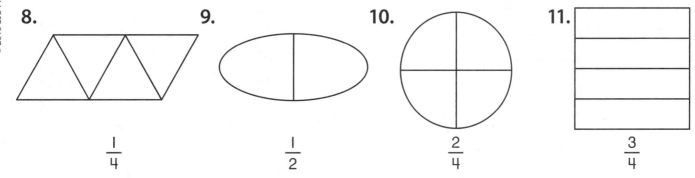

8. $\frac{1}{4}$

9. $\frac{1}{2}$

10. $\frac{2}{4}$

11. $\frac{3}{4}$

Circle the fraction that names the shaded part of the set.

12.

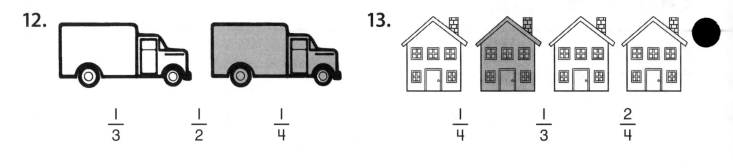

$\frac{1}{3}$ $\frac{1}{2}$ $\frac{1}{4}$

13.

$\frac{1}{4}$ $\frac{1}{3}$ $\frac{2}{4}$

Circle the equal share for each man.
Complete the sentence.

14.

2 men shared 4 tools.

Each man got ☐ tools.

15.

3 men shared 6 screws.

Each man got ☐ screws.

Complete the sentence.

16.

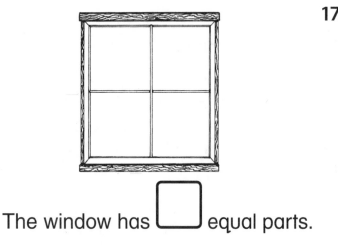

The window has ☐ equal parts.

17.

The mirror has ☐ equal parts.

Cumulative Review

Complete the addition problems.
Reorder the addends to write the related addition fact.

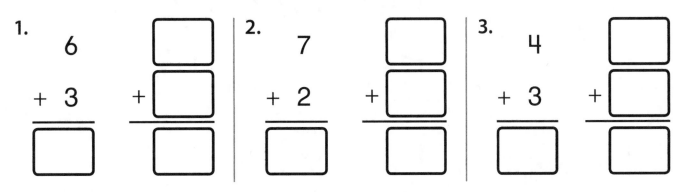

1.
6
+ 3
___

+ □
□
___
□

2.
7
+ 2
___

+ □
□
___
□

3.
4
+ 3
___

+ □
□
___
□

Draw squares to picture the story. Complete the sentences.

4. Lisa made 2 sandwiches.

   She made 3 more sandwiches.

   How many sandwiches did Lisa make in all?

   Lisa made □ sandwiches in all.

   □ + □ = □

Count by 1s, by 5s, or by 10s. Write the value of each set.

5. □ ¢

6. □ ¢

7. □ ¢

Write the time under each clock.
Write the hours passed for each job.

8.

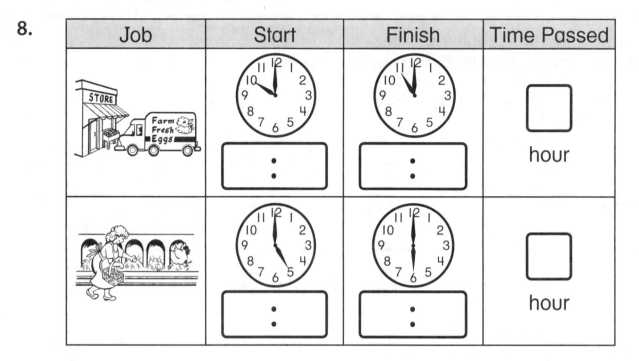

Job	Start	Finish	Time Passed
STORE Farm Fresh Eggs	[clock] :	[clock] :	☐ hour
	[clock] :	[clock] :	☐ hour

Draw the hour hand to show 1 hour later.

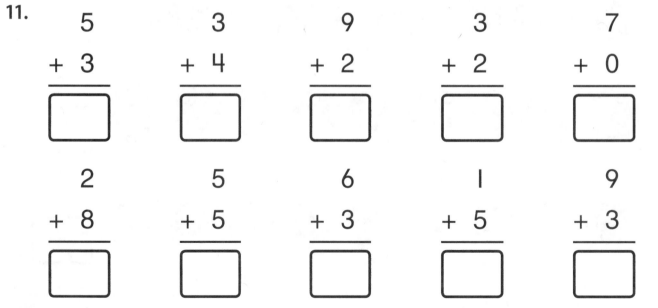

9.

10.

Complete the addition problems.

11.

$$5 + 3 = \boxed{}$$
$$3 + 4 = \boxed{}$$
$$9 + 2 = \boxed{}$$
$$3 + 2 = \boxed{}$$
$$7 + 0 = \boxed{}$$

$$2 + 8 = \boxed{}$$
$$5 + 5 = \boxed{}$$
$$6 + 3 = \boxed{}$$
$$1 + 5 = \boxed{}$$
$$9 + 3 = \boxed{}$$

Count Back 1 or 2; Subtract 0

Draw back jumps to subtract.
Complete the subtraction sentence.

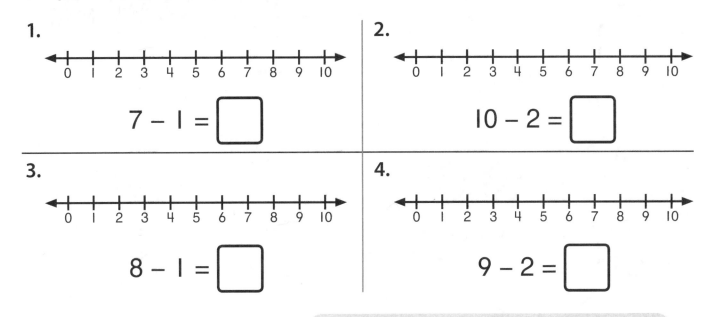

1.

0 1 2 3 4 5 6 7 8 9 10

7 − 1 = ☐

2.

0 1 2 3 4 5 6 7 8 9 10

10 − 2 = ☐

3.

0 1 2 3 4 5 6 7 8 9 10

8 − 1 = ☐

4.

0 1 2 3 4 5 6 7 8 9 10

9 − 2 = ☐

● Complete the subtraction problem.

> When 0 is subtracted from a number, the answer is that number.

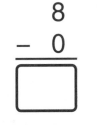 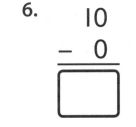 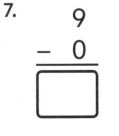 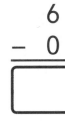 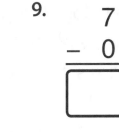

5.
```
  8
− 0
────
☐
```

6.
```
  10
−  0
────
☐
```

7.
```
  9
− 0
────
☐
```

8.
```
  6
− 0
────
☐
```

9.
```
  7
− 0
────
☐
```

Complete the subtraction sentences.

10. Subtract 0

5 − 0 = ☐

3 − 0 = ☐

2 − 0 = ☐

11. *Count Back 1*

9 − 1 = ☐

6 − 1 = ☐

10 − 1 = ☐

12. *Count Back 2*

10 − 2 = ☐

8 − 2 = ☐

8 − 2 = ☐

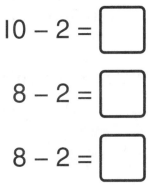

Cross out to subtract. Complete the subtraction problem.

1.
$$\begin{array}{r} 5 \\ -\ 3 \\ \hline \end{array}$$

2.
$$\begin{array}{r} 6 \\ -\ 0 \\ \hline \end{array}$$

3.
$$\begin{array}{r} 4 \\ -\ 4 \\ \hline \end{array}$$

4.
$$\begin{array}{r} 3 \\ -\ 2 \\ \hline \end{array}$$

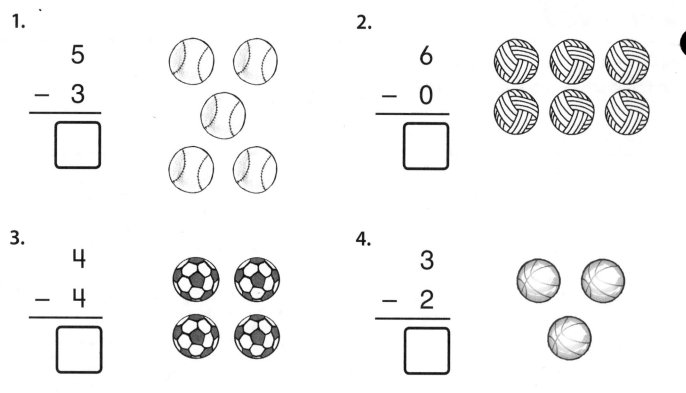

Draw shapes to picture the story.
Cross out to subtract. Complete the sentences.

5. Tom has 3 flags.
   He lost 1 flag.
   How many flags
   does Tom have now?

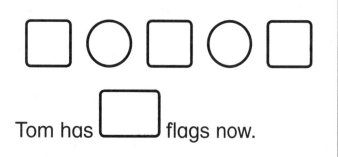

Tom has ☐ flags now.

6. Pam has 6 caps.
   She gave 4 caps away.
   How many caps
   does Pam have left?

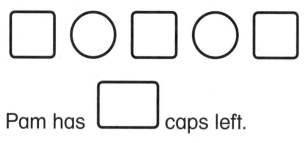

Pam has ☐ caps left.

Write the value of the coin.

7. ☐ ¢

8. ☐ ¢

9. ☐ ¢

Subtract All or Nearly All

Subtract all

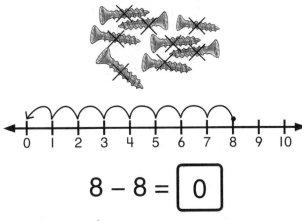

$$8 - 8 = \boxed{0}$$

Subtract nearly all

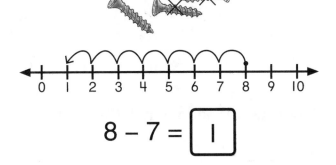

$$8 - 7 = \boxed{1}$$

Cross out to subtract.
Complete the subtraction sentence.

1.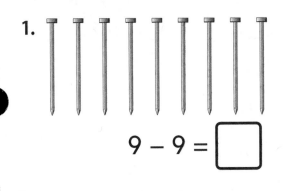

$$9 - 9 = \boxed{}$$

2.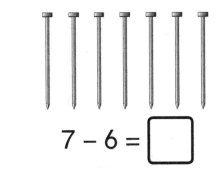

$$7 - 6 = \boxed{}$$

Draw back jumps to subtract.
Complete the subtraction sentence.

3.

$$9 - 8 = \boxed{}$$

4.

$$6 - 6 = \boxed{}$$

Complete the subtraction problem.

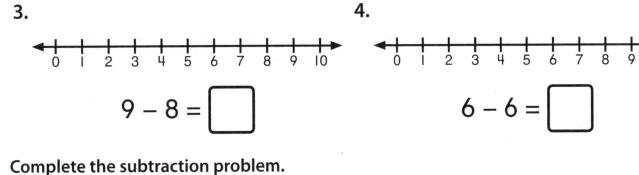

5.
$$\begin{array}{r} 5 \\ -\ 5 \\ \hline \boxed{} \end{array}$$

6.
$$\begin{array}{r} 7 \\ -\ 7 \\ \hline \boxed{} \end{array}$$

7.
$$\begin{array}{r} 10 \\ -\ 10 \\ \hline \boxed{} \end{array}$$

8.
$$\begin{array}{r} 5 \\ -\ 4 \\ \hline \boxed{} \end{array}$$

9.
$$\begin{array}{r} 4 \\ -\ 3 \\ \hline \boxed{} \end{array}$$

Circle the fraction that names the shaded part.

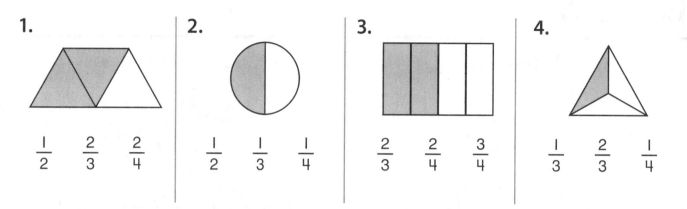

1.
$\frac{1}{2}$ $\frac{2}{3}$ $\frac{2}{4}$

2.
$\frac{1}{2}$ $\frac{1}{3}$ $\frac{1}{4}$

3.
$\frac{2}{3}$ $\frac{2}{4}$ $\frac{3}{4}$

4.
$\frac{1}{3}$ $\frac{2}{3}$ $\frac{1}{4}$

Color the shape to match the fraction.

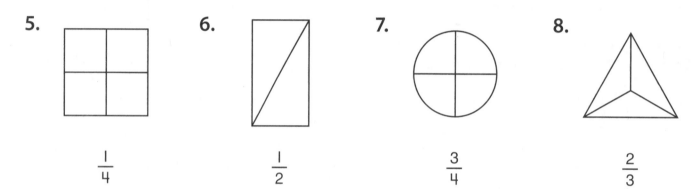

5.
$\frac{1}{4}$

6.
$\frac{1}{2}$

7.
$\frac{3}{4}$

8.
$\frac{2}{3}$

Complete the subtraction sentences.

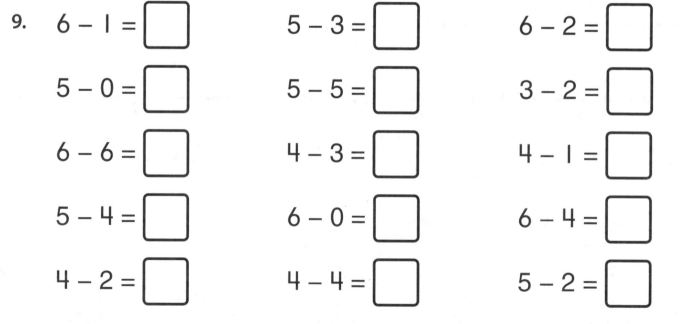

9. $6 - 1 = \boxed{}$ $5 - 3 = \boxed{}$ $6 - 2 = \boxed{}$

$5 - 0 = \boxed{}$ $5 - 5 = \boxed{}$ $3 - 2 = \boxed{}$

$6 - 6 = \boxed{}$ $4 - 3 = \boxed{}$ $4 - 1 = \boxed{}$

$5 - 4 = \boxed{}$ $6 - 0 = \boxed{}$ $6 - 4 = \boxed{}$

$4 - 2 = \boxed{}$ $4 - 4 = \boxed{}$ $5 - 2 = \boxed{}$

Compare Sets

Compare the sets. Complete the sentences.

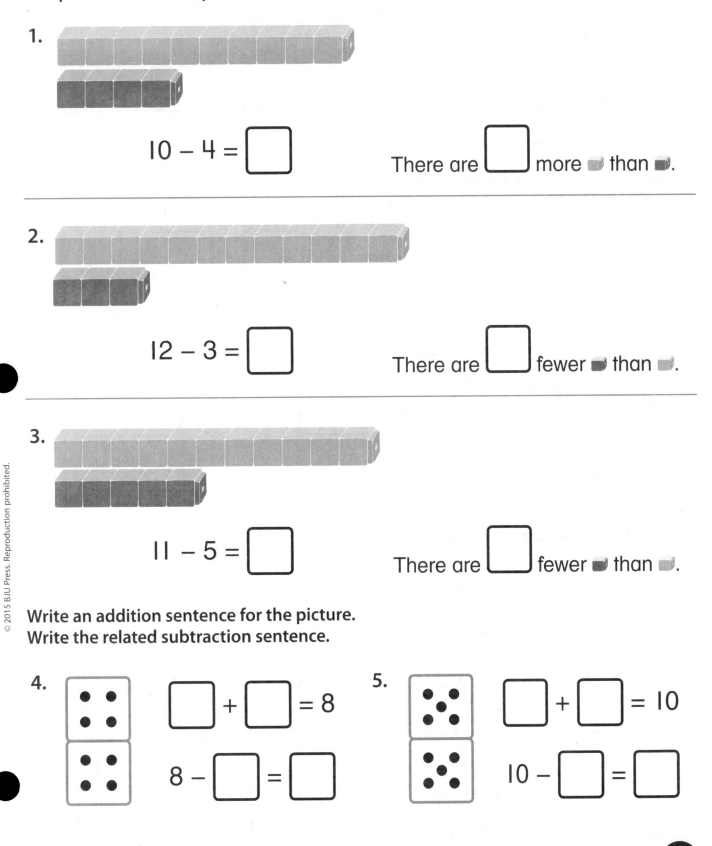

1.

$$10 - 4 = \boxed{}$$

There are $\boxed{}$ more ▬ than ▬.

2.

$$12 - 3 = \boxed{}$$

There are $\boxed{}$ fewer ▬ than ▬.

3.

$$11 - 5 = \boxed{}$$

There are $\boxed{}$ fewer ▬ than ▬.

Write an addition sentence for the picture.
Write the related subtraction sentence.

4.

$$\boxed{} + \boxed{} = 8$$

$$8 - \boxed{} = \boxed{}$$

5.

$$\boxed{} + \boxed{} = 10$$

$$10 - \boxed{} = \boxed{}$$

Draw dots to picture the story.
Complete the sentences.

1. Jay had 6 cars. He gave 2 cars to a friend. How many cars does Jay have left?

   Jay has ⬚ cars left.

   ⬚ – ⬚ = ⬚

2. Maci had 7 dolls. Nana gave her 3 more dolls. How many dolls does Maci have in all?

   Maci has ⬚ dolls in all.

   ⬚ + ⬚ = ⬚

Write the time.

3. [:]

   3 o'clock

4. [:]

   10 o'clock

5. [:]

   7 o'clock

Complete the addition problems.

6.
```
    5          2
  + 2        + 5
  ____       ____
  [  ]       [  ]
```

7.
```
    7          2
  + 2        + 7
  ____       ____
  [  ]       [  ]
```

8.
```
    6          2
  + 2        + 6
  ____       ____
  [  ]       [  ]
```

9.
```
    8          2
  + 2        + 8
  ____       ____
  [  ]       [  ]
```

Missing Addend;
Subtract from 10

Draw more to make a set of 10. Complete the related facts.

1.

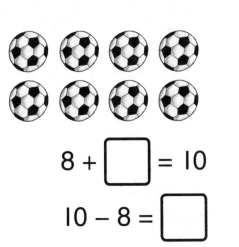

$8 + \boxed{} = 10$

$10 - 8 = \boxed{}$

2.

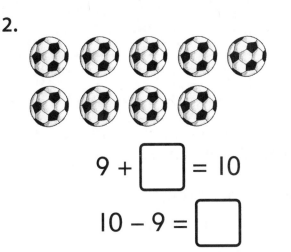

$9 + \boxed{} = 10$

$10 - 9 = \boxed{}$

Complete the subtraction sentence.

3. $10 - 7 = \boxed{}$

4. $10 - 4 = \boxed{}$

5. $10 - 5 = \boxed{}$

6. $10 - 9 = \boxed{}$

7. $10 - 6 = \boxed{}$

8. $10 - 8 = \boxed{}$

Draw more gifts to picture the story.
Complete the sentences.

9. Anna has 3 birthday gifts.
   She will get 5 gifts in all.
   How many gifts will Anna get?

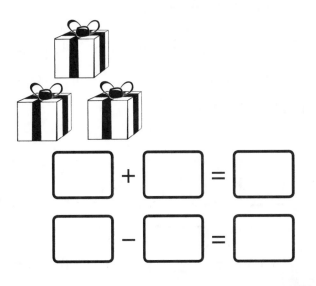

$\boxed{} + \boxed{} = \boxed{}$

$\boxed{} - \boxed{} = \boxed{}$

Write the time.

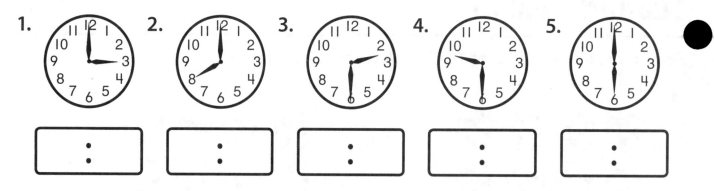

1.
2.
3.
4.
5.

Circle the correct number sentence for the story.
Complete the sentence.

6. Alex had 5 nuts.
He gave 2 nuts to Sam.
How many nuts does Alex
have now?

$$5 + 2 = 7$$

$$5 - 2 = 3$$

Alex has ⬚ nuts now.

7. Kim painted 4 pictures for
Grandmother. She painted 2 more
pictures for Mom. How many
pictures did Kim paint?

$$4 + 2 = 6$$

$$4 - 2 = 2$$

Kim painted ⬚ pictures.

Write a number sentence for the story.
Complete the sentence.

8. Mom put 4 red roses and 4 pink
roses in a vase. How many roses
are in the vase?

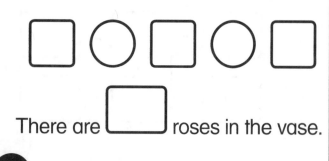

There are ⬚ roses in the vase.

9. There were 6 bugs on the bush.
Then 3 bugs left. How many bugs
are still on the bush?

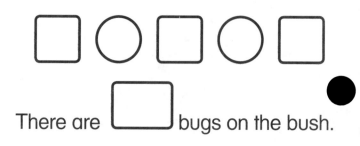

There are ⬚ bugs on the bush.

Fact Families

Write the related facts for the fact family.

1.

$(2)(4)(6)$

Which number represents the whole? Which numbers represent the parts?

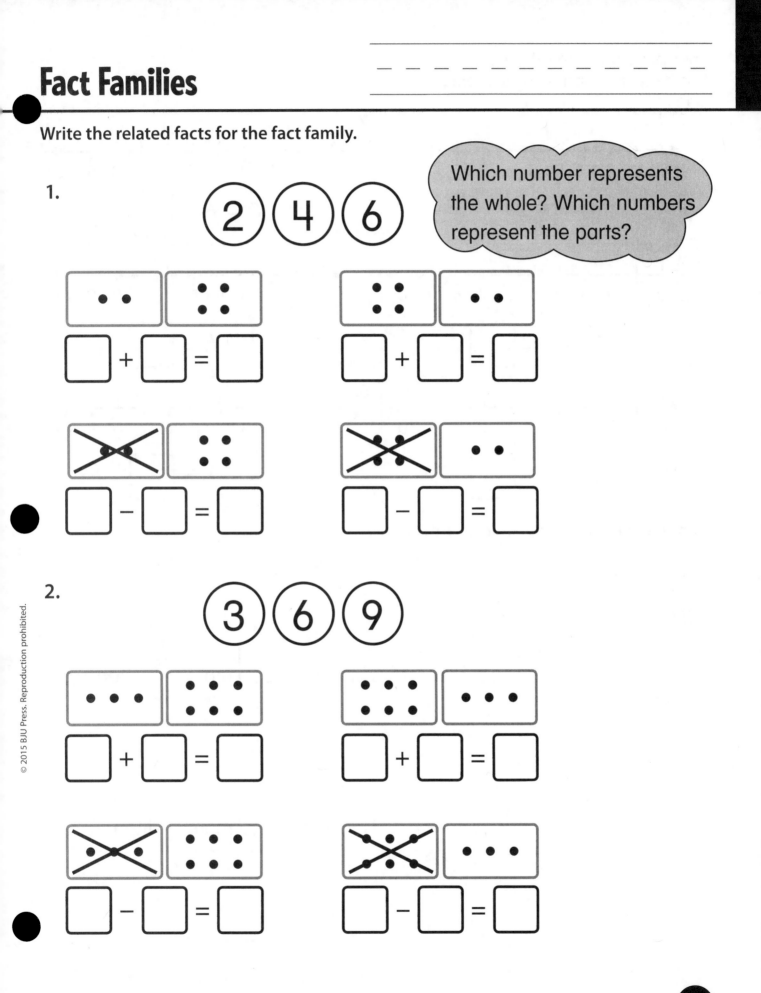

□ + □ = □

□ + □ = □

□ − □ = □

□ − □ = □

2.

$(3)(6)(9)$

□ + □ = □

□ + □ = □

□ − □ = □

□ − □ = □

Draw back jumps to subtract.
Complete the subtraction sentence.

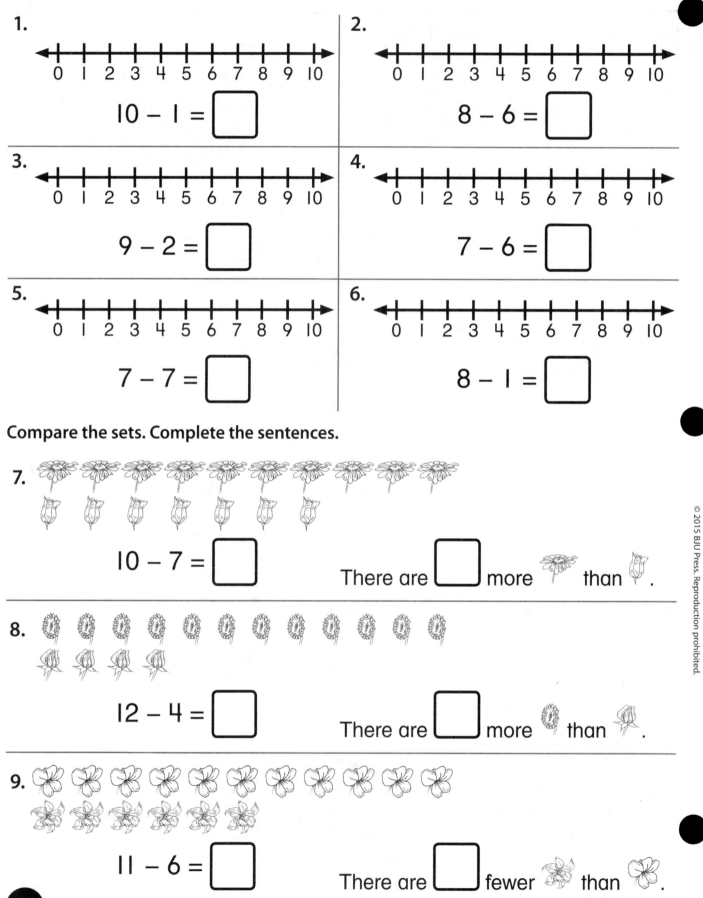

1.

$10 - 1 = \boxed{}$

2.

$8 - 6 = \boxed{}$

3.

$9 - 2 = \boxed{}$

4.

$7 - 6 = \boxed{}$

5.

$7 - 7 = \boxed{}$

6.

$8 - 1 = \boxed{}$

Compare the sets. Complete the sentences.

7.

$10 - 7 = \boxed{}$

There are $\boxed{}$ more 🌼 than 🌷.

8.

$12 - 4 = \boxed{}$

There are $\boxed{}$ more 🌼 than 🌷.

9.

$11 - 6 = \boxed{}$

There are $\boxed{}$ fewer 🌼 than 🌸.

152

Fact Families for 11

Write the number of monkeys to name the fact family.
Write the related facts.

1.

◯ monkeys by a tree   ◯ monkeys running away   ◯ monkeys in all

☐ + ☐ = ☐   ☐ – ☐ = ☐

☐ + ☐ = ☐   ☐ – ☐ = ☐

Complete the sentences.

2. 5 monkeys ate a banana. There are 11 monkeys in all. How many monkeys did not eat a banana?

☐ monkeys did not eat a banana.

☐ + ☐ = ☐

☐ – ☐ = ☐

3. 2 monkeys took a nap. There are 11 monkeys in all. How many monkeys did not take a nap?

☐ monkeys did not take a nap.

☐ + ☐ = ☐

☐ – ☐ = ☐

Write the number of bees to name the fact family.
Write the related facts.

1.

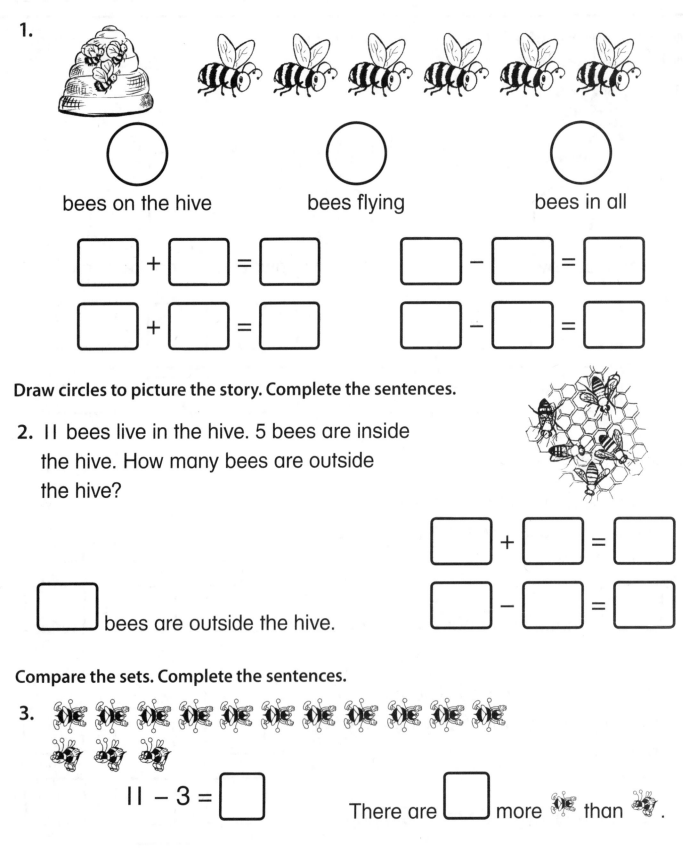

bees on the hive   bees flying   bees in all

☐ + ☐ = ☐   ☐ − ☐ = ☐

☐ + ☐ = ☐   ☐ − ☐ = ☐

Draw circles to picture the story. Complete the sentences.

2. 11 bees live in the hive. 5 bees are inside the hive. How many bees are outside the hive?

☐ bees are outside the hive.

☐ + ☐ = ☐

☐ − ☐ = ☐

Compare the sets. Complete the sentences.

3.

11 − 3 = ☐   There are ☐ more 🐝 than 🐝.

Fact Families for 12

Write the numbers for the fact family.
Write the related facts.

1.

◯ horses standing   ◯ horses running   ◯ horses in all

☐ + ☐ = ☐

☐ + ☐ = ☐

☐ – ☐ = ☐

☐ – ☐ = ☐

2.

◯ gray horses   ◯ white horses   ◯ horses in all

☐ + ☐ = ☐

☐ + ☐ = ☐

☐ – ☐ = ☐

☐ – ☐ = ☐

Write numbers for another fact family for 12.

3.   ◯   ◯   ◯

Complete the sentences.

4. 12 horses were in the pasture altogether.
2 horses were eating grass. How many
horses were not eating grass?

☐ + ☐ = ☐

☐ – ☐ = ☐

☐ horses were not eating grass.

Circle the fraction that names the shaded part of the set.

1.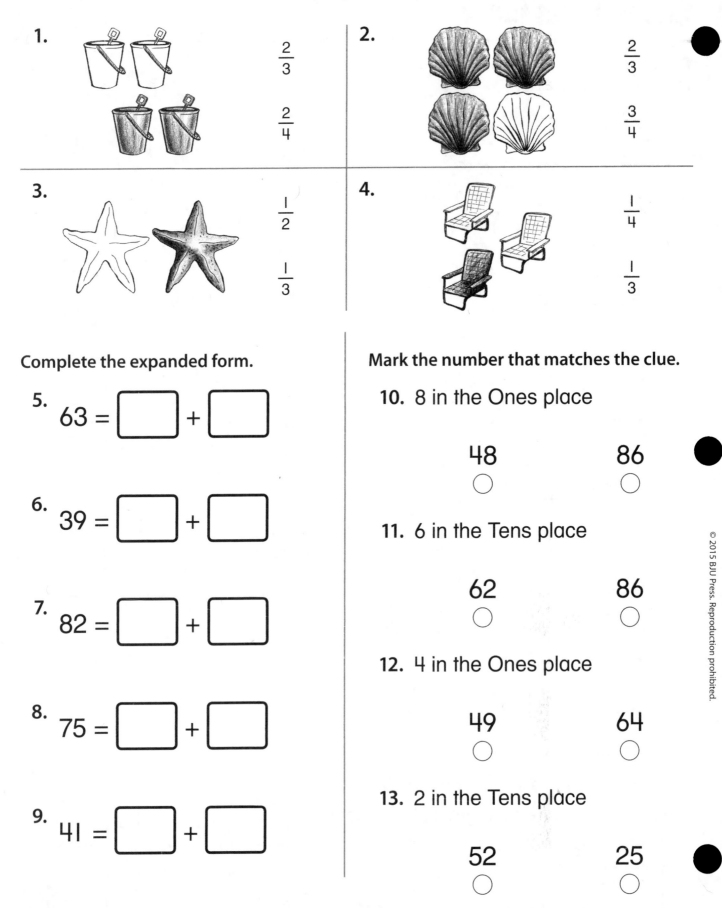

$\frac{2}{3}$

$\frac{2}{4}$

2.

$\frac{2}{3}$

$\frac{3}{4}$

3.

$\frac{1}{2}$

$\frac{1}{3}$

4.

$\frac{1}{4}$

$\frac{1}{3}$

Complete the expanded form.

5. 63 = ☐ + ☐

6. 39 = ☐ + ☐

7. 82 = ☐ + ☐

8. 75 = ☐ + ☐

9. 41 = ☐ + ☐

Mark the number that matches the clue.

10. 8 in the Ones place

48 ○   86 ○

11. 6 in the Tens place

62 ○   86 ○

12. 4 in the Ones place

49 ○   64 ○

13. 2 in the Tens place

52 ○   25 ○

Chapter 10 Review

Draw back jumps to subtract.
Complete the subtraction sentence.

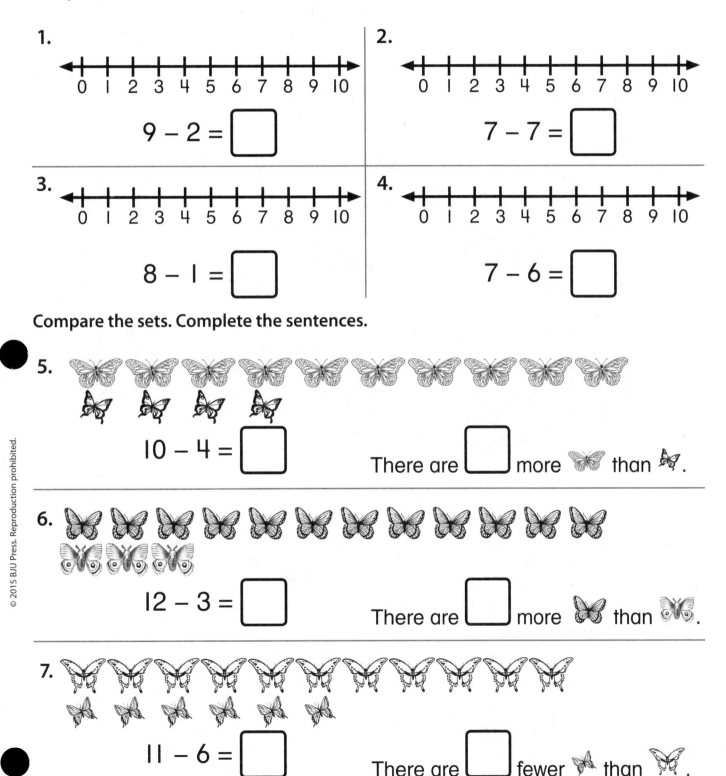

1.

0 1 2 3 4 5 6 7 8 9 10

$9 - 2 = \boxed{}$

2.

0 1 2 3 4 5 6 7 8 9 10

$7 - 7 = \boxed{}$

3.

0 1 2 3 4 5 6 7 8 9 10

$8 - 1 = \boxed{}$

4.

0 1 2 3 4 5 6 7 8 9 10

$7 - 6 = \boxed{}$

Compare the sets. Complete the sentences.

5.

$10 - 4 = \boxed{}$

There are $\boxed{}$ more 🦋 than 🦋.

6.

$12 - 3 = \boxed{}$

There are $\boxed{}$ more 🦋 than 🦋.

7.

$11 - 6 = \boxed{}$

There are $\boxed{}$ fewer 🦋 than 🦋.

Complete the related facts.

8. 7 + ☐ = 10

    10 − 7 = ☐

9. 5 + ☐ = 11

    11 − 5 = ☐

10. 4 + ☐ = 12

    12 − 4 = ☐

Write the number of butterflies to name the fact family.
Write the related facts.

11.

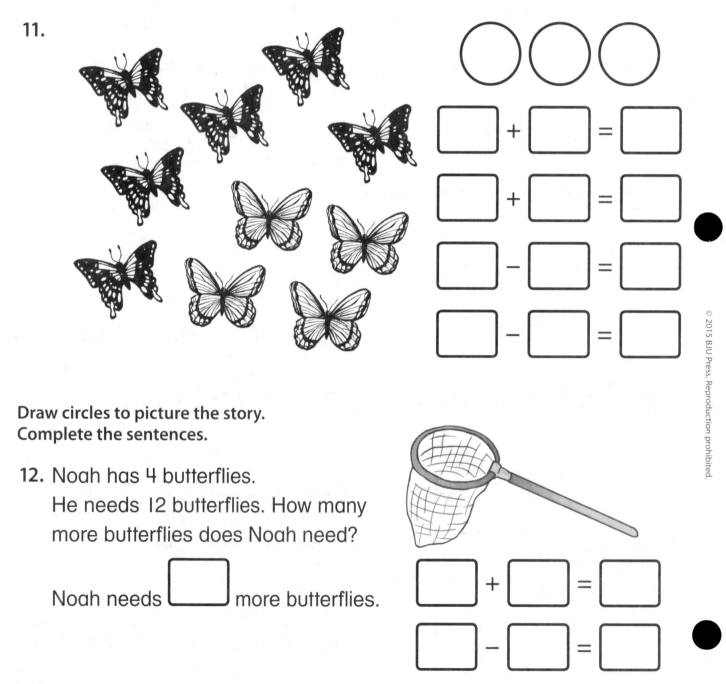

☐ ☐ ☐

☐ + ☐ = ☐

☐ + ☐ = ☐

☐ − ☐ = ☐

☐ − ☐ = ☐

Draw circles to picture the story.
Complete the sentences.

12. Noah has 4 butterflies.
    He needs 12 butterflies. How many
    more butterflies does Noah need?

    Noah needs ☐ more butterflies.

    ☐ + ☐ = ☐

    ☐ − ☐ = ☐

Cumulative Review

Circle the longest object. Put an *X* on the shortest object.

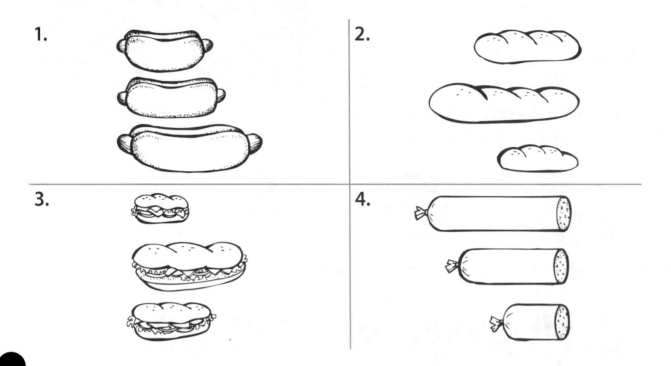

1.

2.

3.

4.

Complete the subtraction sentences.

5.
$6 - 1 = \boxed{}$ $4 - 2 = \boxed{}$ $5 - 0 = \boxed{}$ $4 - 1 = \boxed{}$

$3 - 2 = \boxed{}$ $6 - 3 = \boxed{}$ $2 - 2 = \boxed{}$ $6 - 4 = \boxed{}$

Write the times.

6.

Circle each shape that shows halves.

7.

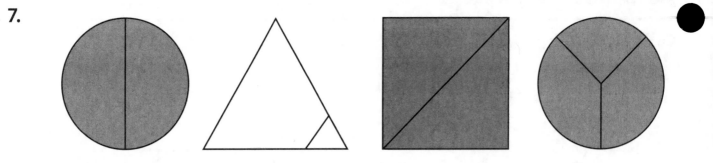

Circle the coin with the greatest value.
Draw a box around the coin with the least value.

8.

Draw lines to match the sets that have the same value.

9.

Write the total value as you *count on*.
Do you have enough money to buy the item? Circle *yes* or *no*.

10.

☐¢ ☐¢ ☐¢ ☐¢ ☐¢   30¢   yes
                                            no

Draw a line to match the number to its number word.

11. one	2	**12.** 10	zero	**13.** four	8
three	3	7	ten	eight	5
two	1	0	seven	five	4

Attributes of Shapes

Color each shape that has corners.

1.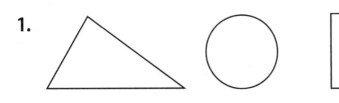

Color each shape that is closed.

Color each shape that has a curved side.

2.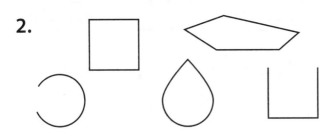

3.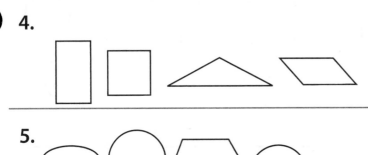

Circle the 3 shapes that belong together.
Mark the sentence that explains why they belong together.

4.

   ○ They all have 4 sides.

   ○ They all have 3 sides.

5.

   ○ They all have straight sides.

   ○ They all have a curved side.

Draw the 3 shapes where they belong in the Venn diagram.

6.

Straight
Sides

Curved
Sides

Count to 100 by 10s.

1. 10 [ ] [ ] [ ] [ ] 60 [ ] [ ] [ ] [ ] ●

Complete the subtraction problems.

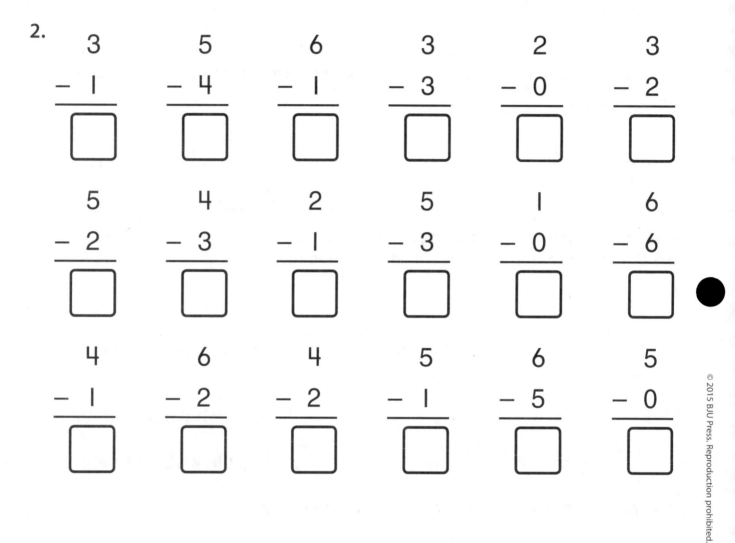

2.

3	5	6	3	2	3
− 1	− 4	− 1	− 3	− 0	− 2
☐	☐	☐	☐	☐	☐

5	4	2	5	1	6
− 2	− 3	− 1	− 3	− 0	− 6
☐	☐	☐	☐	☐	☐

●

4	6	4	5	6	5
− 1	− 2	− 2	− 1	− 5	− 0
☐	☐	☐	☐	☐	☐

Complete the related facts.

3. 6 + ☐ = 10

10 − 6 = ☐

4. 8 + ☐ = 11

11 − 8 = ☐

5. 7 + ☐ = 12

12 − 7 = ☐ ●

Draw Shapes

Draw a shape that is exactly the same.

1.

2.

Draw a different shape with the same number of sides and corners.

3.

4.

Draw a shape with 5 corners and 5 sides.

Draw a shape with 2 long sides and 2 short sides.

5.

6.

Draw back jumps to subtract.
Complete the subtraction sentence.

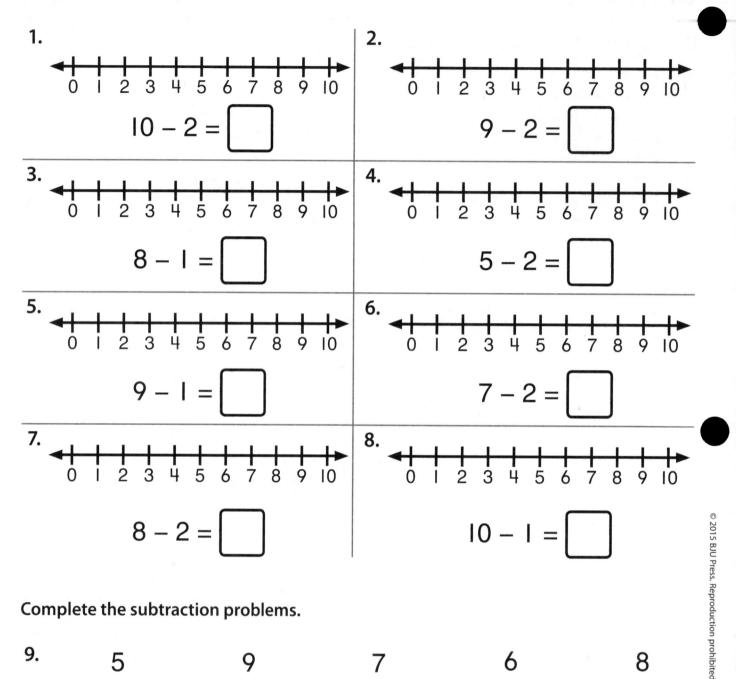

1.

$10 - 2 = \boxed{}$

2.

$9 - 2 = \boxed{}$

3.

$8 - 1 = \boxed{}$

4.

$5 - 2 = \boxed{}$

5.

$9 - 1 = \boxed{}$

6.

$7 - 2 = \boxed{}$

7.

$8 - 2 = \boxed{}$

8.

$10 - 1 = \boxed{}$

Complete the subtraction problems.

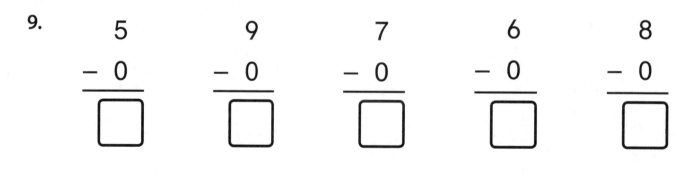

9.

$$\begin{array}{r} 5 \\ -\ 0 \\ \hline \boxed{} \end{array} \qquad \begin{array}{r} 9 \\ -\ 0 \\ \hline \boxed{} \end{array} \qquad \begin{array}{r} 7 \\ -\ 0 \\ \hline \boxed{} \end{array} \qquad \begin{array}{r} 6 \\ -\ 0 \\ \hline \boxed{} \end{array} \qquad \begin{array}{r} 8 \\ -\ 0 \\ \hline \boxed{} \end{array}$$

Composite Shapes

Use the key to color the shapes.

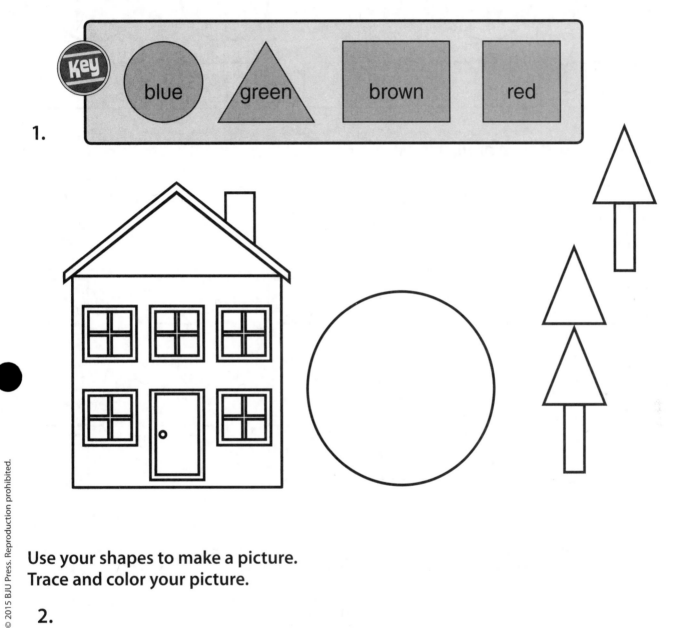

1.

Use your shapes to make a picture.
Trace and color your picture.

2.

Write the time.

1.

| : | | : | | : | | : | | : |

Complete the subtraction problems.

2.

0	4	6	5	2	3
− 0	− 0	− 3	− 5	− 1	− 0

2	6	4	6	1	4
− 2	− 4	− 4	− 0	− 1	− 2

Draw the 3 shapes where they belong in the Venn diagram.

3.

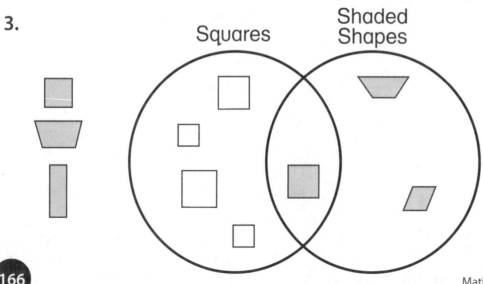

Squares   Shaded Shapes

Math 1 Reviews • Chapter 11, Lesson 83

Compose Shapes

Mark the picture that comes next.

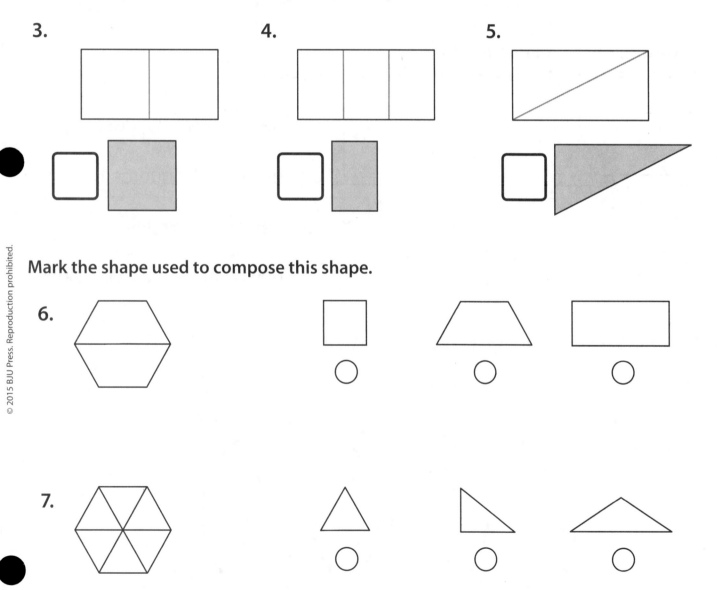

Write the number needed to compose the shape.

3.

4.

5.

Mark the shape used to compose this shape.

6.

7.

Color each shape that has corners.

1.

Color each shape that is closed.

2.

Color each shape that has a curved side.

3.

Circle the 3 shapes that belong together.
Mark the sentence that explains why they belong together.

4.

○ They all have 3 sides.

○ They are all squares.

5.

○ They are all circles.

○ They all have a curved side.

Draw the 3 shapes where they belong in the Venn diagram.

6.

Curved
Sides

Straight
Sides

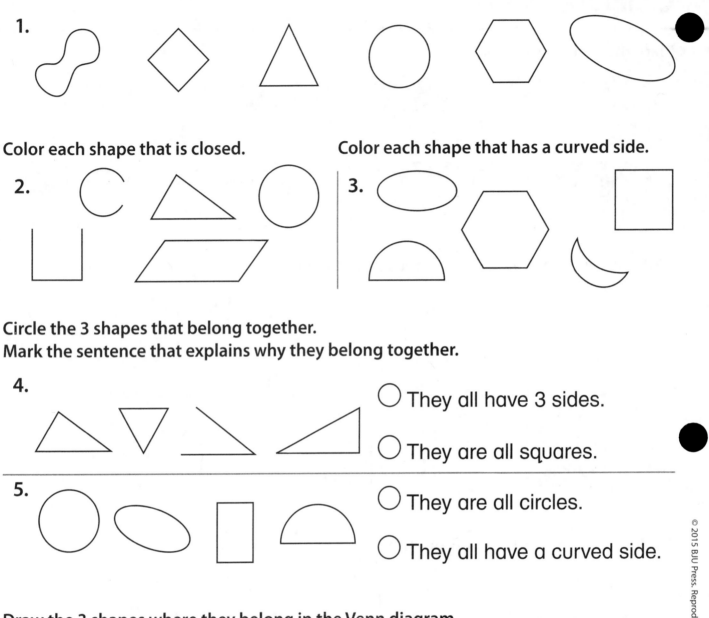

Color each shape that has 4 sides.

1.

Color each shape that has a curved side.

2.

Put an *X* on the shape that is different from the others.
Mark the sentence that explains why it is different.

3.

○ It does not have straight sides and corners.
○ It has straight sides and corners.

Draw a shape that is exactly the same.   Draw a shape with 3 corners.

4.   5.

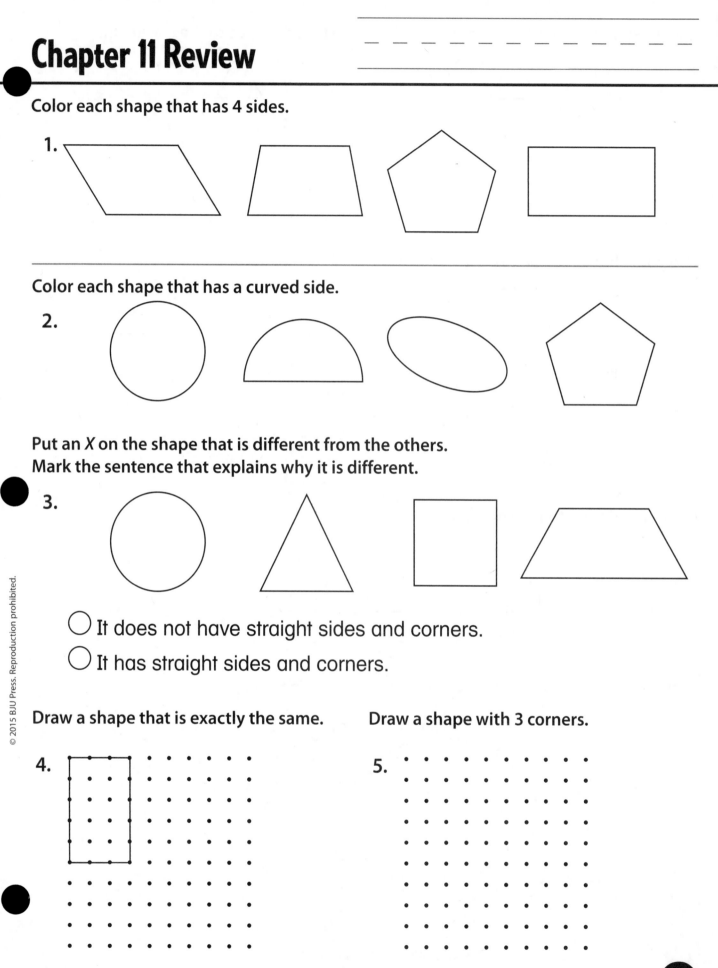

Use these shapes to draw a house.

6.

Use these shapes to draw a clown.

7.

Use your shapes to compose the shape.
Write the numbers needed.

8.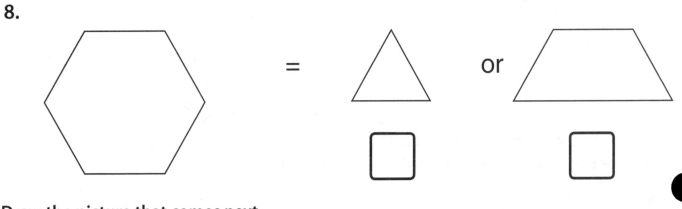

Draw the picture that comes next.

9.

Draw the 3 shapes where they belong in the Venn diagram.

10.

4 Sides   Shaded

Cumulative Review

Circle the number of equal parts.

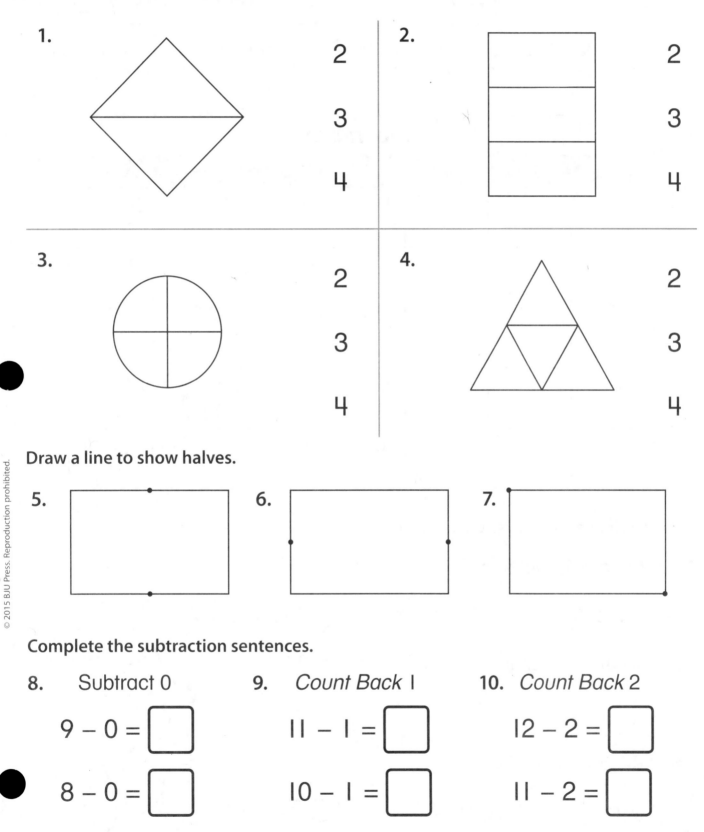

1.
2
3
4

2.
2
3
4

3.
2
3
4

4.
2
3
4

Draw a line to show halves.

5.

6.

7.

Complete the subtraction sentences.

8. Subtract 0

$9 - 0 = \boxed{}$

$8 - 0 = \boxed{}$

9. *Count Back* 1

$11 - 1 = \boxed{}$

$10 - 1 = \boxed{}$

10. *Count Back* 2

$12 - 2 = \boxed{}$

$11 - 2 = \boxed{}$

Number the days of the week in order.

11.

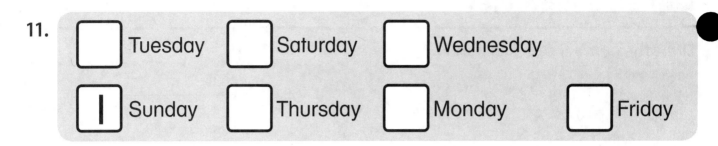

	Tuesday		Saturday		Wednesday
I	Sunday		Thursday		Monday		Friday

December						
Sunday	Monday	Tuesday	Wednesday	Thursday	Friday	Saturday
		1	2	3	4	5
6	7	8	9	10	11	12
13	14	15	16	17	18	19
20	21	22	23	24	25	26
27	28	29	30	31		

Use the calendar to answer the question.

12. What day is December 8?

○ Monday   ○ Tuesday   ○ Wednesday

13. How many Wednesdays are in the month?

○ 3   ○ 4   ○ 5

14. What day is Christmas?

○ Thursday   ○ Friday   ○ Saturday

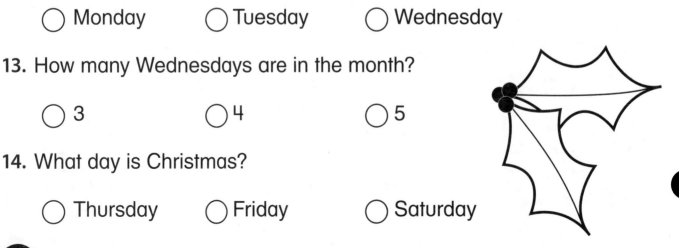

172

Group to Add

Draw tens and ones to picture the numbers.
Use the expanded form to write the addends.
Add tens to tens. Add ones to ones.
Complete the addition sentence.

1.

2.

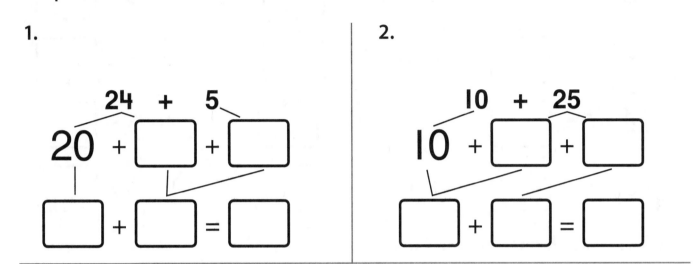

Write the value of each addend. Write the sum.

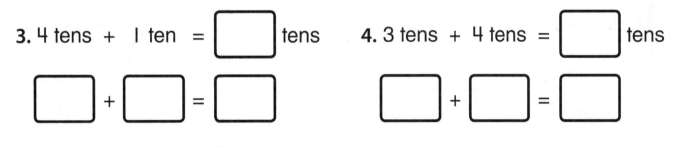

3. 4 tens + 1 ten = ☐ tens

☐ + ☐ = ☐

4. 3 tens + 4 tens = ☐ tens

☐ + ☐ = ☐

Draw tens and ones to picture the numbers.
Add tens to tens. Add ones to ones.
Complete the addition sentence.

5.

6.

7.

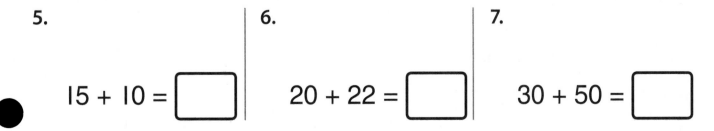

15 + 10 = ☐

20 + 22 = ☐

30 + 50 = ☐

Complete the number sentences.
Write the numbers to name the fact family.

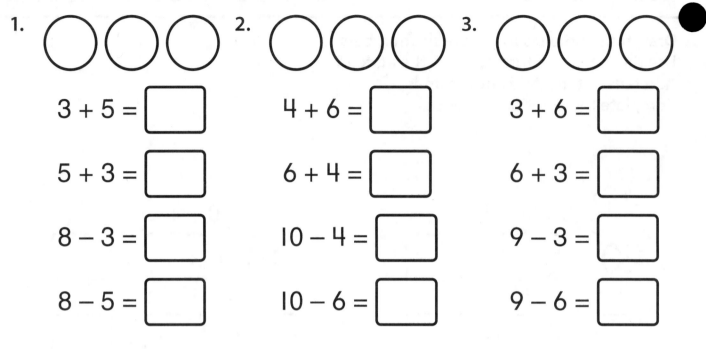

1.
◯ ◯ ◯

3 + 5 = ☐
5 + 3 = ☐
8 − 3 = ☐
8 − 5 = ☐

2.
◯ ◯ ◯

4 + 6 = ☐
6 + 4 = ☐
10 − 4 = ☐
10 − 6 = ☐

3.
◯ ◯ ◯

3 + 6 = ☐
6 + 3 = ☐
9 − 3 = ☐
9 − 6 = ☐

Write the related facts for the fact family.

4.

③ ⑦ ⑩

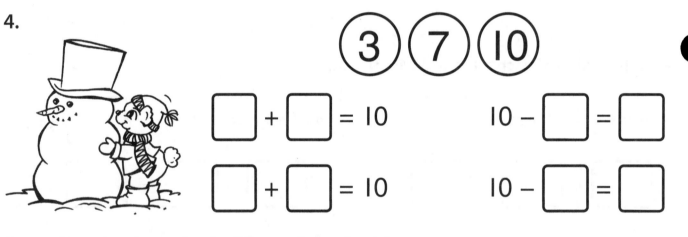

☐ + ☐ = 10

☐ + ☐ = 10

10 − ☐ = ☐

10 − ☐ = ☐

Put an X on the shape that is different from the others.

5.

6.

Color each shape that has only 3 sides.

7.

Add Ones & Add Tens

Complete the addition problem.

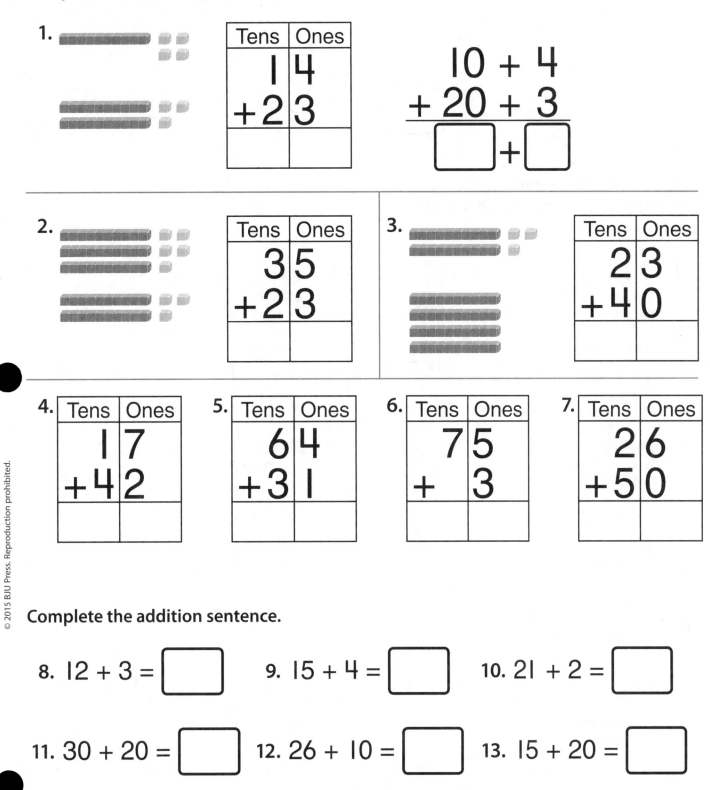

1.

Tens	Ones
1	4
+2	3

$$10 + 4$$
$$+ 20 + 3$$
$$\boxed{} + \boxed{}$$

2.

Tens	Ones
3	5
+2	3

3.

Tens	Ones
2	3
+4	0

4.

Tens	Ones
1	7
+4	2

5.

Tens	Ones
6	4
+3	1

6.

Tens	Ones
7	5
+	3

7.

Tens	Ones
2	6
+5	0

Complete the addition sentence.

8. $12 + 3 = \boxed{}$　　**9.** $15 + 4 = \boxed{}$　　**10.** $21 + 2 = \boxed{}$

11. $30 + 20 = \boxed{}$　　**12.** $26 + 10 = \boxed{}$　　**13.** $15 + 20 = \boxed{}$

**Draw tens and ones to picture the numbers.
Complete the addition sentence.**

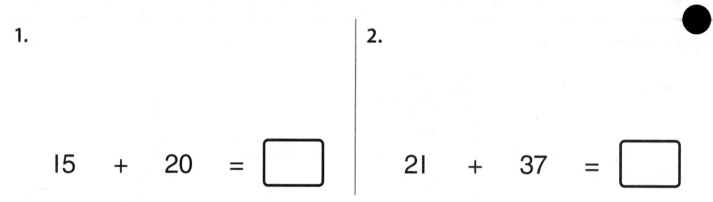

1.

15   +   20   = ☐

2.

21   +   37   = ☐

**Write the number represented.
Circle the single cubes to make pairs.
Circle *even* or *odd*.**

3.

☐   even

           odd

4.

☐   even

           odd

5.

☐   even

           odd

6.

☐   even

           odd

**Write the number represented.
Write the expanded form.**

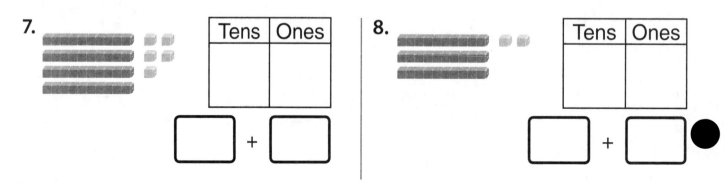

7.

Tens	Ones

☐ + ☐

8.

Tens	Ones

☐ + ☐

2-Digit Addition

Complete the addition problem.

1.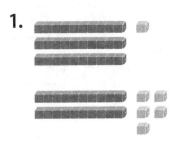

Tens	Ones
3	1
+2	5

Mark the 2 that equal 13 + 24.

2. ◯ 1 ten + 3 ones + 2 tens + 4 ones

◯ 10 + 3 + 20 + 4

◯ 10 + 3 + 40 + 2

Complete the addition problem.

3.
Tens	Ones
1	2
+2	6

4.
Tens	Ones
2	9
+3	0

5.
Tens	Ones
2	5
+4	2

6.
Tens	Ones
2	8
+2	1

Write an addition sentence for the story.
Complete the sentence.

7. Mrs. Smith has 32 crayons in the art center.
She has 24 crayons at her desk.
How many crayons does Mrs. Smith have altogether?

Mrs. Smith has ⬚ crayons altogether.

⬚ + ⬚ = ⬚

Write the expanded form for the addition sentence above.

8. ⬚ + ⬚ + ⬚ + ⬚ = ⬚

Draw tens and ones to picture the numbers.
Complete the addition sentence.

1.

21   +   15   =   ☐

2.

16   +   32   =   ☐

Count to 100 by 10s. Write the missing numbers.

3.   10   ☐   ☐   40   ☐ ☐ ☐ ☐ ☐ ☐

Complete the number sequence.

4.   12   13   14   ☐

5.   45   50   55   ☐

6.   18   20   22   ☐

7.   38   40   42   ☐

Compare the numbers.
Circle the correct sign.

> is greater than   < is less than

8.

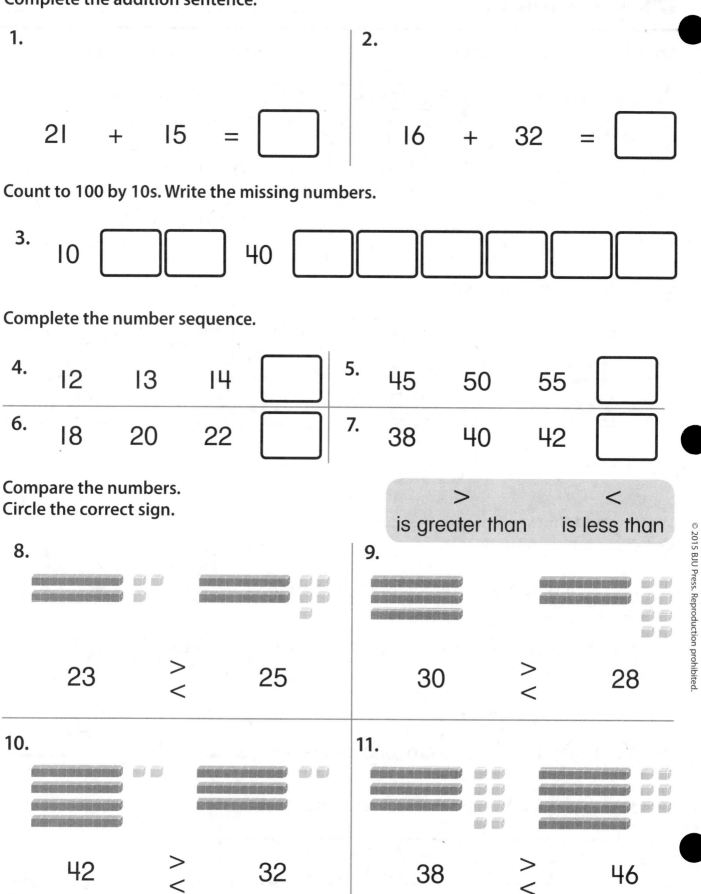

23   >   25
     <

9.

30   >   28
     <

10.

42   >   32
     <

11.

38   >   46
     <

More 2-Digit Addition

Complete the addition problem.

1.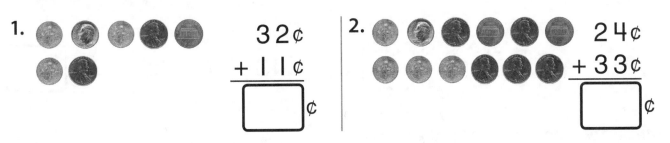

$$
\begin{array}{r}
32¢ \\
+11¢ \\
\hline
\end{array}
$$
☐ ¢

2.
$$
\begin{array}{r}
24¢ \\
+33¢ \\
\hline
\end{array}
$$
☐ ¢

Draw tens and ones to picture the numbers.
Complete the addition problem.

3.
$$
\begin{array}{r}
14 \\
+25 \\
\hline
\end{array}
$$
☐

4.
$$
\begin{array}{r}
40 \\
+12 \\
\hline
\end{array}
$$
☐

Complete the addition problem.

5.
$$
\begin{array}{r}
13¢ \\
+12¢ \\
\hline
\end{array}
$$
☐ ¢

6.
$$
\begin{array}{r}
31¢ \\
+26¢ \\
\hline
\end{array}
$$
☐ ¢

7.
$$
\begin{array}{r}
35¢ \\
+52¢ \\
\hline
\end{array}
$$
☐ ¢

8.
$$
\begin{array}{r}
21¢ \\
+23¢ \\
\hline
\end{array}
$$
☐ ¢

Draw coins to picture the story.
Complete the sentences.

9. Colton had 9 cents. He spent
5 cents. How many cents does
Colton have now?

Colton has ☐ cents now.

☐ ¢ ◯ ☐ ¢ ◯ ☐ ¢

Draw tens and ones to picture the numbers.
Complete the addition sentence.

1.

$$23 \quad + \quad 31 \quad = \quad \boxed{}$$

2.

$$13 \quad + \quad 42 \quad = \quad \boxed{}$$

Write an addition sentence for the story.
Complete the sentence.

3. Luke found 13 bugs to put in his box. His sister gave him 4 more bugs. How many bugs does Luke have now?

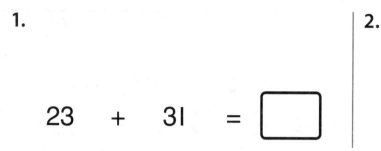

Luke has $\boxed{}$ bugs now.

$$\boxed{} + \boxed{} = \boxed{}$$

Mark the value of the coin.

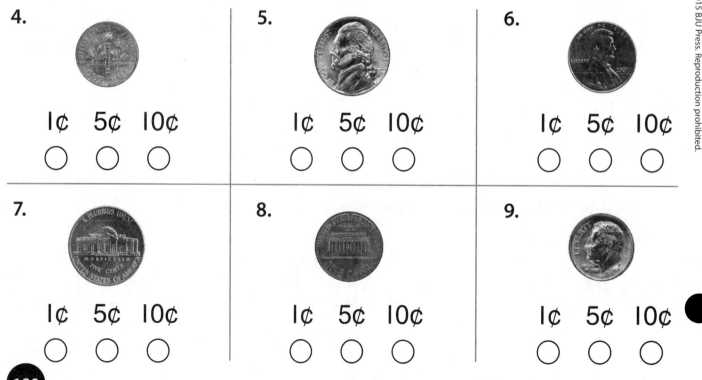

4.

1¢   5¢   10¢
○   ○   ○

5.

1¢   5¢   10¢
○   ○   ○

6.

1¢   5¢   10¢
○   ○   ○

7.

1¢   5¢   10¢
○   ○   ○

8.

1¢   5¢   10¢
○   ○   ○

9.

1¢   5¢   10¢
○   ○   ○

Rename 10 Ones

Write the number of tens and ones.
Circle 10 ones and rename.
Complete the addition sentence.

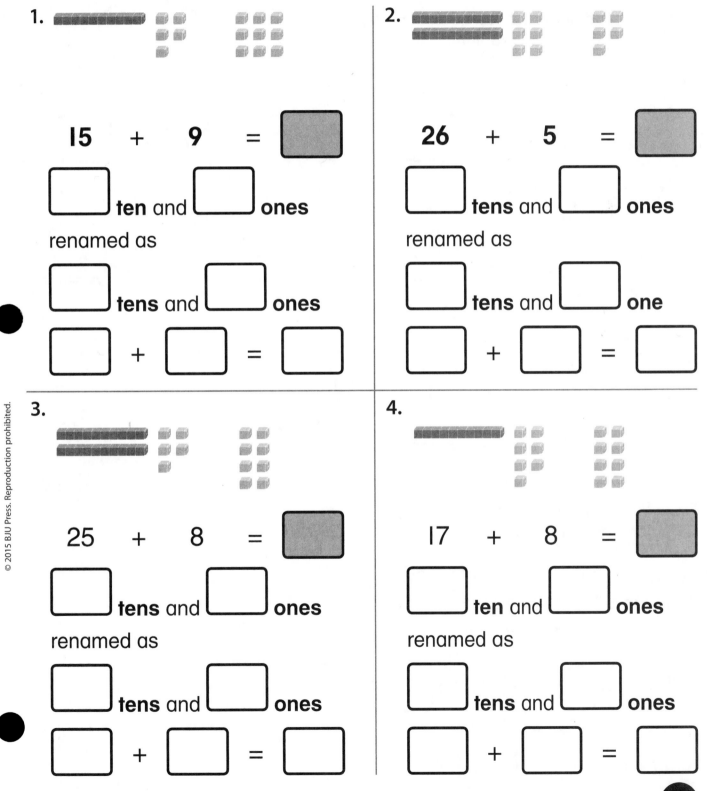

1.

15 + 9 = ⬜

[ ] **ten** and [ ] **ones**

renamed as

[ ] **tens** and [ ] **ones**

[ ] + [ ] = [ ]

2.

26 + 5 = ⬜

[ ] **tens** and [ ] **ones**

renamed as

[ ] **tens** and [ ] **one**

[ ] + [ ] = [ ]

3.

25 + 8 = ⬜

[ ] **tens** and [ ] **ones**

renamed as

[ ] **tens** and [ ] **ones**

[ ] + [ ] = [ ]

4.

17 + 8 = ⬜

[ ] **ten** and [ ] **ones**

renamed as

[ ] **tens** and [ ] **ones**

[ ] + [ ] = [ ]

Write the number represented. Complete the addition problem.

1.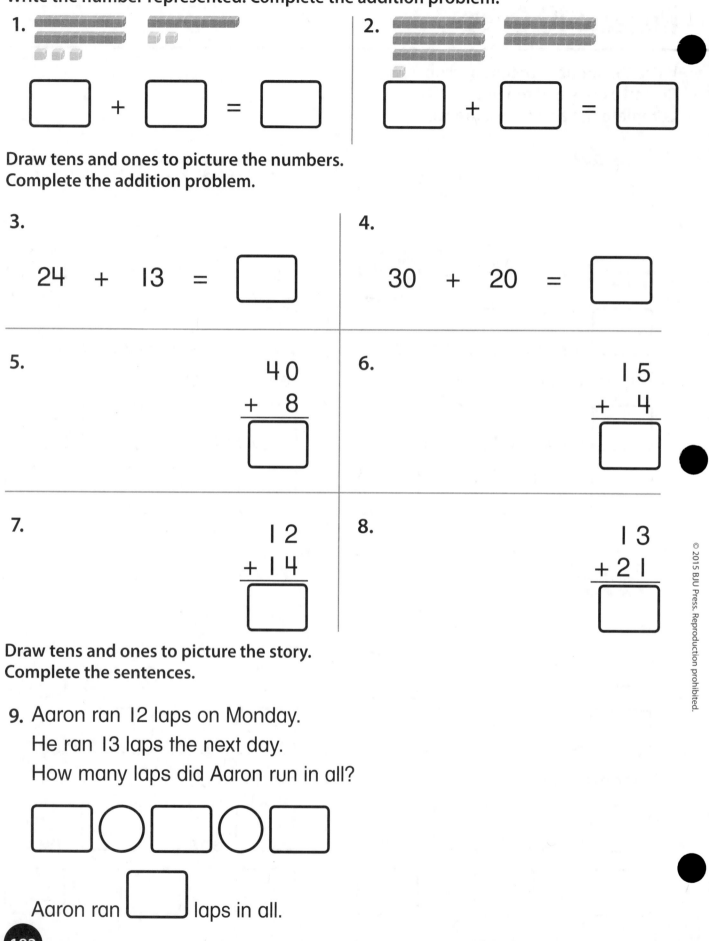

□ + □ = □

2.

□ + □ = □

Draw tens and ones to picture the numbers.
Complete the addition problem.

3.

24 + 13 = □

4.

30 + 20 = □

5.

```
  4 0
+   8
─────
  □
```

6.

```
  1 5
+   4
─────
  □
```

7.

```
  1 2
+ 1 4
─────
  □
```

8.

```
  1 3
+ 2 1
─────
  □
```

Draw tens and ones to picture the story.
Complete the sentences.

9. Aaron ran 12 laps on Monday.
   He ran 13 laps the next day.
   How many laps did Aaron run in all?

□ ○ □ ○ □

Aaron ran □ laps in all.

More Renaming

Write the number of tens and ones.
Circle 10 ones and rename.
Complete the addition sentence.

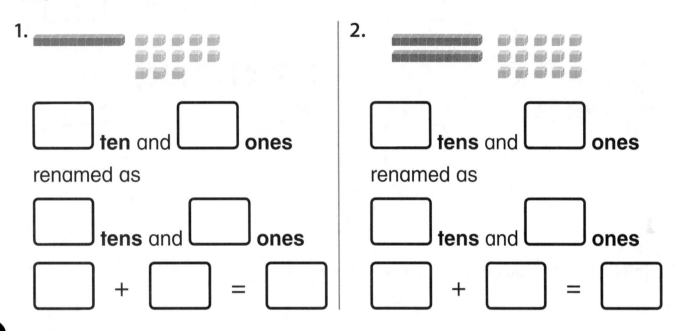

1. [ ] ten and [ ] ones

renamed as

[ ] tens and [ ] ones

[ ] + [ ] = [ ]

2. [ ] tens and [ ] ones

renamed as

[ ] tens and [ ] ones

[ ] + [ ] = [ ]

Complete the addition problem. Rename if needed.
Circle *yes* or *no* to answer the question.

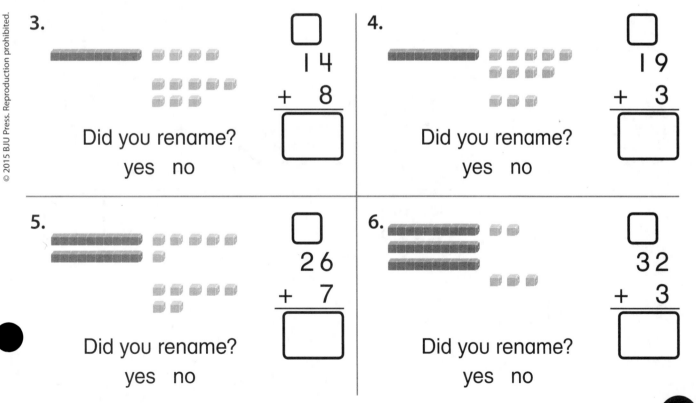

3.

$\begin{array}{r} \square \\ 1\,4 \\ +\quad 8 \\ \hline \square \end{array}$

Did you rename?

yes   no

4.

$\begin{array}{r} \square \\ 1\,9 \\ +\quad 3 \\ \hline \square \end{array}$

Did you rename?

yes   no

5.

$\begin{array}{r} \square \\ 2\,6 \\ +\quad 7 \\ \hline \square \end{array}$

Did you rename?

yes   no

6.

$\begin{array}{r} \square \\ 3\,2 \\ +\quad 3 \\ \hline \square \end{array}$

Did you rename?

yes   no

Complete the addition problem.

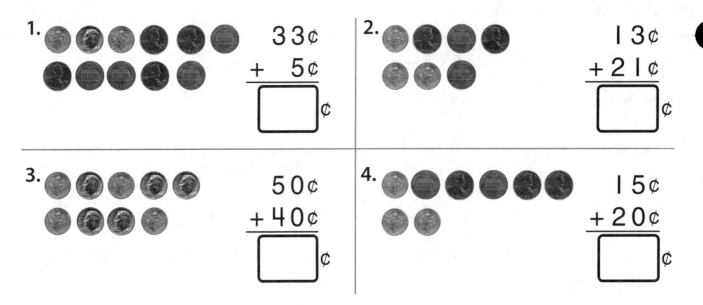

1. 33¢
    + 5¢
    [ ]¢

2. 13¢
    +21¢
    [ ]¢

3. 50¢
    +40¢
    [ ]¢

4. 15¢
    +20¢
    [ ]¢

Complete the addition problem. Rename if needed.

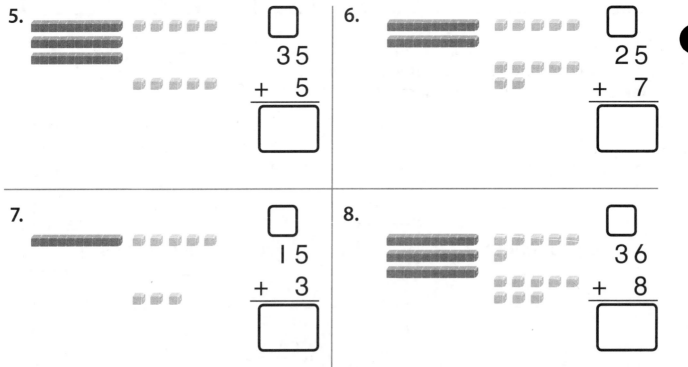

5. [ ]
    35
    + 5
    [ ]

6. [ ]
    25
    + 7
    [ ]

7. [ ]
    15
    + 3
    [ ]

8. [ ]
    36
    + 8
    [ ]

Chapter 12 Review

Draw tens and ones to picture the numbers.
Complete the addition problem.

1.
$$\begin{array}{r} 34 \\ +5 \\ \hline \end{array}$$

2.
$$\begin{array}{r} 31 \\ +23 \\ \hline \end{array}$$

3.
$$\begin{array}{r} 13 \\ +32 \\ \hline \end{array}$$

4.
$$\begin{array}{r} 50 \\ +8 \\ \hline \end{array}$$

5.
$$\begin{array}{r} 43 \\ +24 \\ \hline \end{array}$$

6.
$$\begin{array}{r} 11 \\ +17 \\ \hline \end{array}$$

Draw tens and ones to picture the story.
Complete the sentences.

7. Mrs. Moore graded 12 math tests.
   She graded 17 spelling tests.
   How many tests did she grade in all?

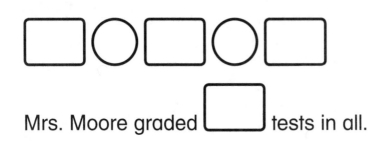

Mrs. Moore graded ▢ tests in all.

Complete the addition problem.

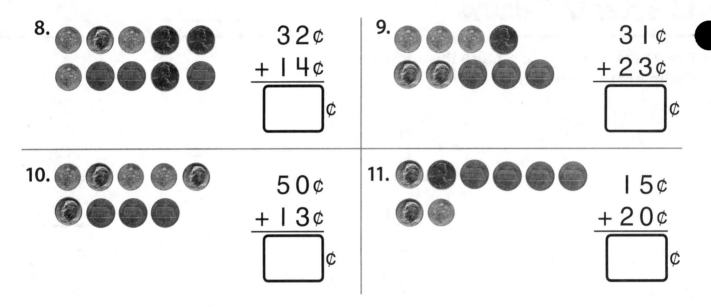

8. $\begin{array}{r} 32 \cent \\ + 14 \cent \\ \hline \end{array}$ ¢

9. $\begin{array}{r} 31 \cent \\ + 23 \cent \\ \hline \end{array}$ ¢

10. $\begin{array}{r} 50 \cent \\ + 13 \cent \\ \hline \end{array}$ ¢

11. $\begin{array}{r} 15 \cent \\ + 20 \cent \\ \hline \end{array}$ ¢

Complete the addition problem. Rename if needed.

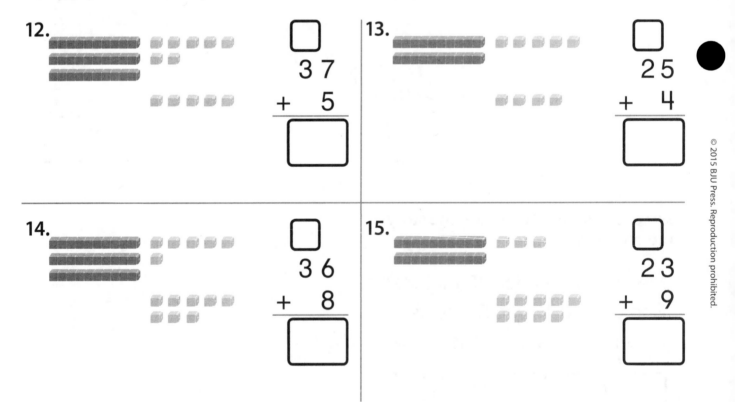

12. $\begin{array}{r} \square \\ 37 \\ + \quad 5 \\ \hline \end{array}$

13. $\begin{array}{r} \square \\ 25 \\ + \quad 4 \\ \hline \end{array}$

14. $\begin{array}{r} \square \\ 36 \\ + \quad 8 \\ \hline \end{array}$

15. $\begin{array}{r} \square \\ 23 \\ + \quad 9 \\ \hline \end{array}$

Cumulative Review

Write the number represented.
Circle the single cubes to make pairs.
Circle *even* or *odd*.

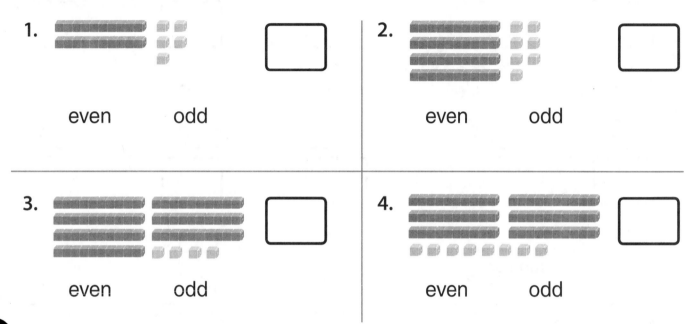

1. [ ]

even   odd

2. [ ]

even   odd

3. [ ]

even   odd

4. [ ]

even   odd

Write the related facts for the fact family.

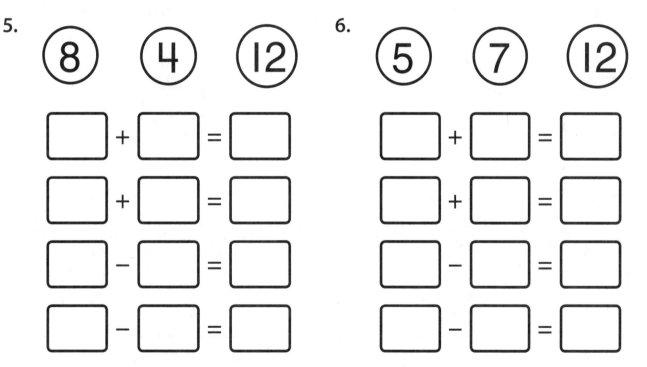

5. (8) (4) (12)

[ ] + [ ] = [ ]

[ ] + [ ] = [ ]

[ ] − [ ] = [ ]

[ ] − [ ] = [ ]

6. (5) (7) (12)

[ ] + [ ] = [ ]

[ ] + [ ] = [ ]

[ ] − [ ] = [ ]

[ ] − [ ] = [ ]

Complete the addition problems.

7.

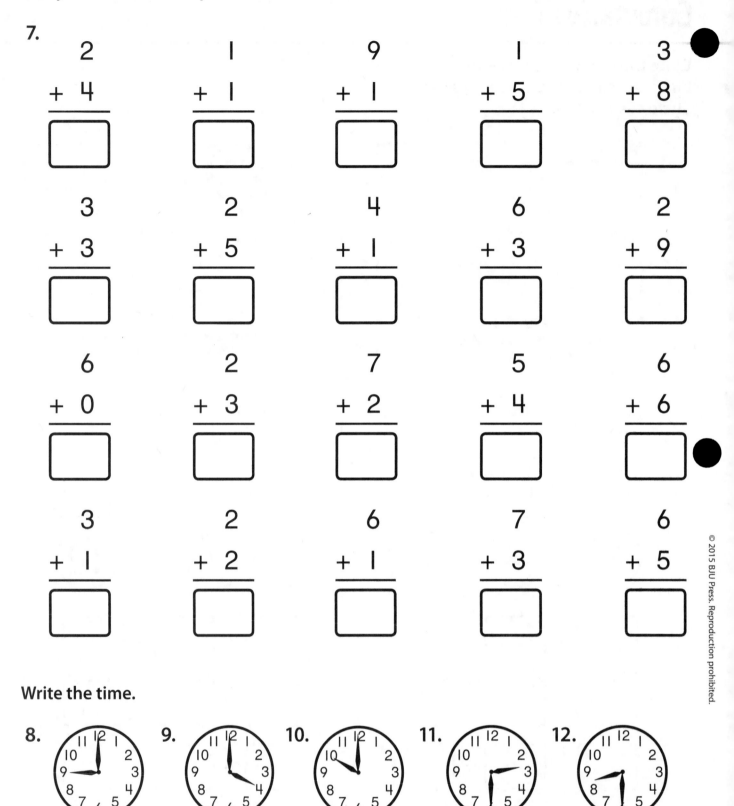

2	1	9	1	3
+ 4	+ 1	+ 1	+ 5	+ 8

3	2	4	6	2
+ 3	+ 5	+ 1	+ 3	+ 9

6	2	7	5	6
+ 0	+ 3	+ 2	+ 4	+ 6

3	2	6	7	6
+ 1	+ 2	+ 1	+ 3	+ 5

Write the time.

8.   **9.**   **10.**   **11.**   **12.**

Math 1 Reviews • Chapter 12, Lesson 94

Subtract Ones & Subtract Tens

Cross out to subtract. Complete the subtraction sentence.

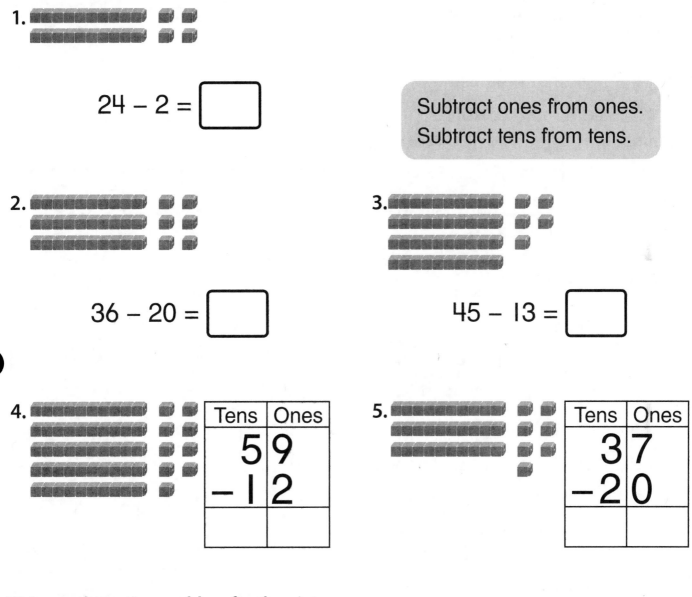

1.

$24 - 2 = \boxed{}$

Subtract ones from ones.
Subtract tens from tens.

2.

$36 - 20 = \boxed{}$

3.

$45 - 13 = \boxed{}$

4.

Tens	Ones
5	9
−1	2

5.

Tens	Ones
3	7
−2	0

Write a subtraction problem for the picture.

6.

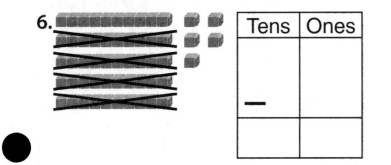

Tens	Ones
−	

7.

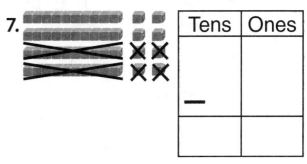

Tens	Ones
−	

Complete the addition sentence.

1. $7 + 3 =$ ☐   2. $8 + 4 =$ ☐   3. $9 + 2 =$ ☐

Draw circles to picture the story.
Complete the sentences.

4. Macy ate 4 carrots with dip.
   She ate 5 more carrots.
   How many carrots did Macy eat in all?

   Macy ate ☐ carrots in all.

   ☐ + ☐ = ☐

Write the number of dimes and pennies.
Write the total value.

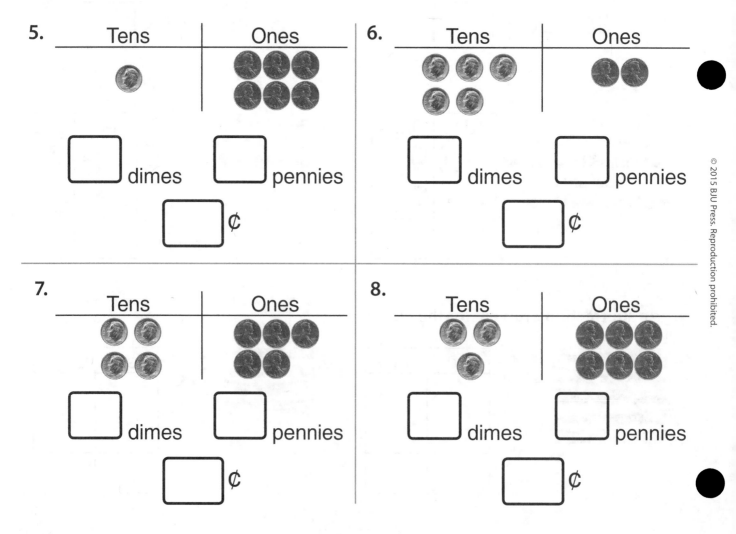

5.
Tens	Ones

   ☐ dimes   ☐ pennies

   ☐ ¢

6.
Tens	Ones

   ☐ dimes   ☐ pennies

   ☐ ¢

7.
Tens	Ones

   ☐ dimes   ☐ pennies

   ☐ ¢

8.
Tens	Ones

   ☐ dimes   ☐ pennies

   ☐ ¢

2-Digit Subtraction

Cross out to subtract. Complete the subtraction problem.

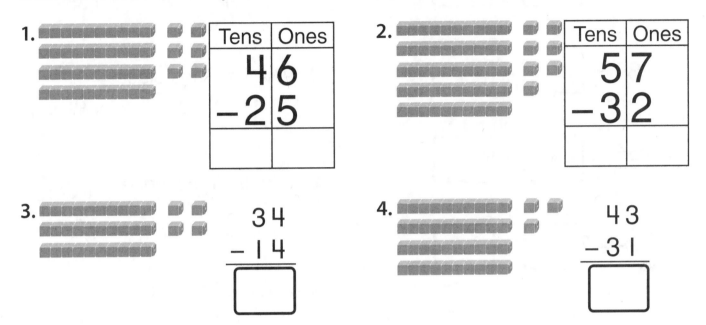

1.
Tens	Ones
4	6
−2	5

2.
Tens	Ones
5	7
−3	2

3.
```
  34
− 14
─────
```

4.
```
  43
− 31
─────
```

Complete the subtraction problem.

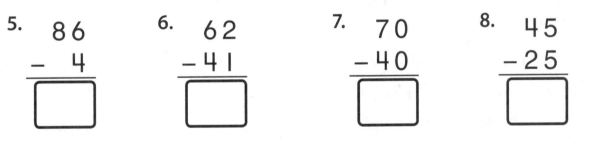

5.
```
  86
−  4
────
```

6.
```
  62
− 41
────
```

7.
```
  70
− 40
────
```

8.
```
  45
− 25
────
```

Draw tens and ones to picture the story.
Complete the sentences.

9. Josiah counted 27 students in the classroom.
   There were 10 boy students.
   How many girl students were there?

There were ☐ girl students.

☐ − ☐ = ☐

Complete the expanded form.

1. 63 = ☐ + ☐

2. 39 = ☐ + ☐

3. 82 = ☐ + ☐

4. 75 = ☐ + ☐

5. 41 = ☐ + ☐

Mark the number that matches the clue.

6. 8 in the Ones place

48 ○   86 ○

7. 4 in the Ones place

49 ○   64 ○

8. 6 in the Tens place

62 ○   86 ○

9. 2 in the Tens place

52 ○   25 ○

Draw tens and ones to picture the story. Complete the sentences.

10. Amy had 28 hair bows. She gave 7 hair bows to her friend. How many hair bows does Amy have now?

Amy has ☐ hair bows now.

☐ – ☐ = ☐

Complete the addition problem.

11.
Tens	Ones
3	2
+4	6

12.
Tens	Ones
	1 8
+	1

13.
Tens	Ones
3	9
+	0

14.
Tens	Ones
6	4
+	3

Subtract Money

Cross out to subtract. Complete the subtraction problem.

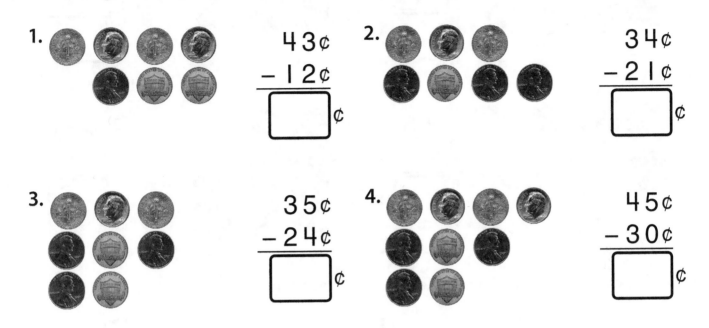

1. $\begin{array}{r} 43¢ \\ -\ 12¢ \\ \hline \end{array}$ ☐ ¢

2. $\begin{array}{r} 34¢ \\ -\ 21¢ \\ \hline \end{array}$ ☐ ¢

3. $\begin{array}{r} 35¢ \\ -\ 24¢ \\ \hline \end{array}$ ☐ ¢

4. $\begin{array}{r} 45¢ \\ -\ 30¢ \\ \hline \end{array}$ ☐ ¢

Complete the subtraction problem.

5. $\begin{array}{r} 58¢ \\ -\ 35¢ \\ \hline \end{array}$ ☐ ¢

6. $\begin{array}{r} 67¢ \\ -\ \ 4¢ \\ \hline \end{array}$ ☐ ¢

7. $\begin{array}{r} 29¢ \\ -\ 18¢ \\ \hline \end{array}$ ☐ ¢

8. $\begin{array}{r} 70¢ \\ -\ 20¢ \\ \hline \end{array}$ ☐ ¢

Draw coins to picture the story. Cross out to subtract. Complete the sentences.

9. Zack had 64 cents. He spent 50 cents for a bottle of water. How many cents does Zack have left?

Zack has ☐ cents left.

☐ ¢ – ☐ ¢ = ☐ ¢

Cross out to subtract. Complete the subtraction problem.

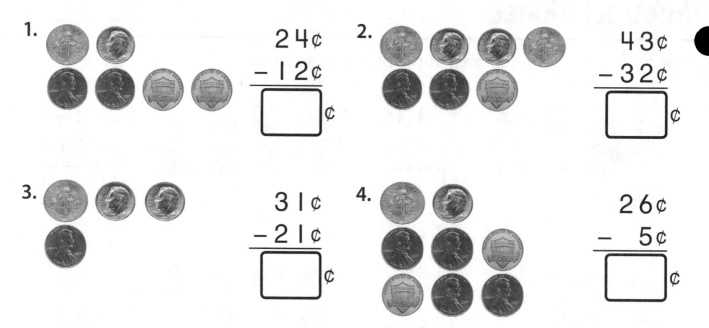

1.
$$\begin{array}{r} 24¢ \\ -12¢ \\ \hline \end{array}$$ ¢

2.
$$\begin{array}{r} 43¢ \\ -32¢ \\ \hline \end{array}$$ ¢

3.
$$\begin{array}{r} 31¢ \\ -21¢ \\ \hline \end{array}$$ ¢

4.
$$\begin{array}{r} 26¢ \\ -5¢ \\ \hline \end{array}$$ ¢

Write the missing addend to complete the addition sentence.

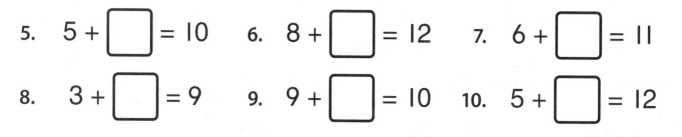

5. $5 + \boxed{} = 10$

6. $8 + \boxed{} = 12$

7. $6 + \boxed{} = 11$

8. $3 + \boxed{} = 9$

9. $9 + \boxed{} = 10$

10. $5 + \boxed{} = 12$

Number the days of the week in order.

11.

☐ Tuesday	☐ Saturday	**4** Wednesday
1 Sunday	☐ Thursday	☐ Monday

☐ Friday

Color each shape that is closed.

12.

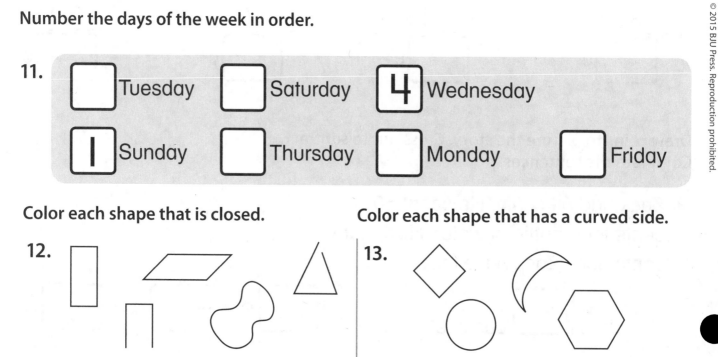

Color each shape that has a curved side.

13.

More 2-Digit Subtraction

Cross out to subtract. Complete the subtraction problem.

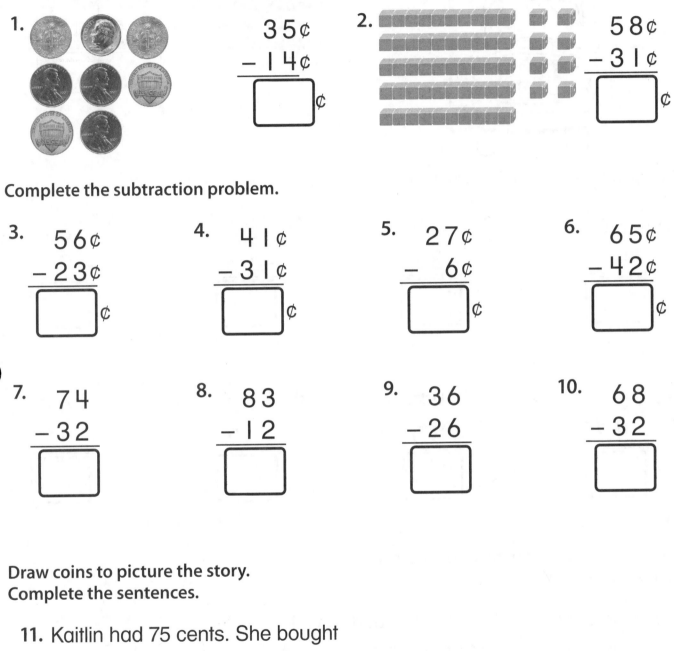

1.
```
  3 5¢
- 1 4¢
┌─────┐
│     │¢
└─────┘
```

2.
```
  5 8¢
- 3 1¢
┌─────┐
│     │¢
└─────┘
```

Complete the subtraction problem.

3.
```
  5 6¢
- 2 3¢
┌─────┐
│     │¢
└─────┘
```

4.
```
  4 1¢
- 3 1¢
┌─────┐
│     │¢
└─────┘
```

5.
```
  2 7¢
-   6¢
┌─────┐
│     │¢
└─────┘
```

6.
```
  6 5¢
- 4 2¢
┌─────┐
│     │¢
└─────┘
```

7.
```
  7 4
- 3 2
┌─────┐
│     │
└─────┘
```

8.
```
  8 3
- 1 2
┌─────┐
│     │
└─────┘
```

9.
```
  3 6
- 2 6
┌─────┐
│     │
└─────┘
```

10.
```
  6 8
- 3 2
┌─────┐
│     │
└─────┘
```

Draw coins to picture the story.
Complete the sentences.

11. Kaitlin had 75 cents. She bought
a book at a yard sale for 50 cents.
How many cents does she have left?

Kaitlin has ☐ cents left.

☐¢ − ☐¢ = ☐¢

Cross out to subtract. Complete the subtraction problem.

1.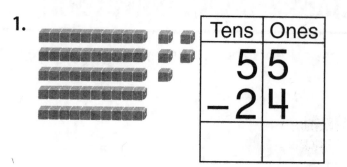

Tens	Ones
5	5
−2	4

Complete the subtraction problem.

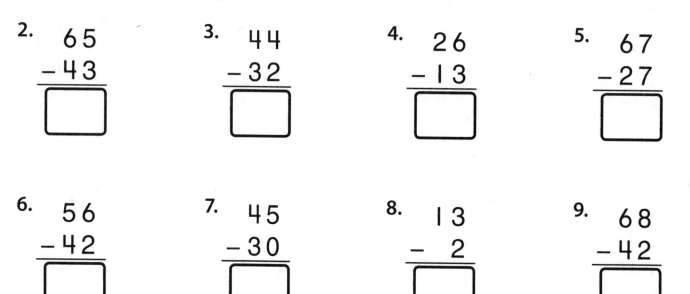

2. 65
   −43
   [ ]

3. 44
   −32
   [ ]

4. 26
   −13
   [ ]

5. 67
   −27
   [ ]

6. 56
   −42
   [ ]

7. 45
   −30
   [ ]

8. 13
   − 2
   [ ]

9. 68
   −42
   [ ]

Draw tens and ones to picture the story.
Complete the sentences.

10. There were 36 trucks in the parking lot.
    The boss sent 22 trucks out on jobs.
    How many trucks are left in the parking lot?

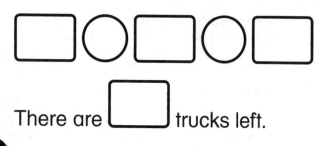

There are [ ] trucks left.

Chapter 13 Review

Cross out to subtract. Complete the subtraction problem.

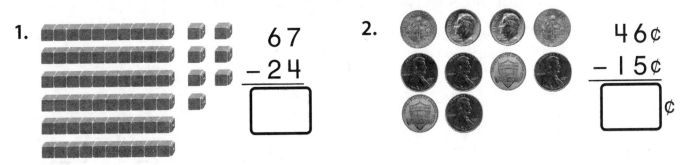

1.
$$\begin{array}{r} 67 \\ -24 \\ \hline \end{array}$$

2.
$$\begin{array}{r} 46¢ \\ -15¢ \\ \hline \end{array}$$
□ ¢

Draw tens and ones to picture the number. Cross out to subtract.
Complete the subtraction problem.

3.
$$\begin{array}{r} 35 \\ -12 \\ \hline \end{array}$$

4.
$$\begin{array}{r} 28 \\ -14 \\ \hline \end{array}$$

Complete the subtraction problems.

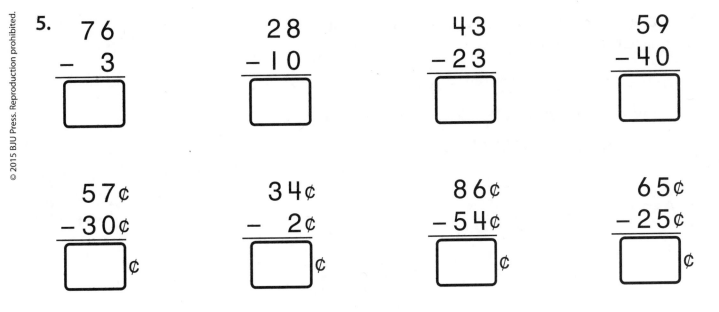

5.
$$\begin{array}{r} 76 \\ -\ 3 \\ \hline \end{array}$$
$$\begin{array}{r} 28 \\ -10 \\ \hline \end{array}$$
$$\begin{array}{r} 43 \\ -23 \\ \hline \end{array}$$
$$\begin{array}{r} 59 \\ -40 \\ \hline \end{array}$$

$$\begin{array}{r} 57¢ \\ -30¢ \\ \hline \end{array}$$ ¢
$$\begin{array}{r} 34¢ \\ -\ 2¢ \\ \hline \end{array}$$ ¢
$$\begin{array}{r} 86¢ \\ -54¢ \\ \hline \end{array}$$ ¢
$$\begin{array}{r} 65¢ \\ -25¢ \\ \hline \end{array}$$ ¢

**Draw tens and ones to picture the story.
Complete the sentences.**

6. Miss Adams made 24 cupcakes.
   She gave 21 cupcakes to her students.
   How many cupcakes are left?

   There are ☐ cupcakes left.   ☐ − ☐ = ☐

---

7. Miss Adams counted 36 drinks. She
   gave 24 drinks to guests. How many
   drinks does Miss Adams have left?

   Miss Adams has ☐ drinks left.   ☐ − ☐ = ☐

**Draw coins to picture the story. Cross out to subtract.
Complete the sentences.**

8. Ashley had 75 cents. She bought a
   cookie for 55 cents. How many cents
   does Ashley have left?

   Ashley has ☐ cents left.   ☐¢ − ☐¢ = ☐¢

Cumulative Review

_____

Draw circles to picture the story.
Complete the sentences.

1. Mom cooked 5 eggs in a pan.
   She cooked 4 eggs in another pan.
   How many eggs did she cook?

2. Sally has 5 sticks of gum. While
   she was playing, she lost 3 sticks
   of gum. How many sticks of gum
   does Sally have left?

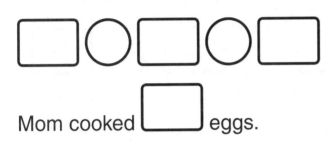

Mom cooked ⬜ eggs.

Sally has ⬜ sticks of gum.

Count the parts in the whole.
Color the shape to match the fraction.

3.
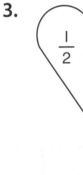
$\frac{1}{2}$

4.
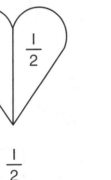
$\frac{3}{4}$

5.
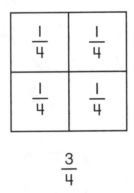
$\frac{2}{3}$

Mark the fraction that names the shaded part.

6.
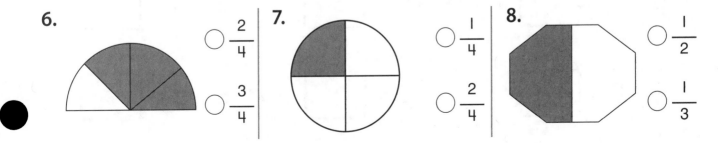

7.

8.

Complete the addition problems.

9.

8	5	3	7	6
+ 0	+ 2	+ 8	+ 1	+ 6

3	4	9	6	8
+ 3	+ 6	+ 0	+ 3	+ 2

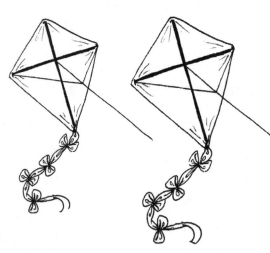

Complete the subtraction sentences.

10. $6 - 6 = \boxed{}$ $8 - 3 = \boxed{}$ $7 - 6 = \boxed{}$

$5 - 4 = \boxed{}$ $9 - 0 = \boxed{}$ $6 - 4 = \boxed{}$

$4 - 2 = \boxed{}$ $8 - 8 = \boxed{}$ $5 - 2 = \boxed{}$

Count Units of Measure

Put an *X* on the longest one. Circle the shortest one.

1.
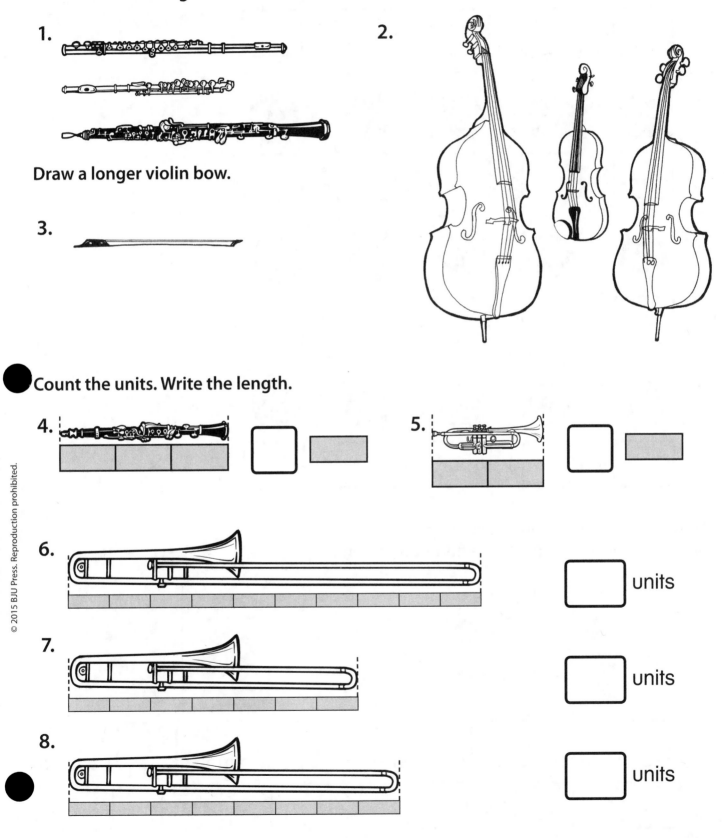

2.

Draw a longer violin bow.

3.

Count the units. Write the length.

4.   ☐   ▬

5.   ☐   ▬

6.   ☐ units

7.   ☐ units

8.   ☐ units

Write the total value as you *count on*.

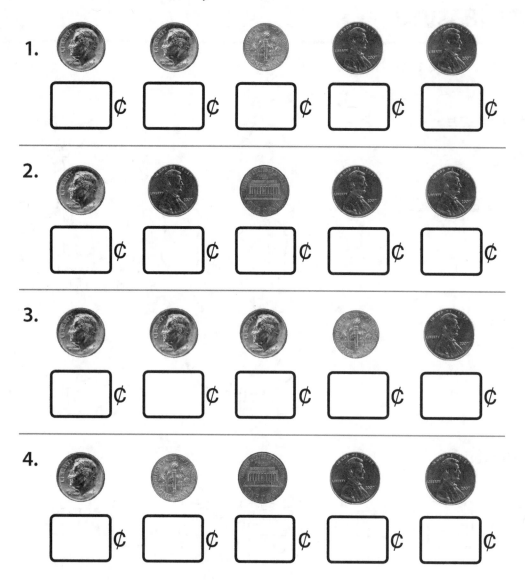

1. ☐¢ ☐¢ ☐¢ ☐¢ ☐¢

2. ☐¢ ☐¢ ☐¢ ☐¢ ☐¢

3. ☐¢ ☐¢ ☐¢ ☐¢ ☐¢

4. ☐¢ ☐¢ ☐¢ ☐¢ ☐¢

Write the number of dimes and pennies.
Write the values. Complete the addition sentence.

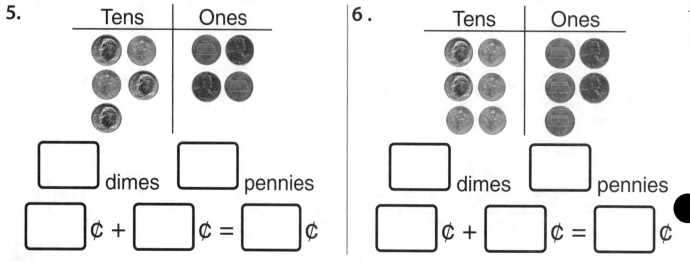

5.

Tens	Ones

☐ dimes ☐ pennies

☐¢ + ☐¢ = ☐¢

6.

Tens	Ones

☐ dimes ☐ pennies

☐¢ + ☐¢ = ☐¢

Measure Length

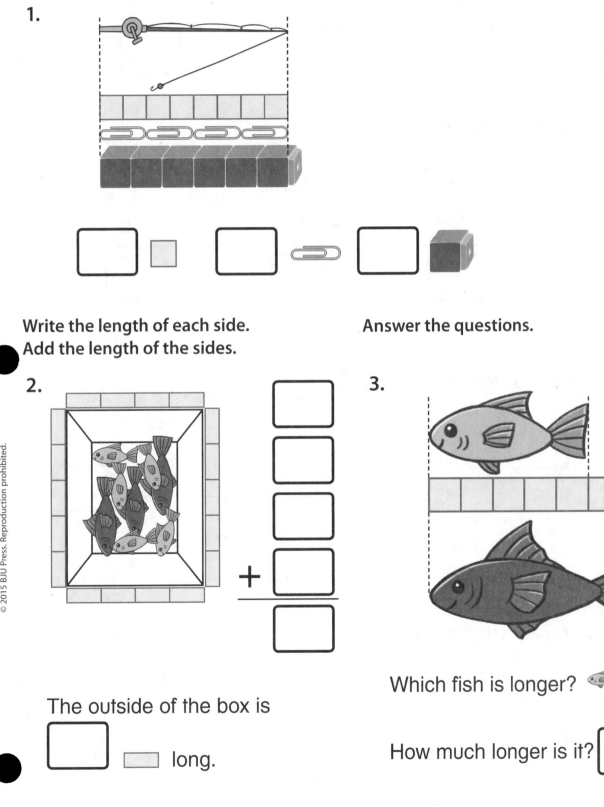

Write the length in different units.

1.

Write the length of each side.
Add the length of the sides.

2.

$+$

The outside of the box is

long.

Answer the questions.

3.

Which fish is longer?

How much longer is it?

© 2015 BJU Press. Reproduction prohibited.

Complete the addition problems.

1.
  24   32   25   60
+ 41   + 15   + 34   + 18

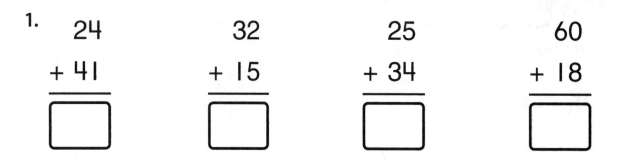

Complete the subtraction problems.

2.
  56   74   62   49
− 24   − 62   − 31   − 25

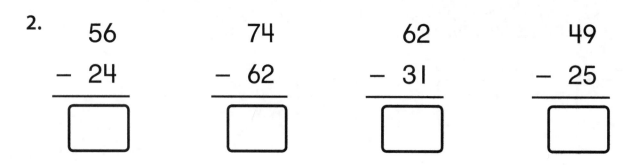

Color 1 part.
Circle the fraction that names the colored part.

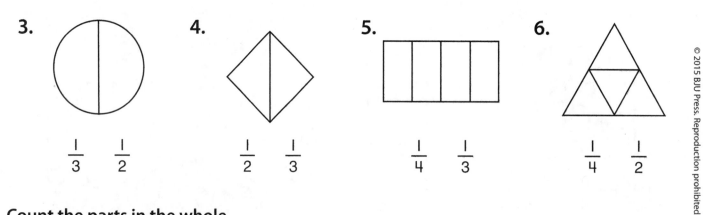

3. $\frac{1}{3}$ $\frac{1}{2}$

4. $\frac{1}{2}$ $\frac{1}{3}$

5. $\frac{1}{4}$ $\frac{1}{3}$

6. $\frac{1}{4}$ $\frac{1}{2}$

Count the parts in the whole.
Color the shape to match the fraction.

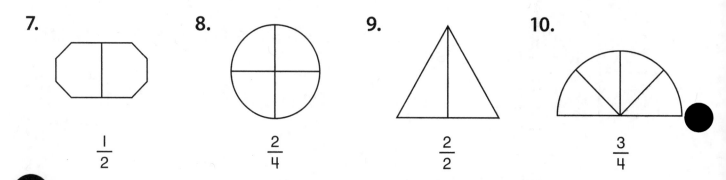

7. $\frac{1}{2}$

8. $\frac{2}{4}$

9. $\frac{2}{2}$

10. $\frac{3}{4}$

Measure Height

Put an X on the taller one. Circle the shorter one.

1.

2.

Draw a flower that is taller.

3.

Write the heights. Answer the question.

4.

Which is taller?

Write the numbers represented.
Write > or < to compare.

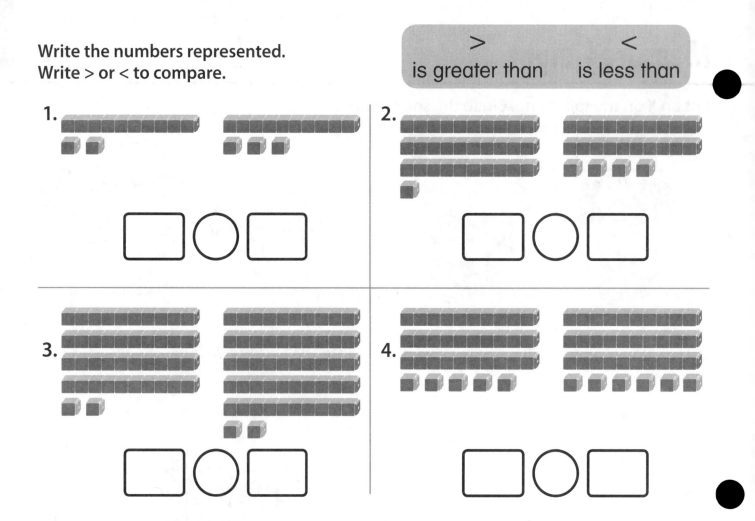

1.

2.

3.

4.

Write the total number of balls for each row. Answer the questions.

Favorite Balls	Total
⚾ ⚾ ⚾ ⚾ ⚾ ⚾ ⚾	
⚽ ⚽ ⚽ ⚽	
🏈 🏈 🏈	

5. Which ball was chosen the most?

6. Which ball was chosen the least?

Measure Using Rulers

Write the length.

1.

2.

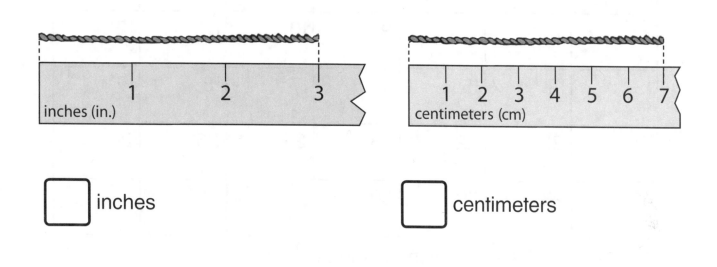

☐ inches

☐ centimeters

Complete the sentences.

3. Ryan's string is 7 inches long. Mel's string is 5 inches long. How many inches longer is Ryan's string than Mel's string?

☐ ○ ☐ ○ ☐

Ryan's string is ☐ inches longer than Mel's string.

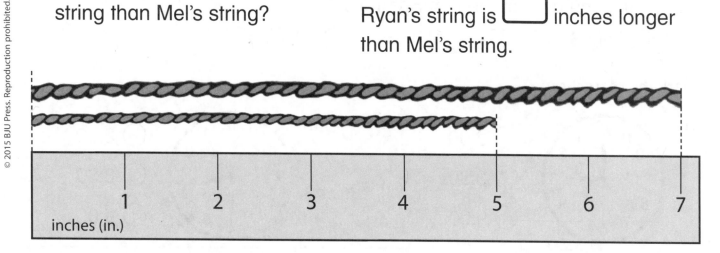

Draw a line to connect the stars.
Measure the line with an inch ruler. Write the length.

4. ★

★ ☐ inches

Use the calendar to answer the question.

April						
Sunday	**Monday**	**Tuesday**	**Wednesday**	**Thursday**	**Friday**	**Saturday**
		1	2	3	4	5
6	7	8	9	10	11	12
13	14	15	16	17	18	19
20	21	22	23	24	25	26
27	28	29	30			

1. Which month does the calendar show?

   ○ March   ○ April   ○ May

2. What day is April 20?

   ○ Sunday   ○ Monday   ○ Tuesday

3. What is the date of the first Saturday?

   ○ April 3   ○ April 4   ○ April 5

Mark the correct time.

4. ○ 3:00
   ○ 3:30
   ○ 4:00

5. ○ 3:00
   ○ 3:30
   ○ 4:00

6. ○ 9:30
   ○ 10:00
   ○ 10:30

7. ○ 9:30
   ○ 10:00
   ○ 10:30

Compare Measurements

Circle to complete the sentences.

1.

Ben   Marie   Alex

Ben is taller than Marie.

Marie is taller than
Ben.

Alex.

So Ben is
taller
shorter
than Alex.

Circle the answer.

Black	
Gray	
Dotted	

2. Which line is the longest? ●——● ●——● ●·····●

3. Which line is shorter than the black line? ●——● ●——● ●·····●

4. Which line is longer than the dotted line
   but shorter than the gray line? ●——● ●——● ●·····●

Mark the picture that matches the statements.

5. The dotted line is longer than the black line.

   The black line is longer than the gray line.

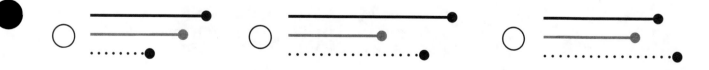

Put an *X* on the shape that is different from the others.

1.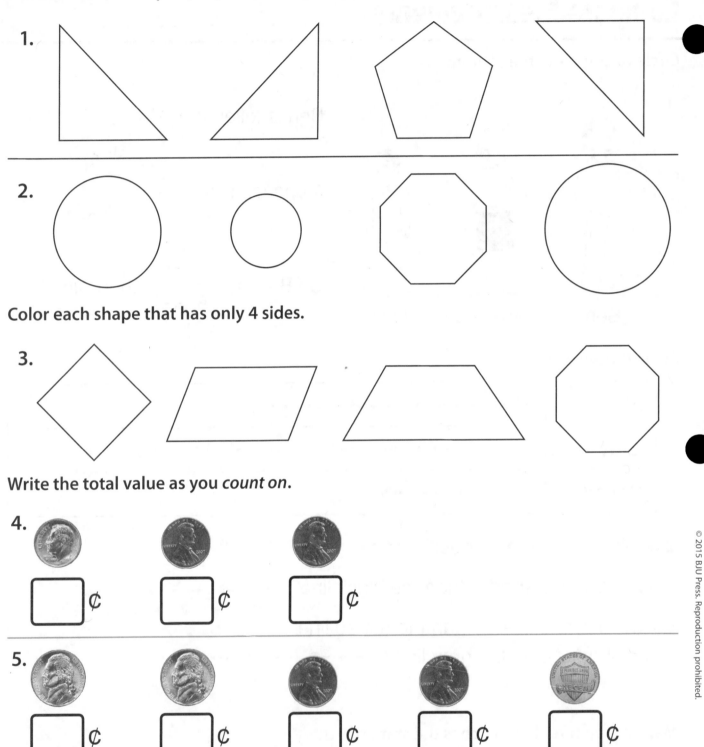

2.

Color each shape that has only 4 sides.

3.

Write the total value as you *count on*.

4. [ ] ¢   [ ] ¢   [ ] ¢

5. [ ] ¢   [ ] ¢   [ ] ¢   [ ] ¢   [ ] ¢

Circle coins to make sets of 10 cents.

6.

Order Objects

Number the branches from shortest to longest.

1.

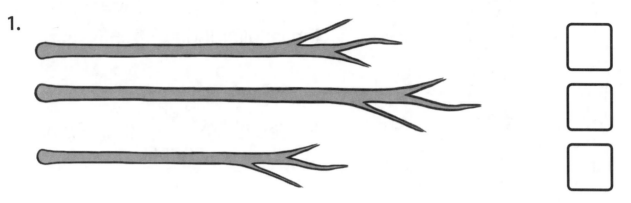

Mark the answer.

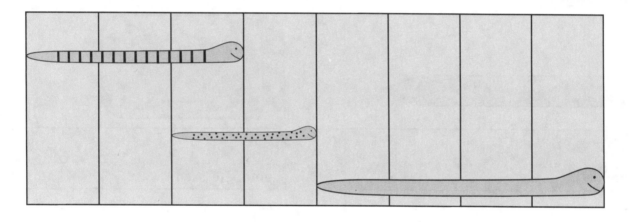

2. Which worm is the longest?

○   ○   ○

3. Which worm is the shortest?

○   ○   ○

4. Which worm is exactly 3 units long?

○   ○   ○

5. If the worms were placed end to
   end, how many units long would they
   measure altogether?

8 units   9 units   10 units
  ○   ○   ○

Circle to complete the sentences.

1.

Ian   Joe   Sam

Joe is taller than Ian.

Ian is taller than [Joe. / Sam.]

So Joe is [taller / shorter] than Sam.

Write the length.

2.

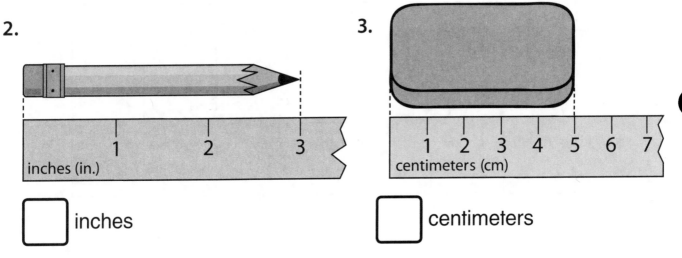

inches (in.)

☐ inches

3.

centimeters (cm)

☐ centimeters

Complete the sentences.

4. Joe's pencil is 6 inches long.
Sam's pencil is 3 inches long.
How many inches longer is Joe's
pencil than Sam's pencil?

☐ ◯ ☐ ◯ ☐

Joe's pencil is ☐ inches longer than Sam's pencil.

Read a Thermometer

Draw a line to match the temperature to the activity.

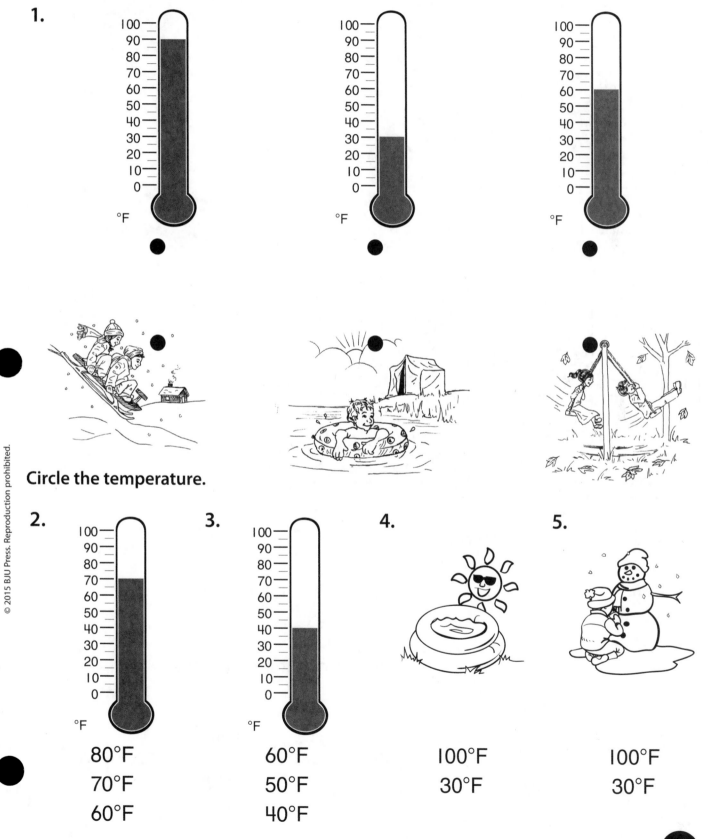

1.

Circle the temperature.

2.

80°F

70°F

60°F

3.

60°F

50°F

40°F

4.

100°F

30°F

5.

100°F

30°F

Write each temperature.
Draw a line to match the temperature to the activity.

Circle the temperature.

1.

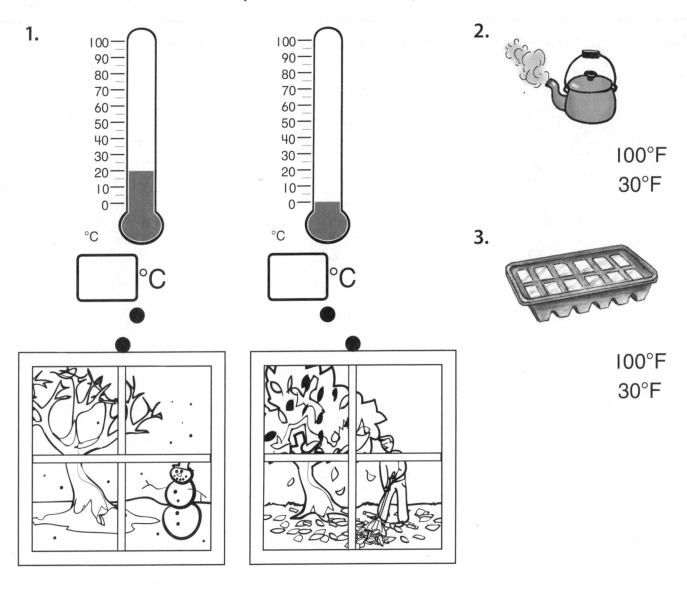

2.

100°F
30°F

3.

100°F
30°F

Circle to complete the sentences.

4.

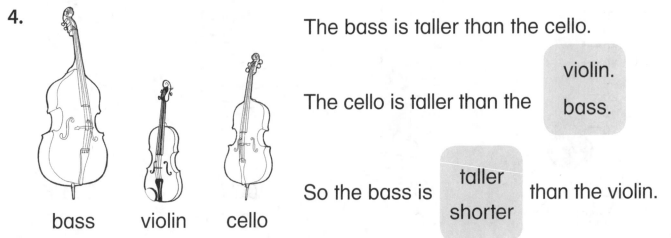

bass   violin   cello

The bass is taller than the cello.

The cello is taller than the ⟨ violin. / bass. ⟩

So the bass is ⟨ taller / shorter ⟩ than the violin.

Chapter 14 Review

Put an *X* on the longest one.
Circle the shortest one.

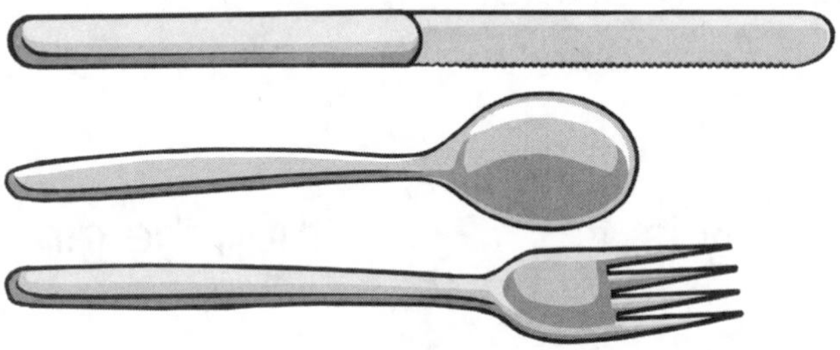

Put an *X* on the taller one.
Circle the shorter one.

1.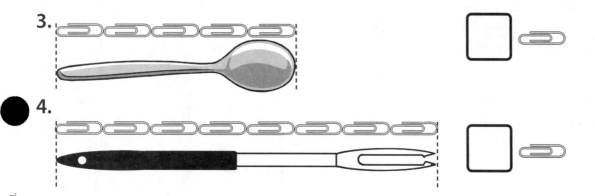

2.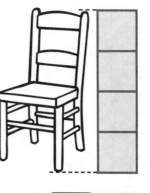

Write the length.

3.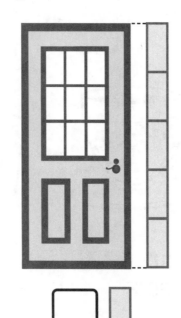

⬜ 🖇

4.

⬜ 🖇

Write the height.

5.

6.

⬜ ⬜

⬜ ⬜

Circle to complete the sentences.

7.

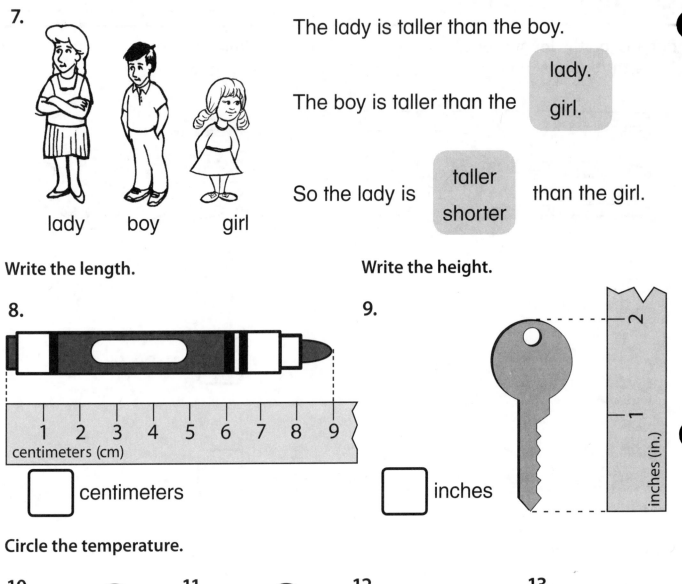

lady   boy   girl

The lady is taller than the boy.

The boy is taller than the | lady. / girl.

So the lady is | taller / shorter | than the girl.

Write the length.

8.

☐ centimeters

Write the height.

9.

☐ inches

Circle the temperature.

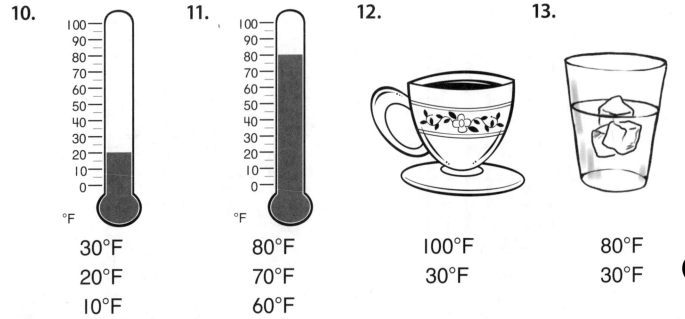

10.

30°F
20°F
10°F

11.

80°F
70°F
60°F

12.

100°F
30°F

13.

80°F
30°F

Cumulative Review

Cross out to subtract.
Complete the subtraction problem.

Complete the subtraction problem.

1.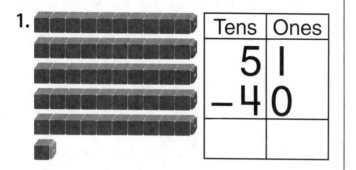

Tens	Ones
5	1
− 4	0

2.
Tens	Ones
4	7
− 1	1

3.
Tens	Ones
2	5
− 1	3

Complete the subtraction problems.

4.

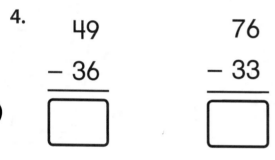 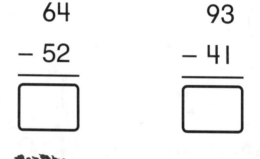

$$49 - 36$$ $$76 - 33$$ $$64 - 52$$ $$93 - 41$$

Draw tens and ones to picture the story.
Complete the sentences.

5. The train had 43 cars. Then 22 cars were taken off. How many cars are in the train now?

6. There are 30 little boxes and 35 big boxes on the train car. How many boxes are there in all?

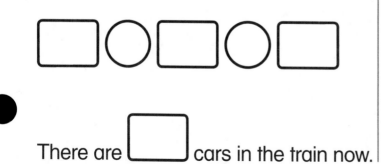

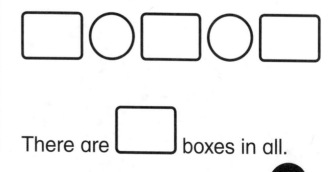

There are ☐ cars in the train now.

There are ☐ boxes in all.

Count to 9 by 1s on the number line.

7.

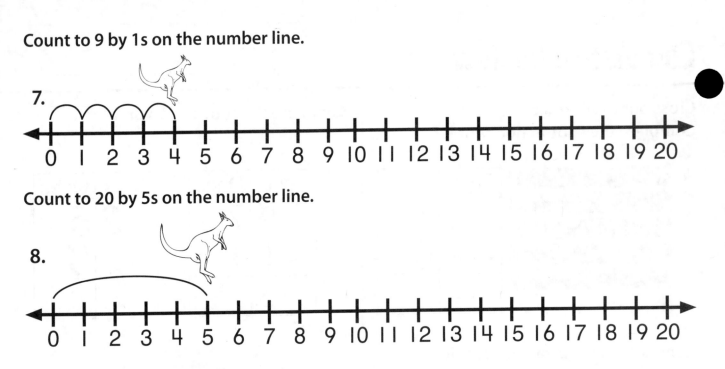

Count to 20 by 5s on the number line.

8.

Complete the number sequence.

9. 30	35	40	☐		**10.** 65	70	75	☐
11. 13	14	15	☐		**12.** 20	30	40	☐
13. 40	50	60	☐		**14.** 41	42	43	☐

Count by fives and connect the dots.

15.

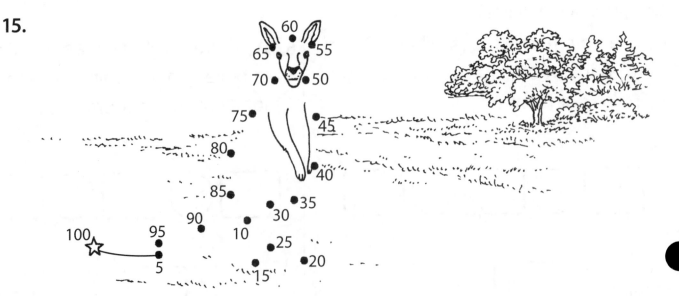

Flat & Curved Surfaces

Circle each object that has at least 1 flat surface.

1.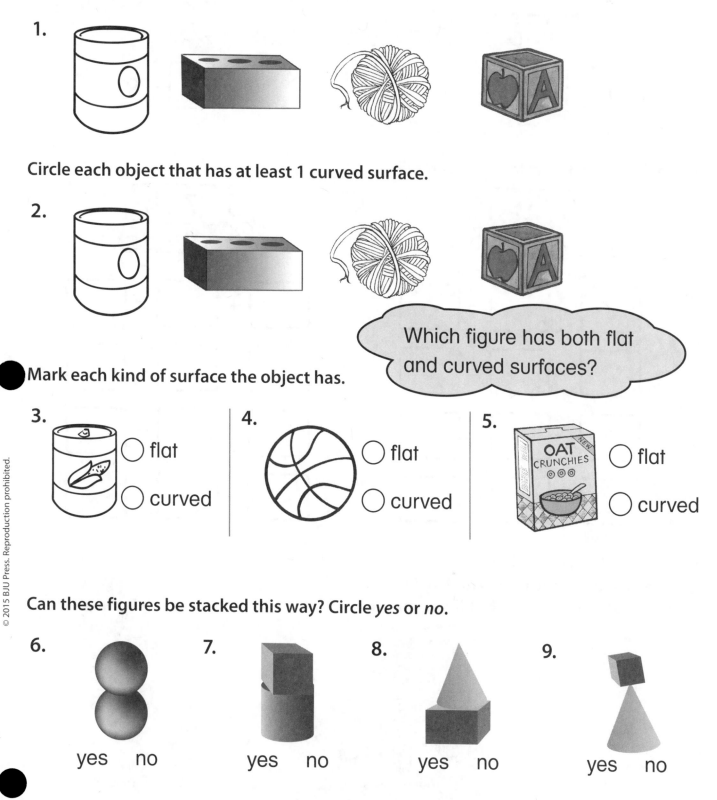

Circle each object that has at least 1 curved surface.

2.

Which figure has both flat and curved surfaces?

Mark each kind of surface the object has.

3. ◯ flat ◯ curved

4. ◯ flat ◯ curved

5. ◯ flat ◯ curved

Can these figures be stacked this way? Circle *yes* or *no*.

6. yes   no

7. yes   no

8. yes   no

9. yes   no

Write the missing addend to complete the addition sentence.

1. $4 + \boxed{} = 7$

2. $8 + \boxed{} = 10$

3. $6 + \boxed{} = 12$

4. $7 + \boxed{} = 9$

Write the related facts for the fact family.

5.

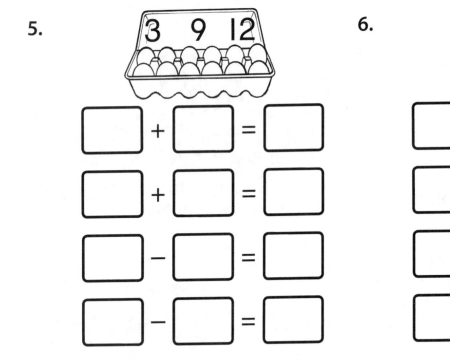

3 9 12

$\boxed{} + \boxed{} = \boxed{}$

$\boxed{} + \boxed{} = \boxed{}$

$\boxed{} - \boxed{} = \boxed{}$

$\boxed{} - \boxed{} = \boxed{}$

6.

5 7 12

$\boxed{} + \boxed{} = \boxed{}$

$\boxed{} + \boxed{} = \boxed{}$

$\boxed{} - \boxed{} = \boxed{}$

$\boxed{} - \boxed{} = \boxed{}$

Circle the third child in line.
Draw a line under the ninth child in line.
Draw a box around the fifth child in line.

7.

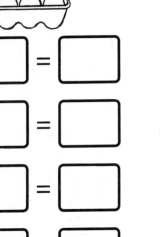

Spheres

Circle each object that has the same attributes as the figure.

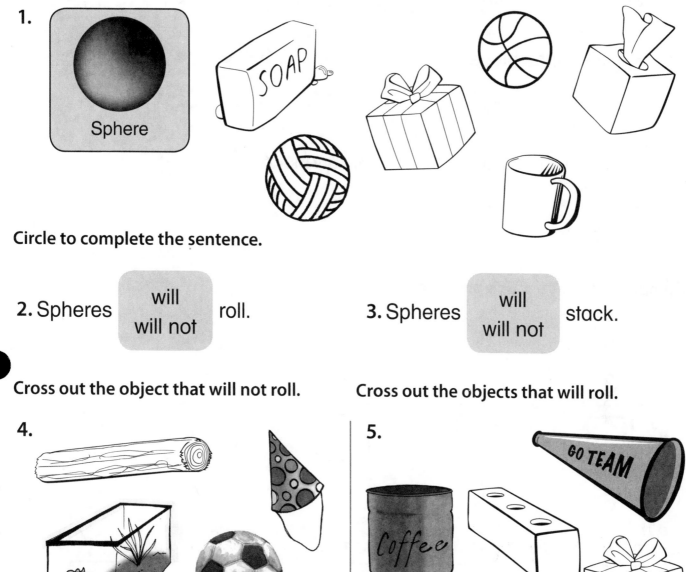

1.

Sphere

SOAP

Circle to complete the sentence.

2. Spheres | will / will not | roll.

3. Spheres | will / will not | stack.

Cross out the object that will not roll.

4.

Cross out the objects that will roll.

5.

GO TEAM

Coffee

Circle the figure that will both roll and stack.

6.

Mark the number that matches the clue.

1. 3 in the Tens place

   34 ○   43 ○

2. 5 in the Ones place

   56 ○   65 ○

3. 7 in the Tens place

   72 ○   27 ○

4. 9 in the Tens place

   19 ○   90 ○

5. 2 tens, 5 ones

   25 ○   52 ○

6. 3 tens, 6 ones

   63 ○   36 ○

Complete the subtraction problems.

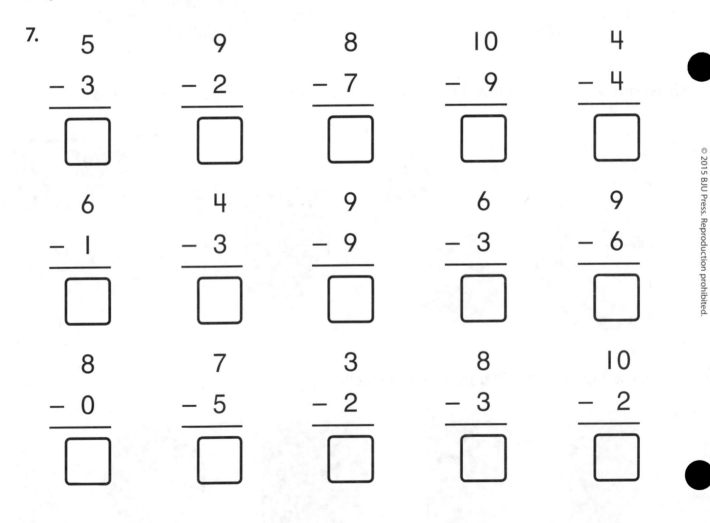

7.

5	9	8	10	4
− 3	− 2	− 7	− 9	− 4

6	4	9	6	9
− 1	− 3	− 9	− 3	− 6

8	7	3	8	10
− 0	− 5	− 2	− 3	− 2

Rectangular Prisms & Cubes

_____

Circle each object that has the same attributes as the figure.

1. Rectangular Prism

2. Cube

Circle each picture of the stacked figures.

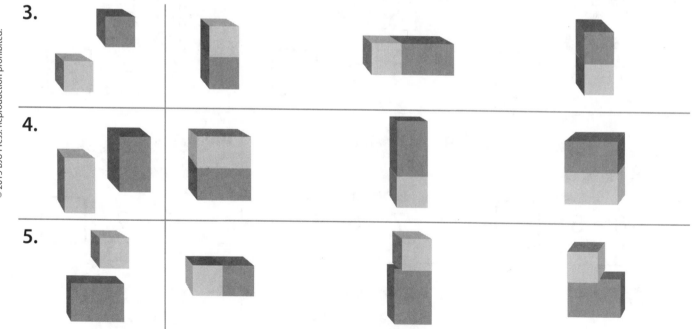

3.

4.

5.

Number the days of the week in order.

1.
[3] Tuesday   [ ] Saturday   [ ] Wednesday

[ ] Sunday   [5] Thursday   [ ] Monday   [ ] Friday

Write the length.

2.

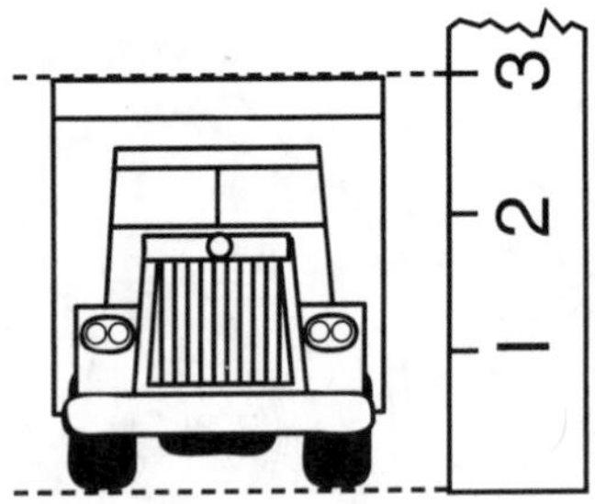

[ ] units

3.

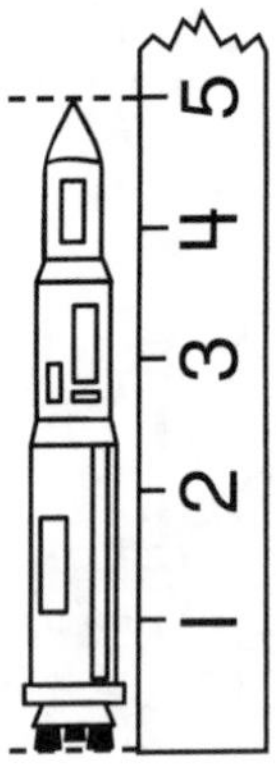

[ ] units

4.

[ ] units

Cross out to subtract. Complete the subtraction sentence.

5.

$7 - 3 = $ [ ]

6.

$8 - 3 = $ [ ]

7.

$9 - 2 = $ [ ]

8.

$8 - 5 = $ [ ]

9.

$7 - 5 = $ [ ]

10.

$10 - 9 = $ [ ]

11.

$7 - 4 = $ [ ]

12.

$10 - 2 = $ [ ]

13.

$8 - 1 = $ [ ]

Cylinders & Cones

Circle each object that has the same attributes as the figure.

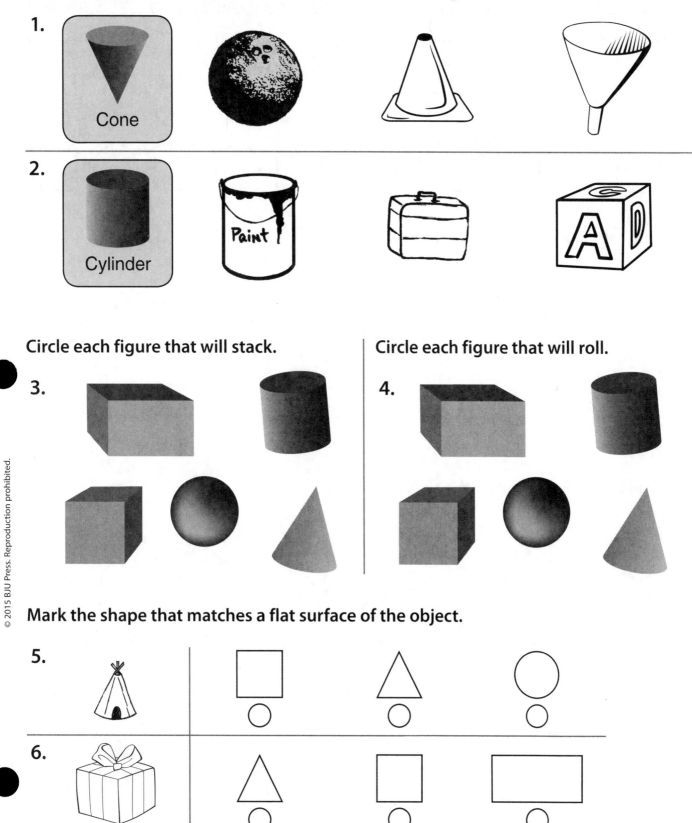

1.
Cone

2.
Cylinder

Circle each figure that will stack.

3.

Circle each figure that will roll.

4.

Mark the shape that matches a flat surface of the object.

5.

6.

Draw shapes to picture the story.
Complete the addition sentence.

1. Lexi colored 5 circles blue. She colored 4 circles yellow. How many circles did she color?

2. Sally had 5 sticks of gum. While she was playing, she lost 3 sticks of gum. How many sticks of gum does Sally have left?

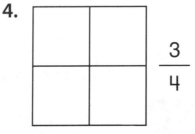 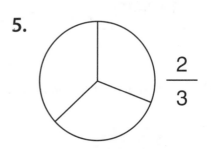

Color the shape to match the fraction.

3. 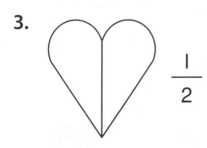 $\dfrac{1}{2}$

4. $\dfrac{3}{4}$

5. $\dfrac{2}{3}$

Mark the fraction that names the shaded part.

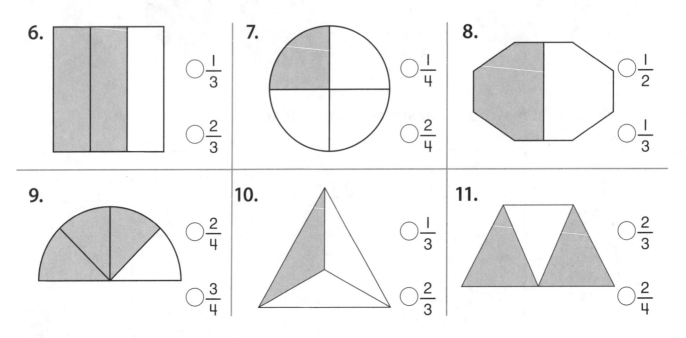

6. ○ $\dfrac{1}{3}$ ○ $\dfrac{2}{3}$

7. ○ $\dfrac{1}{4}$ ○ $\dfrac{2}{4}$

8. ○ $\dfrac{1}{2}$ ○ $\dfrac{1}{3}$

9. ○ $\dfrac{2}{4}$ ○ $\dfrac{3}{4}$

10. ○ $\dfrac{1}{3}$ ○ $\dfrac{2}{3}$

11. ○ $\dfrac{2}{3}$ ○ $\dfrac{2}{4}$

Compose Solid Figures

Circle the combinations that have the same shape.

1.

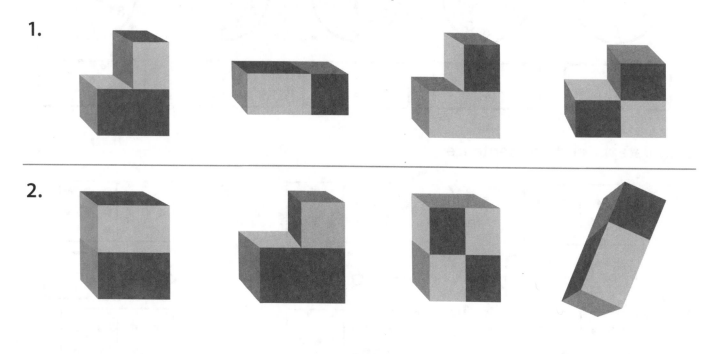

2.

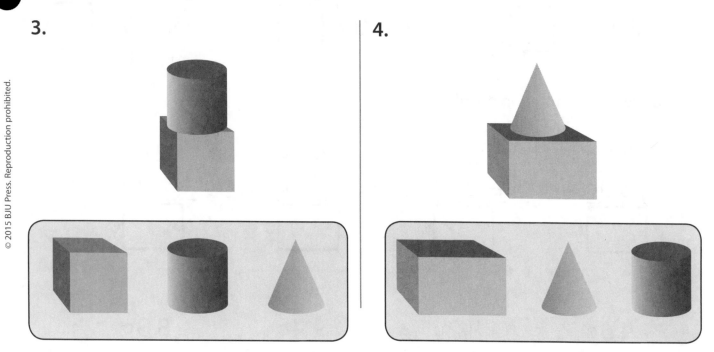

Circle each kind of figure used in the picture.

3.

4.

Write the time.

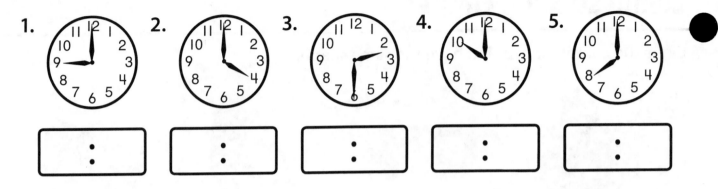

1.
2.
3.
4.
5.

Complete the addition sentence.

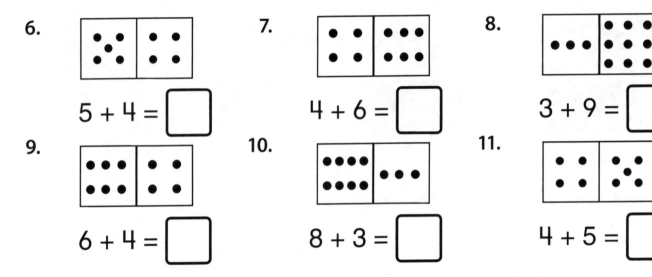

6. 5 + 4 = ☐

7. 4 + 6 = ☐

8. 3 + 9 = ☐

9. 6 + 4 = ☐

10. 8 + 3 = ☐

11. 4 + 5 = ☐

Complete the subtraction problems.

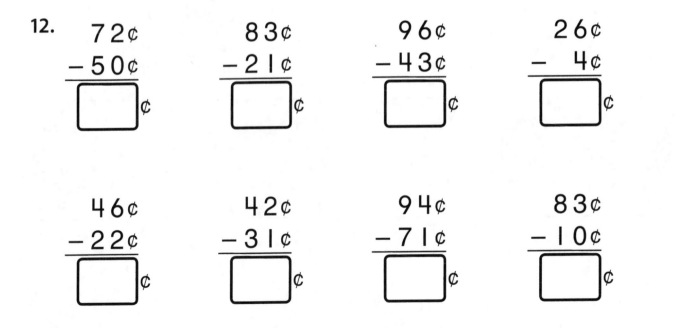

12.

```
  72¢        83¢        96¢        26¢
- 50¢      - 21¢      - 43¢      -  4¢
─────      ─────      ─────      ─────
 ☐ ¢        ☐ ¢        ☐ ¢        ☐ ¢


  46¢        42¢        94¢        83¢
- 22¢      - 31¢      - 71¢      - 10¢
─────      ─────      ─────      ─────
 ☐ ¢        ☐ ¢        ☐ ¢        ☐ ¢
```

Shape Attributes

Circle each object that has a flat surface that matches the shape.

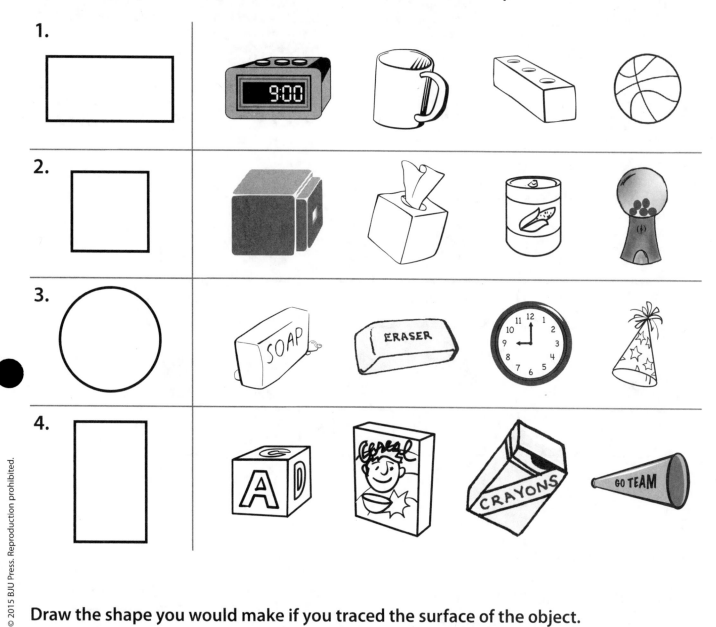

Draw the shape you would make if you traced the surface of the object.

5.

6.

Compare the numbers. Circle the correct sign.

> | is greater than | < | is less than

1.

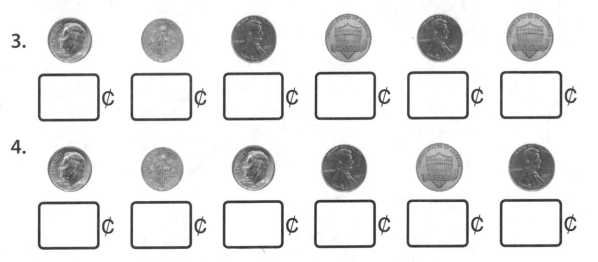

29 $\overset{>}{<}$ 41

2.

57 $\overset{>}{<}$ 23

Write the total value as you *count on*.

3.

[ ] ¢ [ ] ¢ [ ] ¢ [ ] ¢ [ ] ¢ [ ] ¢

4.

[ ] ¢ [ ] ¢ [ ] ¢ [ ] ¢ [ ] ¢ [ ] ¢

Complete the sentences.

5. Joy caught 8 bugs. She put them in a jar. She caught 6 more bugs. She put them in a different jar. How many bugs did Joy catch?

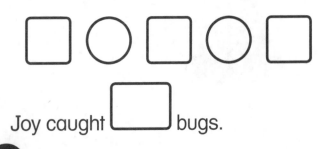

[ ] ◯ [ ] ◯ [ ]

[ ]

Joy caught [ ] bugs.

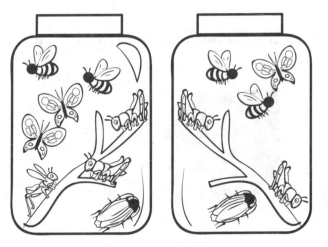

Extend Patterns

Circle the one that extends the pattern.

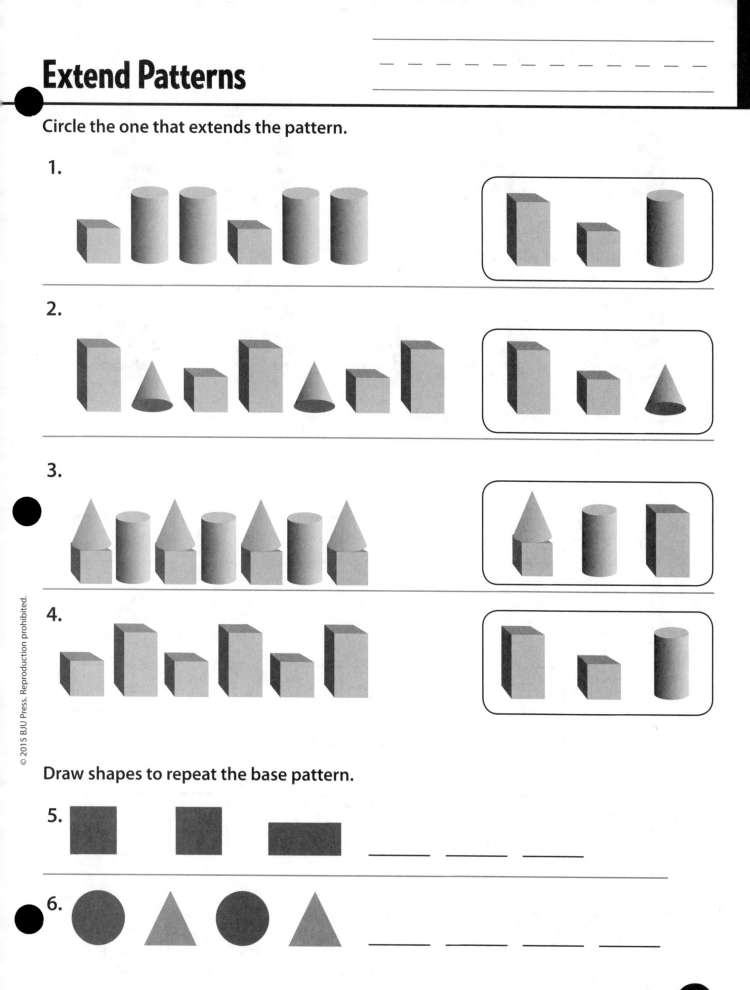

1.

2.

3.

4.

Draw shapes to repeat the base pattern.

5.

6.

Circle each figure that will roll.

1.

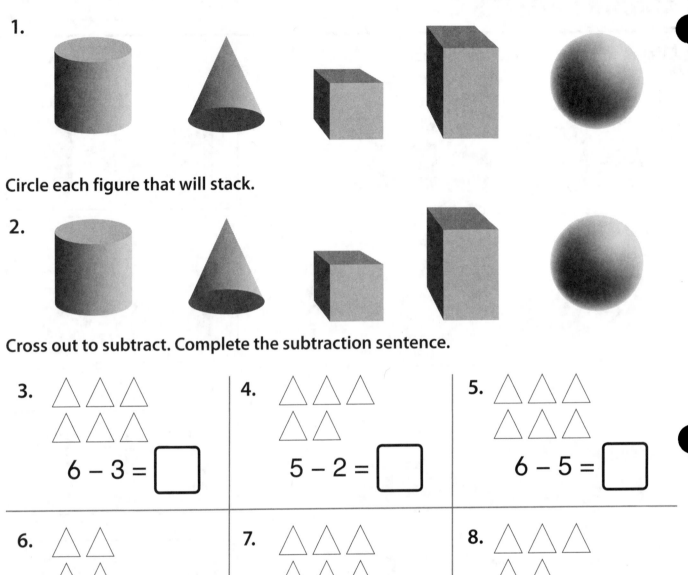

Circle each figure that will stack.

2.

Cross out to subtract. Complete the subtraction sentence.

3. $6 - 3 = \boxed{}$

4. $5 - 2 = \boxed{}$

5. $6 - 5 = \boxed{}$

6. $4 - 2 = \boxed{}$

7. $6 - 4 = \boxed{}$

8. $5 - 3 = \boxed{}$

Write the number that comes *before*, *after*, or *between*.

9. 60 ◯ 62

10. 43 ◯

11. ⬜ 87

12. 78 ♡ 80

13. ⬜ 99

14. 64 ◯

Chapter 15 Review

Mark the figure that has the same attributes as the object.

1.  ○ cylinder ○ ○ ○ cube

2. ○ rectangular prism ○ ○ ○ cube

3. 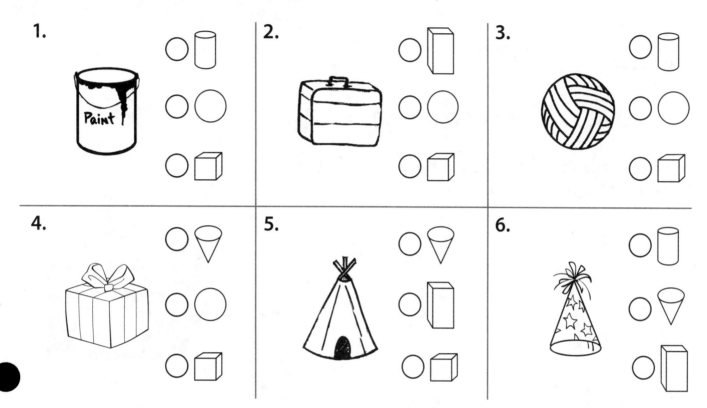 ○ cylinder ○ ○ ○ cube

4. ○ cone ○ ○ ○ cube

5. ○ cone ○ rectangular prism ○ cube

6. ○ cylinder ○ cone ○ rectangular prism

Circle each shape that will roll. Put an *X* on each shape that will stack.

7.

Mark each attribute of the shape.

8.
   ○ flat surface
   ○ curved surface
   ○ corner

9.
   ○ flat surface
   ○ curved surface
   ○ corner

10.
   ○ flat surface
   ○ curved surface
   ○ corner

11.
   ○ flat surface
   ○ curved surface
   ○ corner

Match each figure to its name.

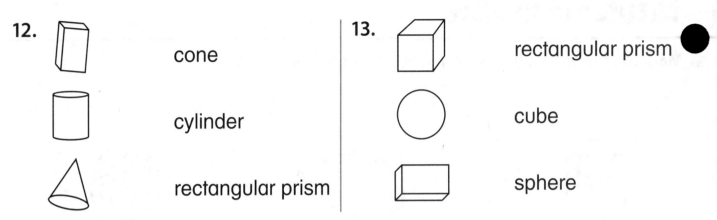

12.

cone

cylinder

rectangular prism

13.

rectangular prism

cube

sphere

Jim traced the flat surface of an object on his paper. Circle the object he traced.

14.

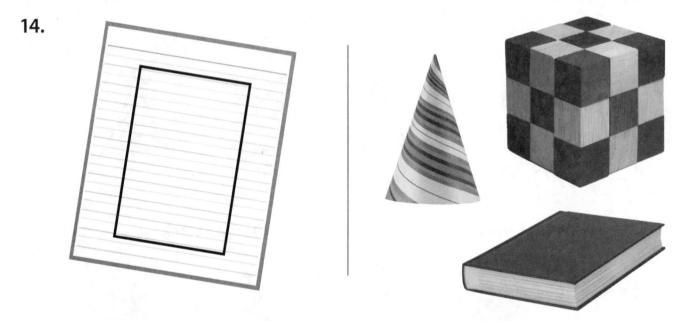

Circle the one that extends the pattern.

15.

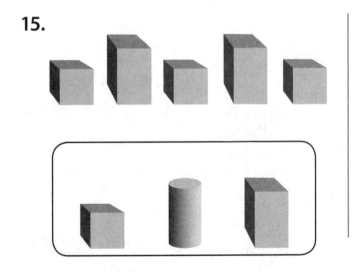

16.

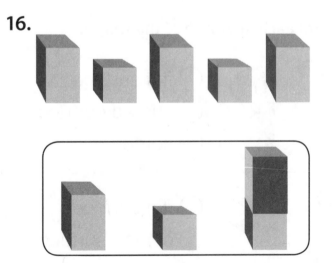

Cumulative Review

Complete the addition problems.

1.

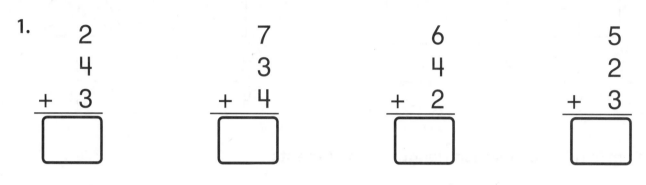

```
    2            7            6            5
    4            3            4            2
 +  3         +  4         +  2         +  3
 _____       _____       _____       _____
```

Write the time.

2.   3.   4.   5.

```
  [  :  ]      [  :  ]      [  :  ]      [  :  ]
```

Complete the addition problems.

6.

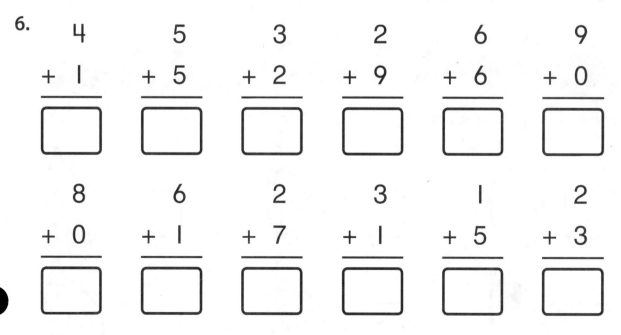

```
    4            5            3            2            6            9
 +  1         +  5         +  2         +  9         +  6         +  0
 _____       _____       _____       _____       _____       _____



    8            6            2            3            1            2
 +  0         +  1         +  7         +  1         +  5         +  3
 _____       _____       _____       _____       _____       _____
```

Color the shape to match the fraction.

7.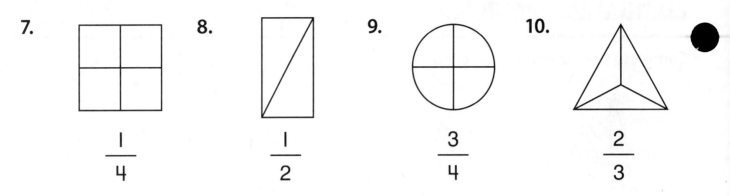
$\dfrac{1}{4}$

8.
$\dfrac{1}{2}$

9.
$\dfrac{3}{4}$

10.
$\dfrac{2}{3}$

Use an inch ruler to draw each length. Start at the star.

11. 3 inches

12. 2 inches

13. 5 inches

Draw a line under the third duck.
Circle the ninth duck.
Draw a box around the seventh duck.

14.

Write the number that comes *before*.

15. [   ] 20

16. [   ] 43

17. [   ] 16

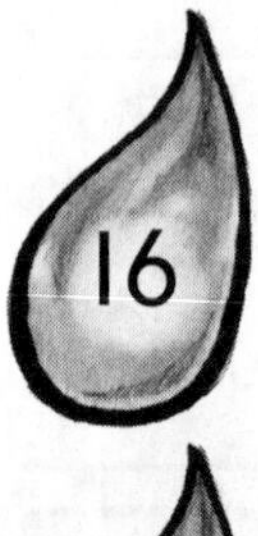

18. [   ] 7

19. [   ] 68

20. [   ] 31

Hundreds, Tens & Ones

Count to 900 by 100s. Write the missing numbers.

1.

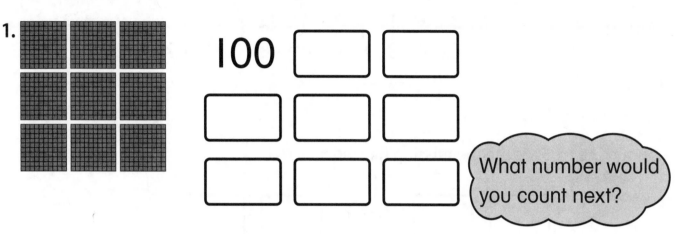

100 ☐ ☐

☐ ☐ ☐

☐ ☐ ☐

What number would you count next?

Write the number of hundreds, tens, and ones.

2.
Hundreds	Tens	Ones

3.
Hundreds	Tens	Ones

Write the number of hundreds, tens, and ones.
Write the number represented.

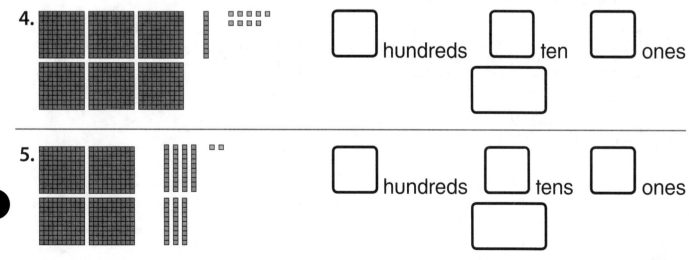

4. ☐ hundreds ☐ ten ☐ ones

☐

5. ☐ hundreds ☐ tens ☐ ones

☐

Count to 20 by 2s on the number line.
Circle the numbers you land on.

1.

Count to 30 by 5s. Write the missing numbers.

2. 5 ☐ ☐ 20 ☐ ☐

Complete the subtraction sentence.

3. 6 − 3 = ☐   4. 7 − 4 = ☐   5. 9 − 4 = ☐

6. 12 − 4 = ☐   7. 11 − 6 = ☐   8. 10 − 7 = ☐

9. 8 − 6 = ☐   10. 10 − 2 = ☐   11. 11 − 8 = ☐

Number the days of the week in order.

12.

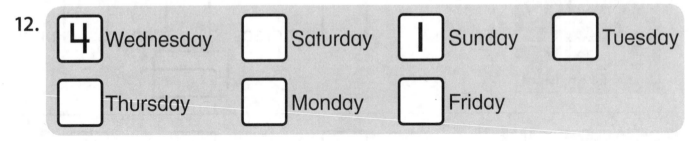

☐ 4 Wednesday   ☐ Saturday   ☐ 1 Sunday   ☐ Tuesday

☐ Thursday   ☐ Monday   ☐ Friday

3-Digit Numbers

Write the number of hundreds, tens, and ones.
Write the number represented.

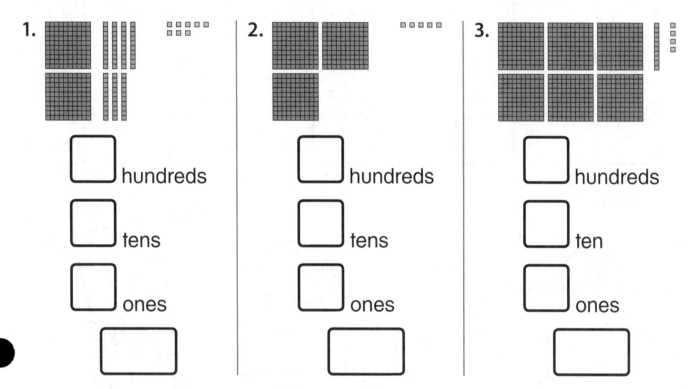

1. ☐ hundreds ☐ tens ☐ ones ☐

2. ☐ hundreds ☐ tens ☐ ones ☐

3. ☐ hundreds ☐ ten ☐ ones ☐

Draw hundreds, tens, and ones to picture the number.

4. 326

Write the number represented.
Count on and write the number sequence.

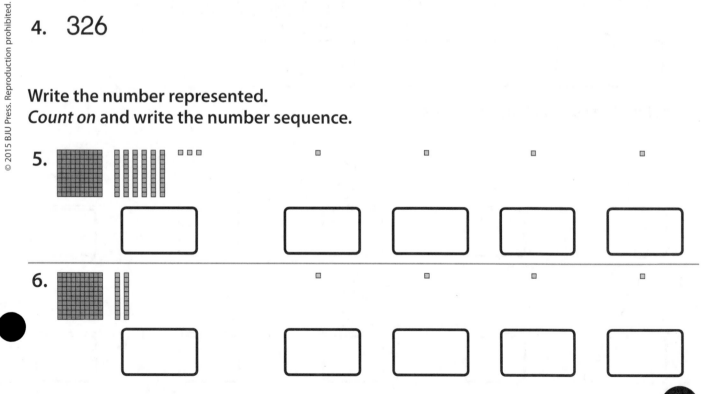

5. ☐ ☐ ☐ ☐ ☐

6. ☐ ☐ ☐ ☐ ☐

Complete the addition problems.

1.

32	16	75	80	43
+ 43	+ 52	+ 21	+ 17	+ 14

50	63	71	20	35
+ 26	+ 36	+ 15	+ 23	+ 54

Write the time.

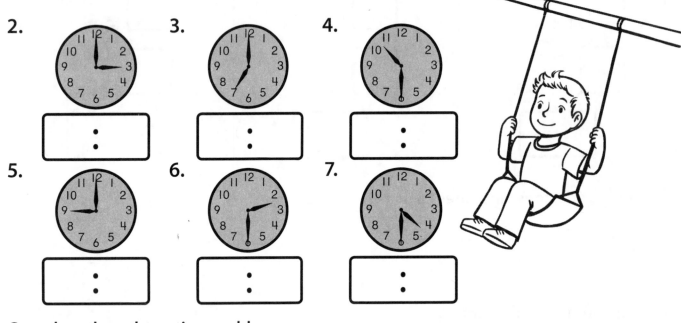

2. 3. 4.

5. 6. 7.

Complete the subtraction problems.

8.

11	9	12	10	7
− 4	− 5	− 3	− 7	− 2

10	8	11	7	8
− 2	− 6	− 2	− 3	− 4

3-Digit Place Value

Picture the number.
Complete the expanded form.

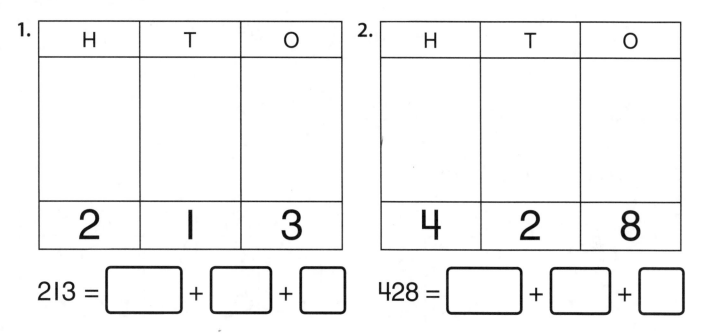

1.

H	T	O
2	1	3

213 = ☐ + ☐ + ☐

2.

H	T	O
4	2	8

428 = ☐ + ☐ + ☐

Draw a line to match the clue to the number.

3.

This number has a 5 in the Ones place.   416

The 5 in this number has a value of 50.   531

This number is equal to 400 + 10 + 6.   195

This number has a 5 in the Hundreds place.   152

Write the number of hundreds, tens, and ones.
Write the number represented.

4.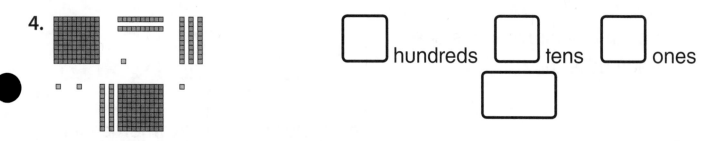

☐ hundreds   ☐ tens   ☐ ones

☐

Write > or < to compare.

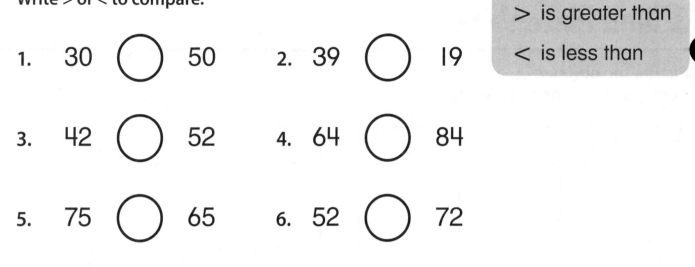
1. 30 ◯ 50   2. 39 ◯ 19

3. 42 ◯ 52   4. 64 ◯ 84

5. 75 ◯ 65   6. 52 ◯ 72

Complete the addition problems.

7.
Tens	Ones
5	3
+2	4

8.
Tens	Ones
3	4
+6	2

9.
Tens	Ones
4	1
+2	6

10.
Tens	Ones
7	0
+2	9

Draw tens and ones to picture the story.
Complete the sentences.

11. Mother baked 40 chocolate chip cookies and 24 sugar cookies. How many cookies did Mother bake in all?

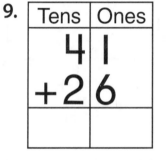

Mother baked ☐ cookies in all.

12. Andy picked 35 strawberries. He gave 13 strawberries to Ann. How many strawberries does Andy have left?

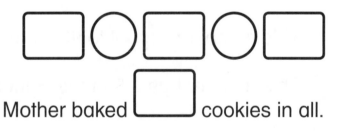

Andy has ☐ strawberries left.

1 More & 1 Less

Use the clues to picture and write the numbers.

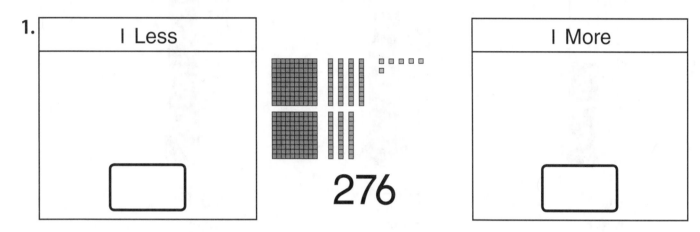

1.

I Less		I More

276

Complete the number sentences to show 1 less and 1 more than 276.

2. $276 - \boxed{} = \boxed{}$ $276 + \boxed{} = \boxed{}$

Underline the digit in the Ones place.
Use the clues to write the numbers.

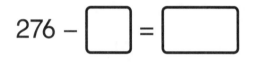

3.

169

I Less   I More

4.

203

I Less   I More

Write the missing number.

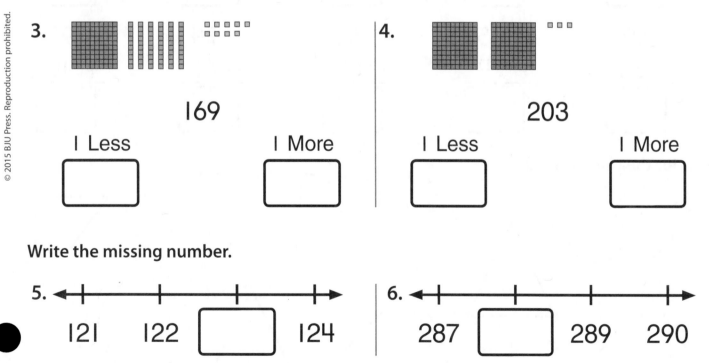

5. 121   122 $\boxed{}$ 124

6. 287 $\boxed{}$ 289   290

Circle the temperature.

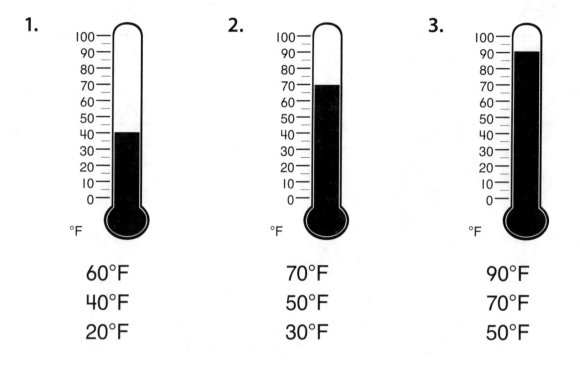

1.
60°F
40°F
20°F

2.
70°F
50°F
30°F

3.
90°F
70°F
50°F

Complete the subtraction problems.

4.
```
  73        85        69        84        48
- 22      - 31      - 23      - 50      - 14
[    ]     [   ]     [   ]     [   ]     [   ]

  97        85        63        74        92
- 34      - 24      - 52      - 61      - 40
[   ]      [   ]     [   ]     [   ]     [   ]
```

Color the triangles red.

5.

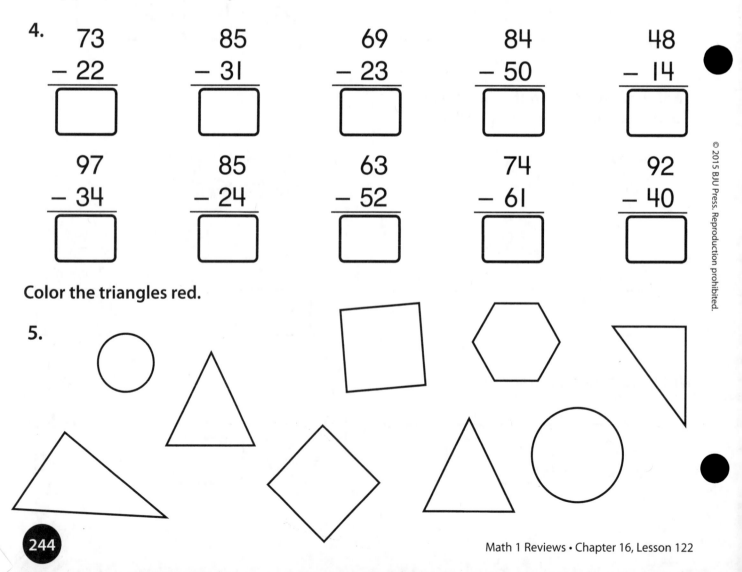

10 More & 10 Less

Write the number represented.
Use the clues to picture and write the numbers.

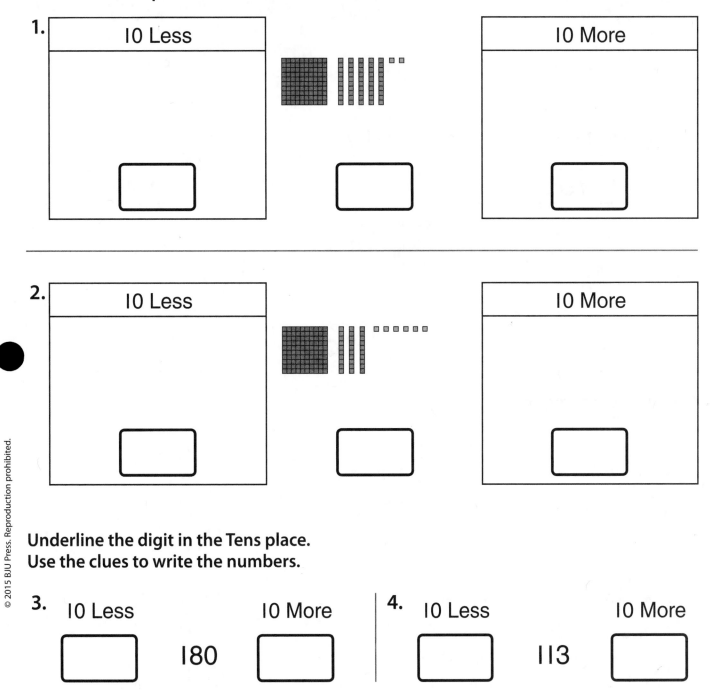

1.

| 10 Less | | 10 More |

2.

| 10 Less | | 10 More |

Underline the digit in the Tens place.
Use the clues to write the numbers.

3.

10 Less   10 More

180

4.

10 Less   10 More

113

Circle the day that comes next.

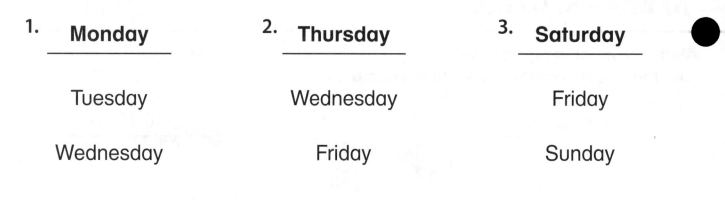

1. **Monday**	2. **Thursday**	3. **Saturday**
Tuesday	Wednesday	Friday
Wednesday	Friday	Sunday

Use the clues to picture and write the numbers.

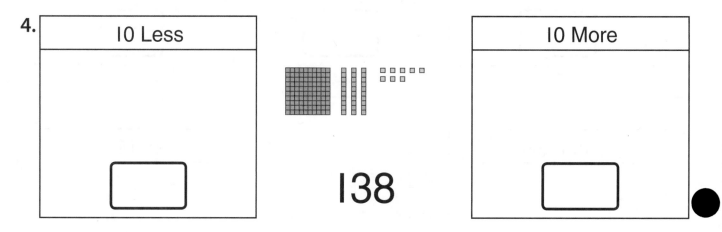

4.

10 Less		10 More

138

Complete the addition problem.

5.
$$\begin{array}{r} 51 \\ + 36 \\ \hline \end{array}$$

6.
$$\begin{array}{r} 38 \\ + 60 \\ \hline \end{array}$$

7.
$$\begin{array}{r} 27 \\ + 42 \\ \hline \end{array}$$

8. On Friday, 72 people went to the zoo. On Saturday, 25 people went to the zoo. How many people went to the zoo altogether?

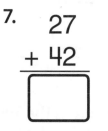

Tens	Ones
7	2
+2	5

_____ people went to the zoo.

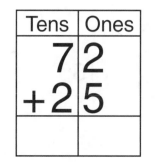

Compare 3-Digit Numbers

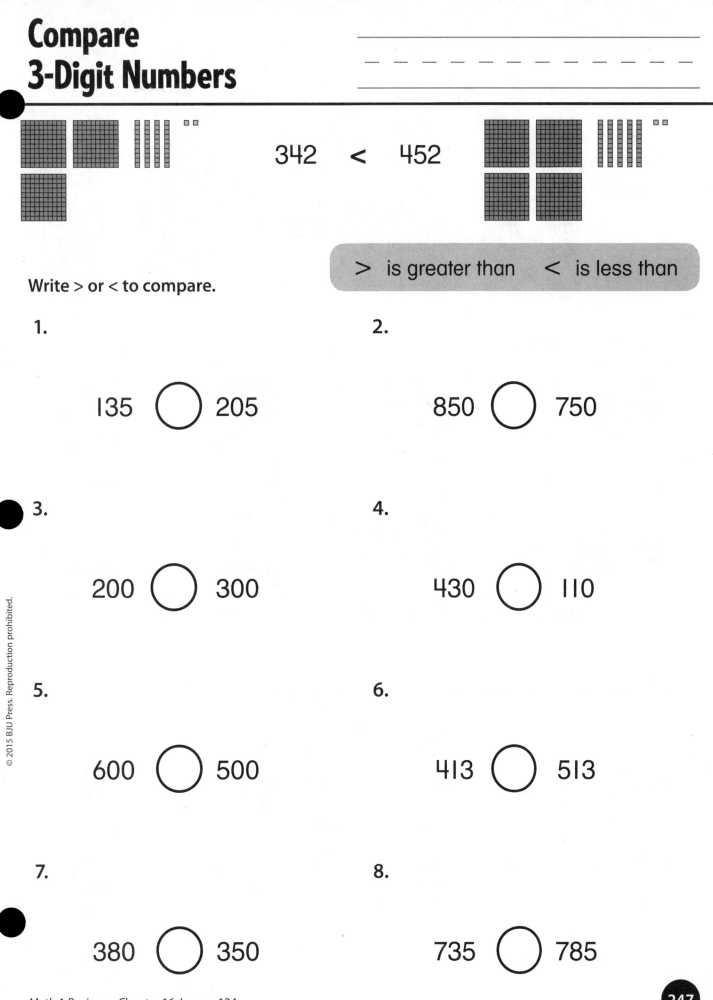

342 < 452

> is greater than   < is less than

Write > or < to compare.

1.

135 ◯ 205

2.

850 ◯ 750

3.

200 ◯ 300

4.

430 ◯ 110

5.

600 ◯ 500

6.

413 ◯ 513

7.

380 ◯ 350

8.

735 ◯ 785

Circle the larger object.

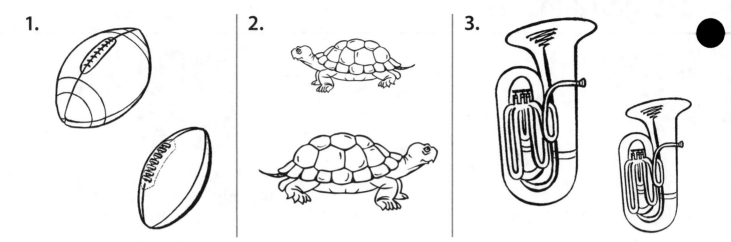

1.

2.

3.

Complete the expanded form.

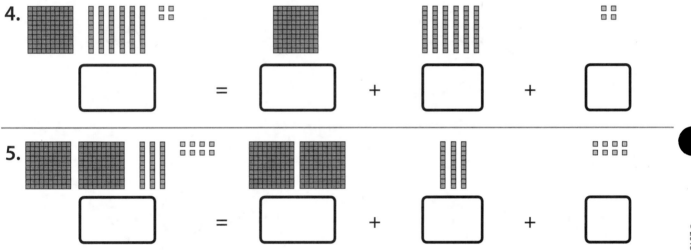

4.

5.

Draw a line to match the number word to the dot pattern.

6. two

   seven

   three

   nine

   four

7. five

   eight

   ten

   one

   six

3-Digit Addition

Complete the addition problem.

1.
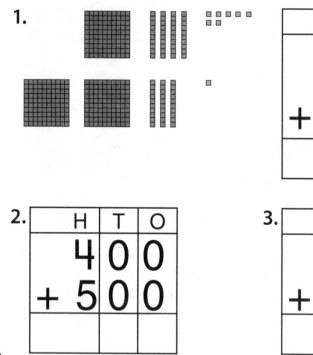

H	T	O
	1	4	7
+ 2	3	1

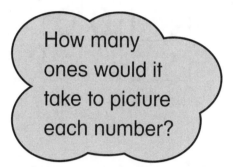

How many ones would it take to picture each number?

2.
H	T	O
4	0	0
+ 5	0	0

3.
H	T	O
2	0	0
+ 2	7	5

4.
H	T	O
3	1	0
+	4	0

Use the clues to picture and write the numbers.

5.
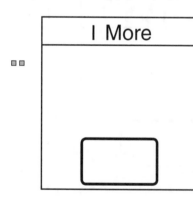

142

1 More

10 More

100 More

Write an addition problem for the story. Complete the sentence.

6. Jared mailed 136 invitation post cards. Eliza mailed 100 post cards. How many post cards did they mail in all?

They mailed [ ] post cards.

H	T	O
+		

Complete the addition problem.

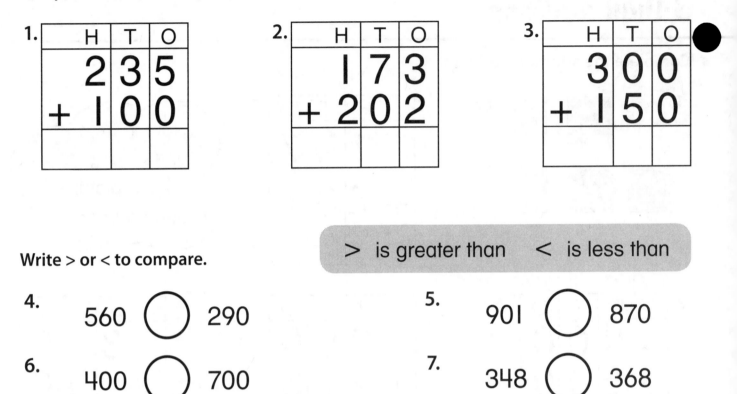

1.

H	T	O
2	3	5
+ 1	0	0

2.

H	T	O
1	7	3
+ 2	0	2

3.

H	T	O
3	0	0
+ 1	5	0

Write > or < to compare.

> is greater than   < is less than

4. 560 ◯ 290

6. 400 ◯ 700

5. 901 ◯ 870

7. 348 ◯ 368

Use the clues to picture and write the numbers.

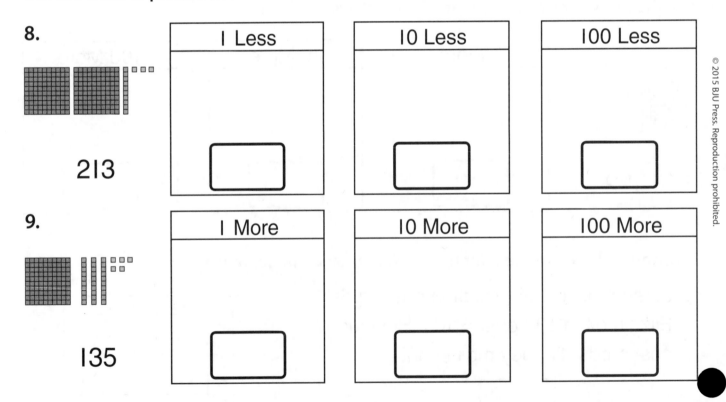

8.

213

I Less
▢

10 Less
▢

100 Less
▢

9.

135

I More
▢

10 More
▢

100 More
▢

Chapter 16 Review

Count to 900 by 100s. Write the missing numbers.

1.

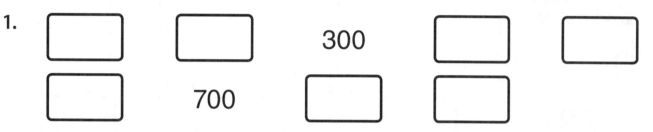

| | | 300 | | |

| | 700 | | | |

Write the number represented.
Count on and write the number sequence.

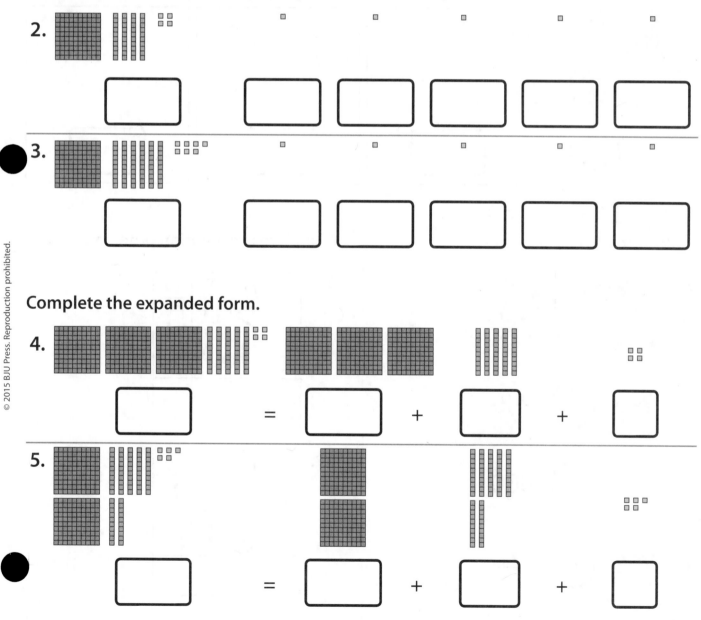

2.

3.

Complete the expanded form.

4.

| | = | | + | | + | |

5.

| | = | | + | | + | |

Use the clues to picture and write the numbers.

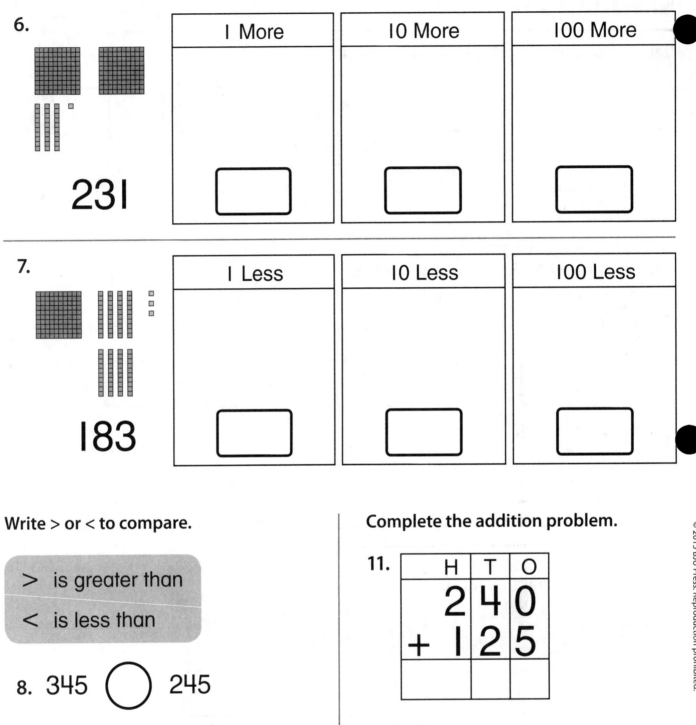

6.

	I More	10 More	100 More
231			

7.

	I Less	10 Less	100 Less
183			

Write > or < to compare.

>	is greater than
<	is less than

8. 345 ◯ 245

9. 600 ◯ 800

10. 750 ◯ 760

Complete the addition problem.

11.
H	T	O
2	4	0
+ 1	2	5

12.
H	T	O
1	8	1
+ 2	1	6

Cumulative Review

Match each clock to the correct time.

1.

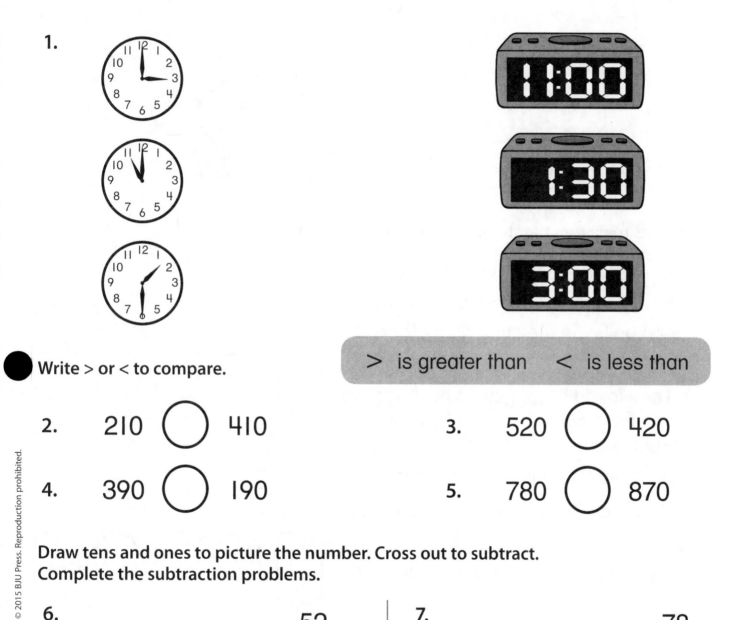

Write > or < to compare.

> is greater than   < is less than

2.   210 ◯ 410

3.   520 ◯ 420

4.   390 ◯ 190

5.   780 ◯ 870

Draw tens and ones to picture the number. Cross out to subtract.
Complete the subtraction problems.

6.
$$\begin{array}{r} 52 \\ -\ 32 \\ \hline \end{array}$$

7.
$$\begin{array}{r} 78 \\ -\ 64 \\ \hline \end{array}$$

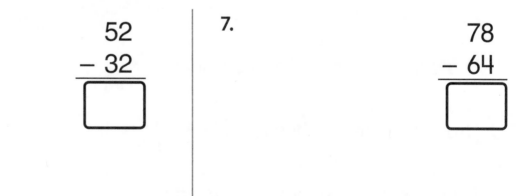

Write the numbers to match the picture.

8.

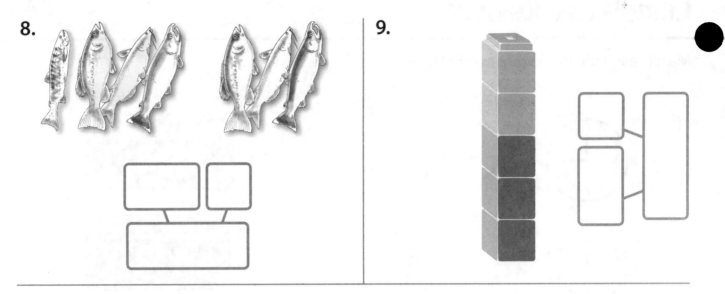

9.

Draw dots to picture the story. Complete the sentences.

10. Ben found 3 golf balls at the park.
Shelly found 5 golf balls. How many
golf balls did they find altogether?

They found ⬜ golf balls altogether. ☐ ◯ ☐ ◯ ☐

11. Paul had 6 tennis balls.
He gave 2 tennis balls to Megan.
How many balls does Paul have left?

Paul has ⬜ tennis balls left. ☐ ◯ ☐ ◯ ☐

12. Draw a shape that has three sides.

13. Draw a shape that has four sides.

14. Draw a shape that has curved sides.

Weight: More or Less

Read the scale. Circle the object that weighs more.

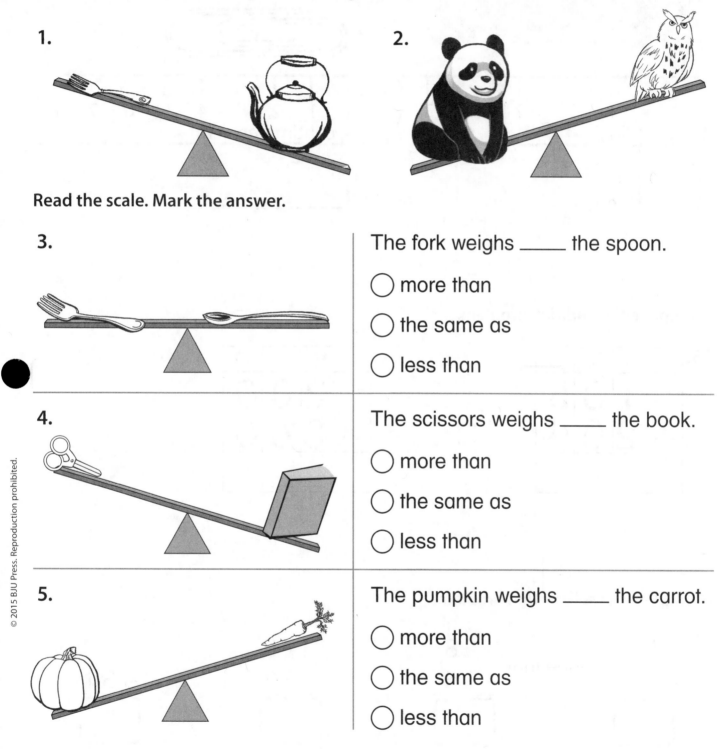

1.

2.

Read the scale. Mark the answer.

3.

The fork weighs _____ the spoon.

○ more than

○ the same as

○ less than

4.

The scissors weighs _____ the book.

○ more than

○ the same as

○ less than

5.

The pumpkin weighs _____ the carrot.

○ more than

○ the same as

○ less than

Write the length.

1.

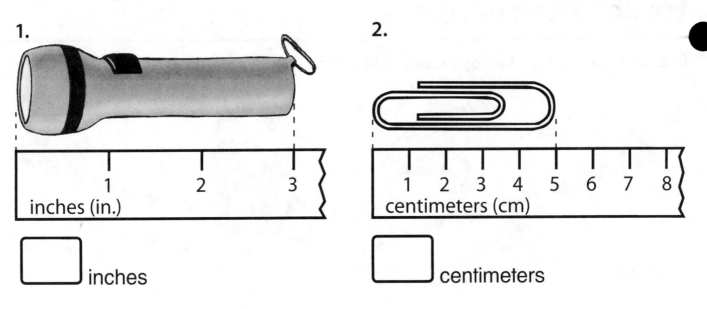

inches (in.)

| | inches

2.

centimeters (cm)

| | centimeters

Complete the addition problem.

3.

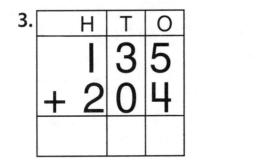

H	T	O
1	3	5
+ 2	0	4

4.

H	T	O
2	0	0
+ 3	6	0

Complete the subtraction problems.

5.

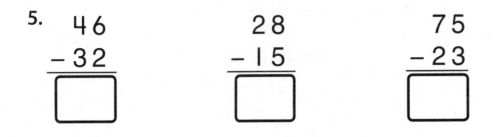

$$\begin{array}{r} 46 \\ -32 \\ \hline \end{array}$$

$$\begin{array}{r} 28 \\ -15 \\ \hline \end{array}$$

$$\begin{array}{r} 75 \\ -23 \\ \hline \end{array}$$

$$\begin{array}{r} 93 \\ -31 \\ \hline \end{array}$$

Compare Weight

Draw the sets of tennis balls on the correct sides of the scale.
Complete the sentence.

1.

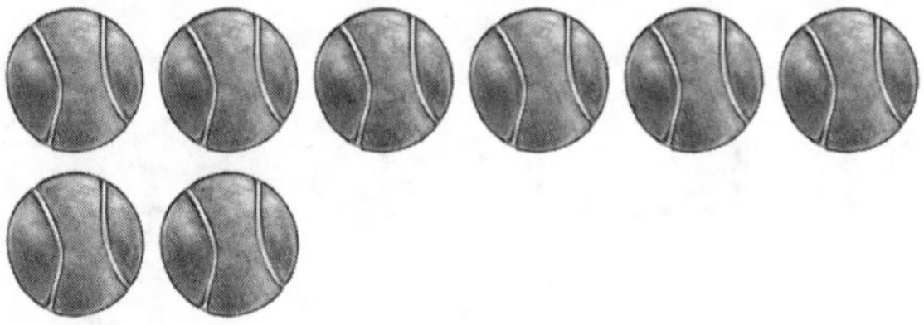

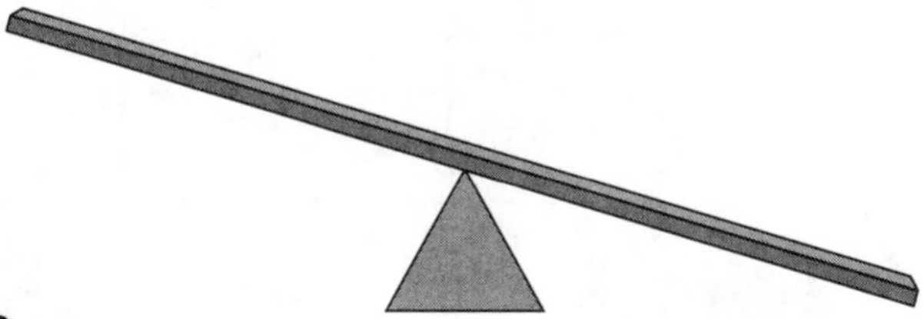

☐ tennis balls weigh less than ☐ tennis balls.

Read the scale. Mark the answer.

2.

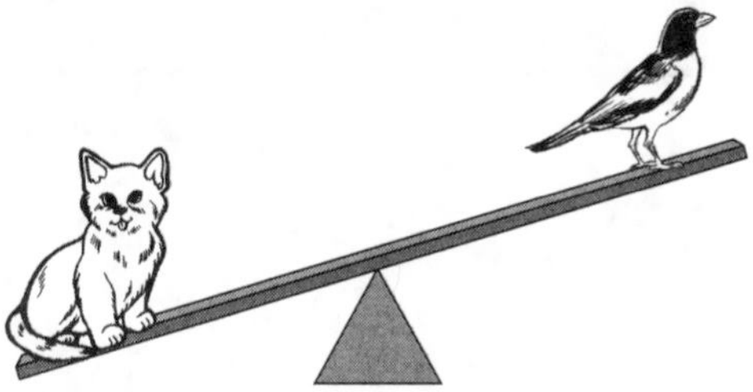

The cat is _____ the bird.

○ heavier than

○ as heavy as

○ lighter than

3.

The cat is _____ the dog.

○ heavier than

○ as heavy as

○ lighter than

Circle the correct scale. Mark the answer.

4.

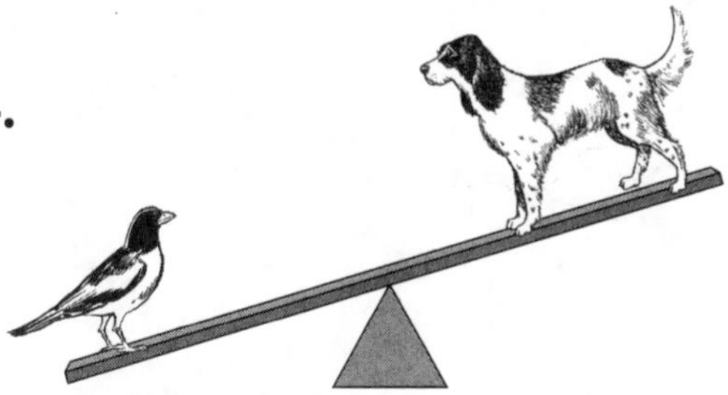

The bird is _____ the dog.

○ heavier than   ○ lighter than

Complete the expanded form.

1.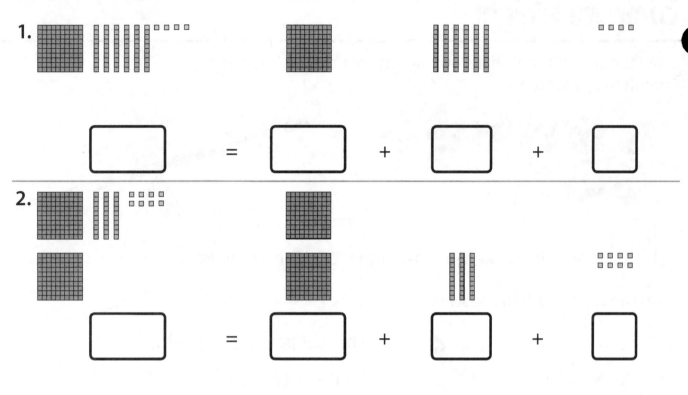

⬜ = ⬜ + ⬜ + ⬜

2.

⬜ = ⬜ + ⬜ + ⬜

Write > or < to compare.

3. 645 ◯ 445

4. 530 ◯ 810

5. 300 ◯ 700

6. 280 ◯ 240

Circle the correct scale. Mark the answer.

7.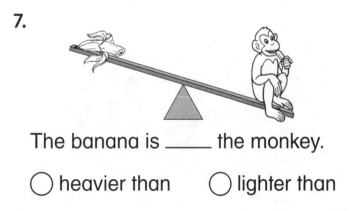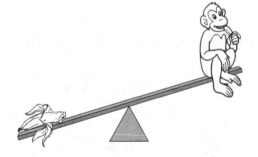

The banana is _____ the monkey.

◯ heavier than   ◯ lighter than

Weight: Heavier or Lighter

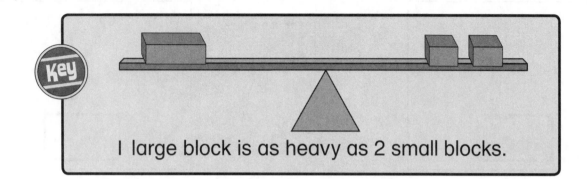

Key

I large block is as heavy as 2 small blocks.

Cross out the scale that is not correct. Use the key.

1.

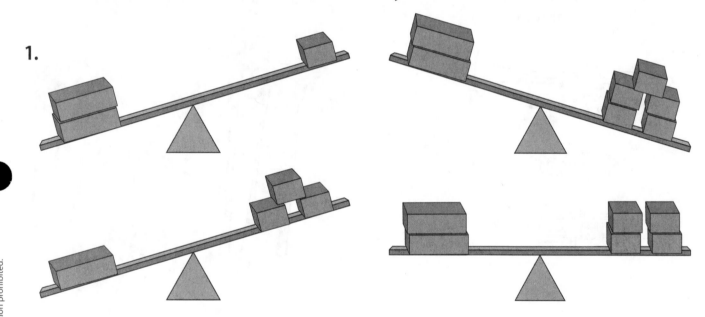

Draw the large blocks needed to balance the scale. Use the key. Complete the sentence.

2.

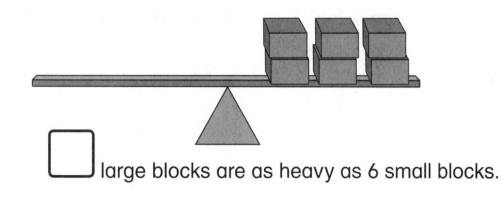

□ large blocks are as heavy as 6 small blocks.

Use the clues to picture and write the numbers.

1.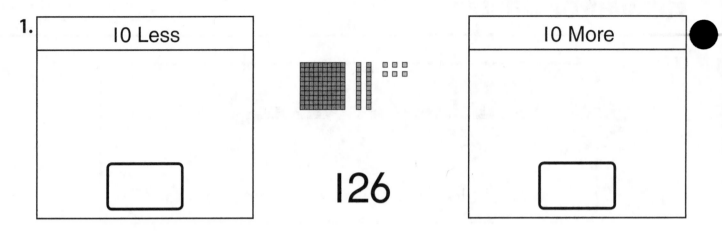

10 Less

126

10 More

Put an X on the longest one.
Circle the shortest one.

2.

3.

Mark the number sentence for the story.

4. Larry bought 9 pencils. He gave 5 pencils to Jennifer. How many pencils does Larry have left?

◯ 9 + 5 = 14

◯ 9 − 5 = 4

5. Betty's rope is 6 feet long. Ella's rope is 8 feet long. How long are their ropes altogether?

◯ 8 + 6 = 14

◯ 8 − 6 = 2

Capacity: More or Less

Circle the container that holds more.
Draw a line under the container that holds less.

1.

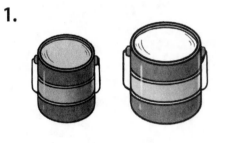

2.

3.

4.

Read the story. Complete the sentence.

5. Container A was full. Holly poured all the
juice from container A into container B.
Which container holds less juice?

Container ☐ holds less juice.

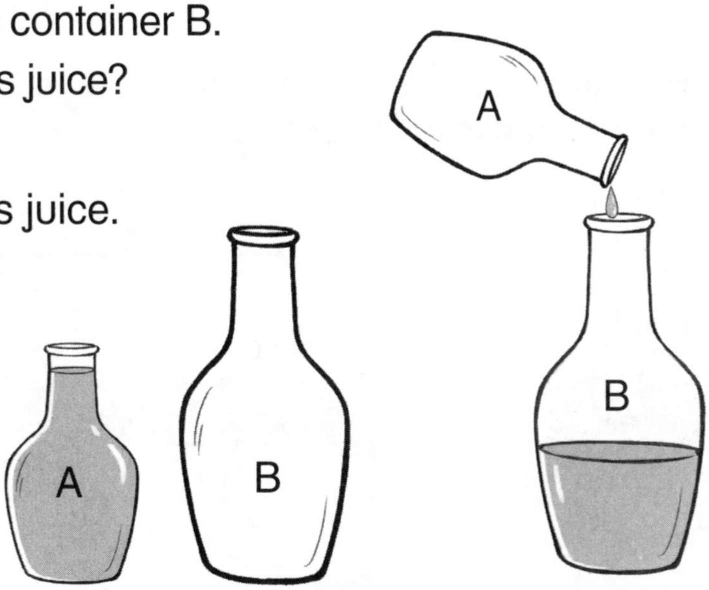

A

A   B   B

Draw a line to match the object to its shape.

1.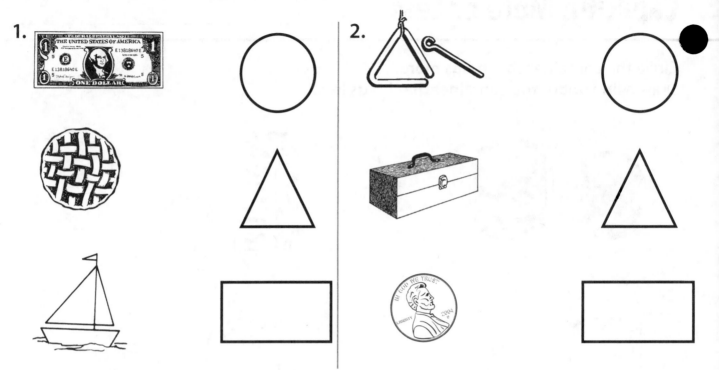

2.

Use the clues to picture and write the numbers.

3.

253

I Less	10 Less	100 Less

Draw a line under the container that holds the least.
Circle the container that holds the most.

4.

Compare Capacity

1 jar fills 2 glasses.

Draw the number of glasses that 3 jars can fill. Use the key.
Complete the sentence.

1.

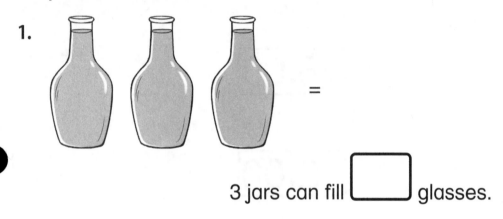

=

3 jars can fill ☐ glasses.

Mark the set that holds less. Use the key.

2.

○   ○

3.

○   ○

Write the number represented.

1.

2.

Match each clock to the correct time.

3.

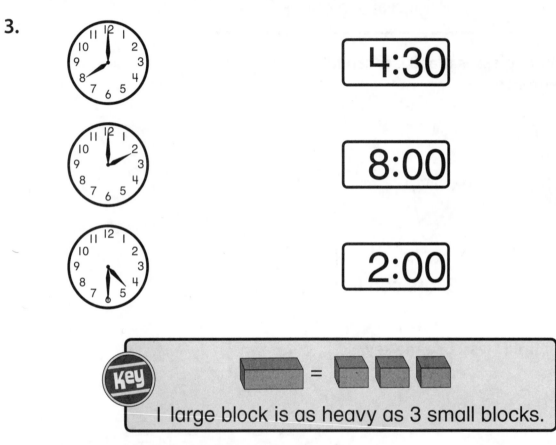

4:30

8:00

2:00

Key 1 large block is as heavy as 3 small blocks.

Draw the small blocks needed to balance the scale.
Use the key. Complete the sentence.

4.

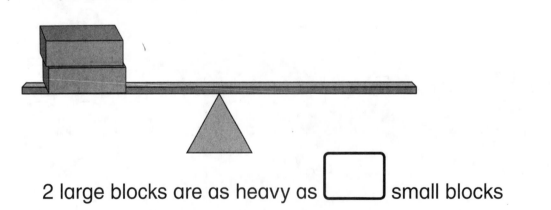

2 large blocks are as heavy as ☐ small blocks

Measurement Tools

Draw a line to the tool Tessa can use to answer her question.

1.

Can I wear my shorts today? ●

How much milk is in the glass? ●

How long is the rope? ●

Is an apple heavier than a grape? ●

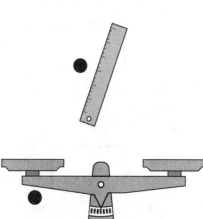

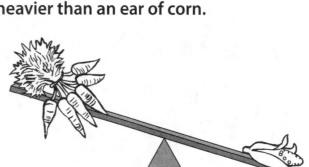

Circle the scale that shows that six carrots are heavier than an ear of corn.

2.

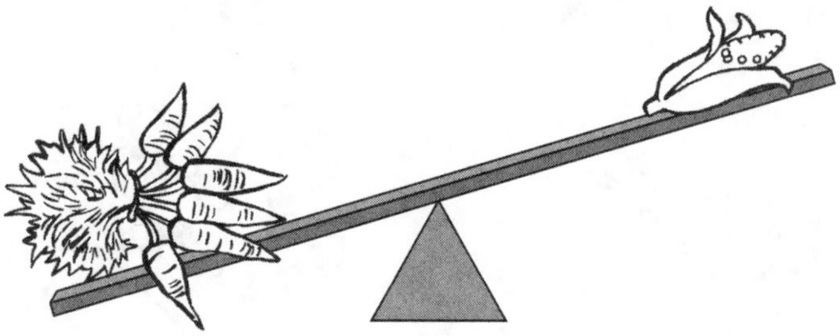

Write the number represented.
Count on and write the number sequence.

1.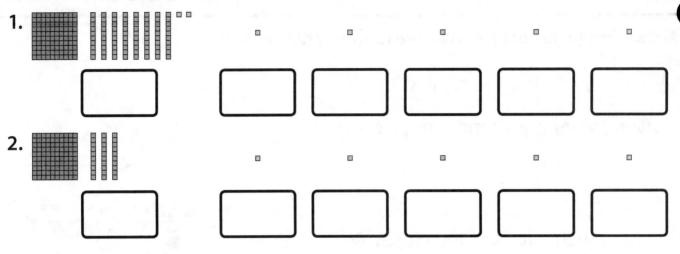

2.

Draw dots to picture the story. Complete the sentences.

3. Katie caught 4 fish. Ben caught 6 fish. How many fish did they catch altogether?

   They caught ⬜ fish altogether.

Draw a line to show 2 equal parts.

4.

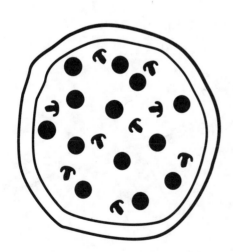  

Chapter 17 Review

Read the scale. Circle the object that weighs more.

1.

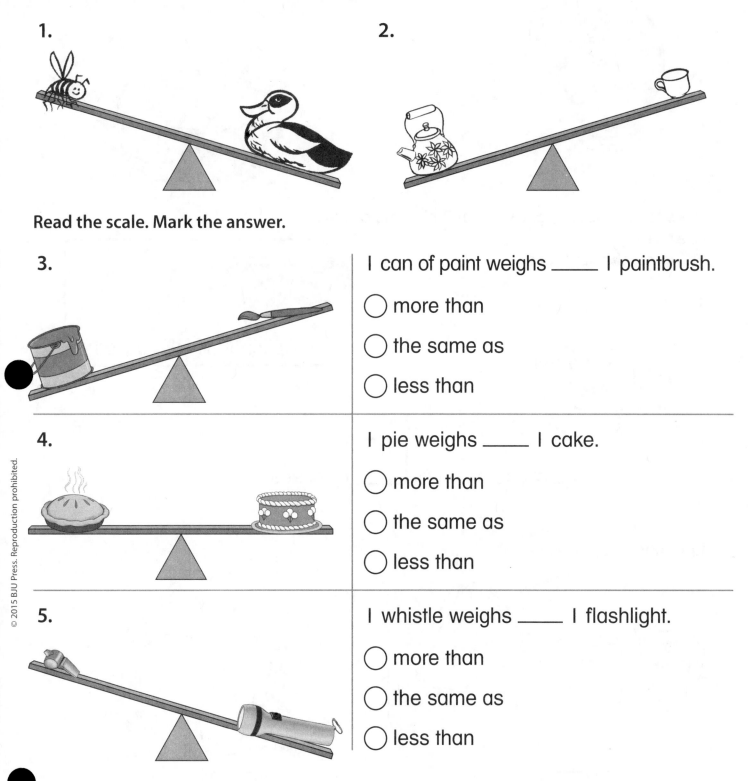

2.

Read the scale. Mark the answer.

3.

I can of paint weighs ____ I paintbrush.

○ more than

○ the same as

○ less than

4.

I pie weighs ____ I cake.

○ more than

○ the same as

○ less than

5.

I whistle weighs ____ I flashlight.

○ more than

○ the same as

○ less than

Circle the container that holds less.
Draw a line under the container that holds more.

6.  **7.**

Draw the number of glasses that 2 pitchers can fill.
Use the key.
Complete the sentence.

8.  =

Key

1 pitcher fills 4 glasses.

2 pitchers can fill ☐ glasses.

Complete the sentence.

9.

10.

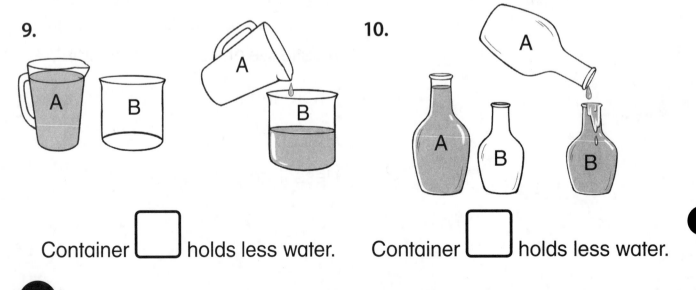

Container ☐ holds less water.   Container ☐ holds less water.

Cumulative Review

Write the related facts for the fact family.

1.

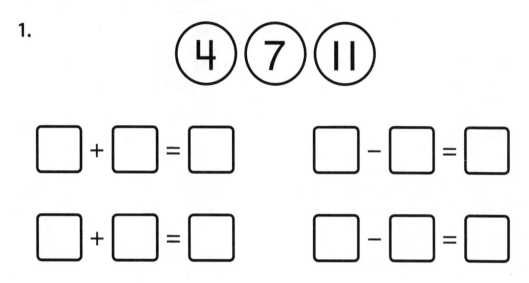

$$\boxed{} + \boxed{} = \boxed{} \qquad \boxed{} - \boxed{} = \boxed{}$$

$$\boxed{} + \boxed{} = \boxed{} \qquad \boxed{} - \boxed{} = \boxed{}$$

Mark the day that comes next.

2. **Sunday**	3. **Tuesday**	4. **Friday**
◯ Saturday	◯ Wednesday	◯ Saturday
◯ Monday	◯ Thursday	◯ Sunday

Draw the sets of oranges on the correct sides of the scale. Complete the sentence.

5.

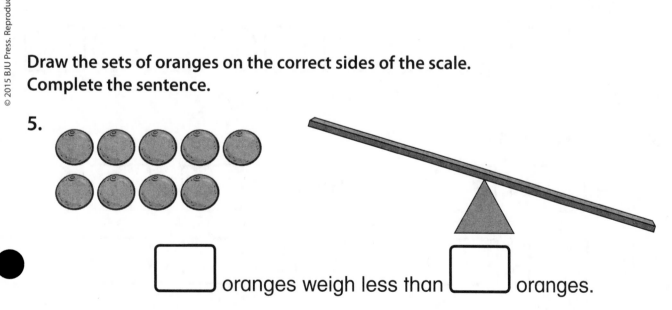

$\boxed{}$ oranges weigh less than $\boxed{}$ oranges.

Circle the container that holds more.
Draw a line under the container that holds less.

6.

7.

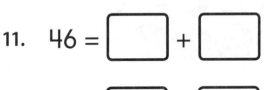

Draw circles to picture the story.
Complete the sentences.

8. Ana is making dinner for her family. She needs 3 cups of wild rice and 2 cups of brown rice. How many cups of rice does Ana need altogether?

   Ana needs ☐ cups of rice.   ☐ ◯ ☐ ☐ ◯ ☐ ●

9. Cory read 6 books for summer reading. Nathan read 4 books. How many more books did Cory read than Nathan?

   Cory read ☐ more books than Nathan.   ☐ ◯ ☐ ☐ ◯ ☐

Complete the expanded form.

10. 63 = ☐ + ☐

11. 46 = ☐ + ☐

12. 91 = ☐ + ☐

13. 75 = ☐ + ☐

Add Doubles

Write the double fact for the picture.

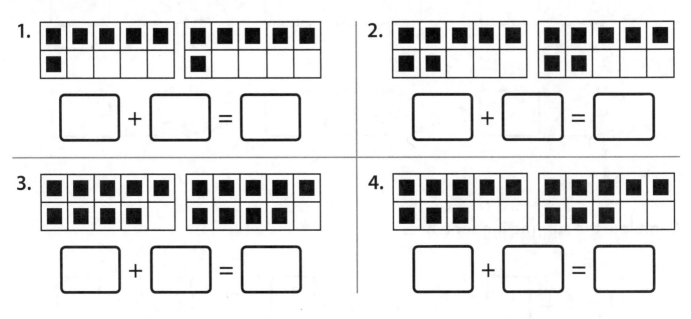

1. ☐ + ☐ = ☐

2. ☐ + ☐ = ☐

3. ☐ + ☐ = ☐

4. ☐ + ☐ = ☐

Draw dots to picture the story.
Complete the sentences.

5. The 3 little bears sat on a hill.
   The 3 big bears sat on a hill.
   How many bears sat on a hill?

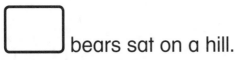 bears sat on a hill.

 ☐ + ☐ = ☐

6. Kim painted 4 pictures for her
   grandmother. She painted 4 more
   pictures for her mom. How many
   pictures did Kim paint?

Kim painted ☐ pictures.

 ☐ + ☐ = ☐

Write the number that comes *after*.

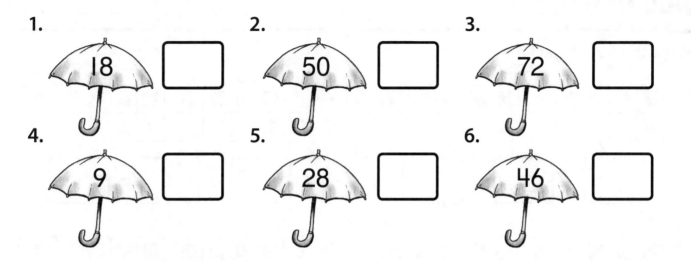

1. 18 ☐

2. 50 ☐

3. 72 ☐

4. 9 ☐

5. 28 ☐

6. 46 ☐

Complete the subtraction sentences.

7. $11 - 6 = $ ☐

$11 - 5 = $ ☐

8. $12 - 3 = $ ☐

$12 - 9 = $ ☐

9. $12 - 4 = $ ☐

$12 - 8 = $ ☐

Write the number for each set.
Circle the basket of the set that has more.

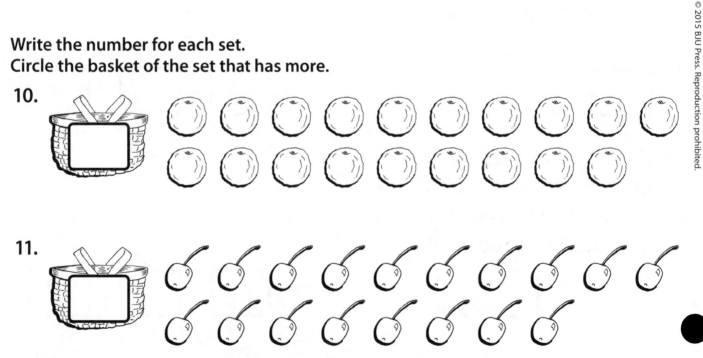

10.

11.

Add Near Doubles

© 2015 BJU Press. Reproduction prohibited.

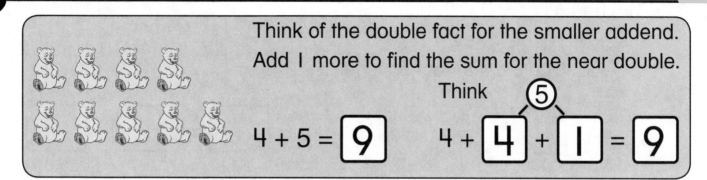

Think of the double fact for the smaller addend.
Add 1 more to find the sum for the near double.

Think ⑤

$4 + 5 = \boxed{9}$

$4 + \boxed{4} + \boxed{1} = \boxed{9}$

Think of the double fact to complete the near double fact.

1.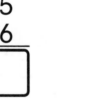

$8 + 9 = \boxed{}$

Think ⑨

$8 + \boxed{} + \boxed{} = \boxed{}$

2.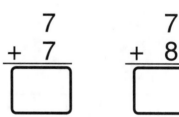

$6 + 7 = \boxed{}$

Think ⑦

$6 + \boxed{} + \boxed{} = \boxed{}$

Complete the double fact and then use it to complete the near double fact.

3.
$$\begin{array}{r} 5 \\ + 5 \\ \hline \boxed{} \end{array} \qquad \begin{array}{r} 5 \\ + 6 \\ \hline \boxed{} \end{array}$$

4.
$$\begin{array}{r} 7 \\ + 7 \\ \hline \boxed{} \end{array} \qquad \begin{array}{r} 7 \\ + 8 \\ \hline \boxed{} \end{array}$$

Draw squares to picture the story.
Complete the sentences.

5. Joey counted 8 black dogs at the pet store. He counted 9 white dogs. How many dogs did he count in all?

Joey counted $\boxed{}$ dogs.

$\boxed{} + \boxed{} = \boxed{}$

Draw squares to picture the story.
Complete the sentences.

1. Pam had 6 hats.
   She gave 4 hats away.
   How many hats does Pam have left?

   Pam has ☐ hats left.   ☐ − ☐ = ☐

Write the total value as you *count on*.

2.

   ☐¢   ☐¢   ☐¢   ☐¢   ☐¢   ☐¢

3. ☐¢   ☐¢   ☐¢   ☐¢   ☐¢

4. ☐¢   ☐¢   ☐¢   ☐¢   ☐¢

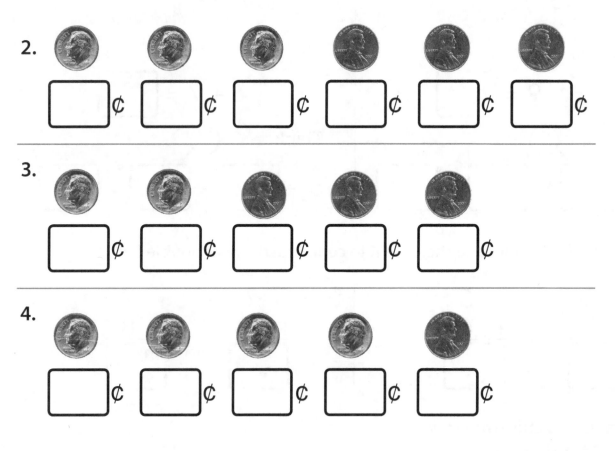

Complete the expanded form.

5. 41 = ☐ + ☐   6. 39 = ☐ + ☐

7. 82 = ☐ + ☐   8. 75 = ☐ + ☐

Add to 10

Draw the part being added to 10.
Complete the addition sentence.

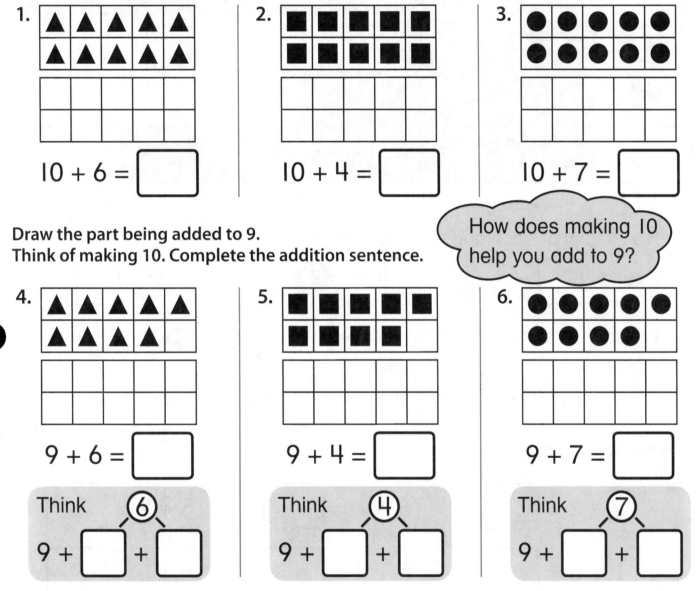

1. 10 + 6 = ☐

2. 10 + 4 = ☐

3. 10 + 7 = ☐

Draw the part being added to 9.
Think of making 10. Complete the addition sentence.

How does making 10 help you add to 9?

4. 9 + 6 = ☐

Think ⑥
9 + ☐ + ☐

5. 9 + 4 = ☐

Think ④
9 + ☐ + ☐

6. 9 + 7 = ☐

Think ⑦
9 + ☐ + ☐

Draw squares to picture the story.
Complete the sentences.

7. There are 9 dogs sleeping in the pen.
There are 3 dogs eating. How many
dogs are there in all?

There are ☐ dogs in all.

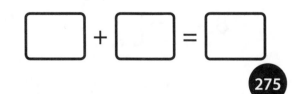

☐ + ☐ = ☐

Use the bar graph to answer the question.

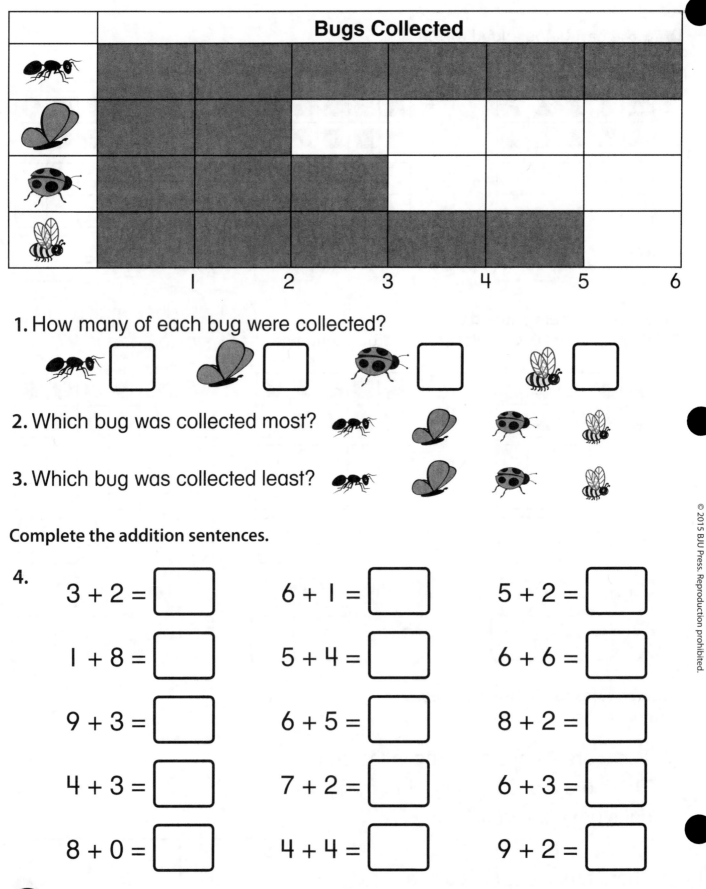

Bugs Collected

| | 1 | 2 | 3 | 4 | 5 | 6 |

1. How many of each bug were collected?

2. Which bug was collected most?

3. Which bug was collected least?

Complete the addition sentences.

4.

$3 + 2 =$ ☐ $6 + 1 =$ ☐ $5 + 2 =$ ☐

$1 + 8 =$ ☐ $5 + 4 =$ ☐ $6 + 6 =$ ☐

$9 + 3 =$ ☐ $6 + 5 =$ ☐ $8 + 2 =$ ☐

$4 + 3 =$ ☐ $7 + 2 =$ ☐ $6 + 3 =$ ☐

$8 + 0 =$ ☐ $4 + 4 =$ ☐ $9 + 2 =$ ☐

Add to 10

Draw the part being added to 6, 7, or 8.
Think of making 10. Complete the addition sentence.

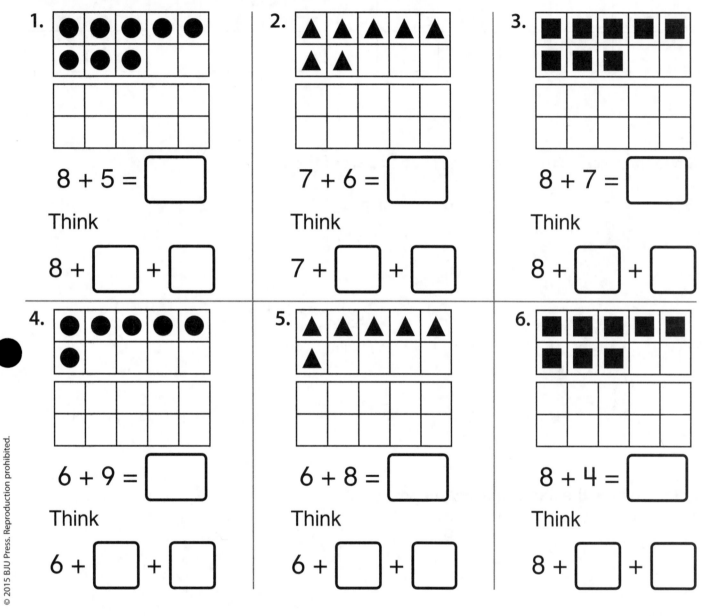

1. 8 + 5 = ☐

Think

8 + ☐ + ☐

2. 7 + 6 = ☐

Think

7 + ☐ + ☐

3. 8 + 7 = ☐

Think

8 + ☐ + ☐

4. 6 + 9 = ☐

Think

6 + ☐ + ☐

5. 6 + 8 = ☐

Think

6 + ☐ + ☐

6. 8 + 4 = ☐

Think

8 + ☐ + ☐

Complete the sentences.

7. At the pet store, Jill saw 7 mice eating apples. She saw 5 mice eating cheese. How many mice did Jill see?

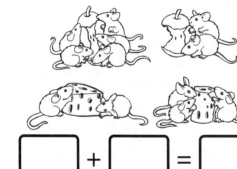

Jill saw ☐ mice.

☐ + ☐ = ☐

Complete the addition problem.

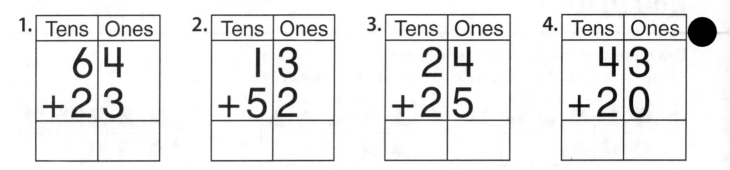

1.

Tens	Ones
6	4
+2	3

2.

Tens	Ones
1	3
+5	2

3.

Tens	Ones
2	4
+2	5

4.

Tens	Ones
4	3
+2	0

Circle the fraction that names the shaded part of the set.

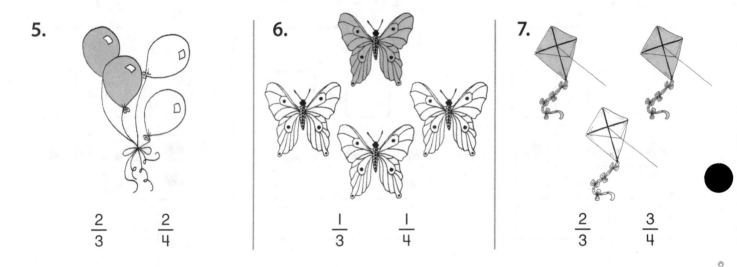

5. $\frac{2}{3}$ $\frac{2}{4}$

6. $\frac{1}{3}$ $\frac{1}{4}$

7. $\frac{2}{3}$ $\frac{3}{4}$

Color to show the named part of the set.

8. $\frac{1}{2}$ of the leaves

9. $\frac{2}{3}$ of the birds

10. $\frac{3}{4}$ of the flags

3 Addends

Use a strategy to combine 2 addends.
Complete the addition sentence.

1. $4 + 4 + 3 = \boxed{}$

2. $4 + 3 + 7 = \boxed{}$

3.
$$
\begin{array}{r}
1 \\
4 \\
+\ 3 \\
\hline
\end{array}
\quad \bigcirc
$$

4.
$$
\begin{array}{r}
8 \\
2 \\
+\ 7 \\
\hline
\end{array}
\quad \bigcirc
$$

What strategies did you use to solve the 3-addend problems?

Write the number in each set. Complete the addition sentence.

5.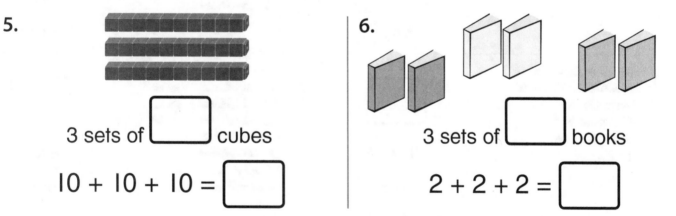

3 sets of $\boxed{}$ cubes

$10 + 10 + 10 = \boxed{}$

6.

3 sets of $\boxed{}$ books

$2 + 2 + 2 = \boxed{}$

Draw cookies to picture the story. Complete the sentences.

7. Mom had 3 plates. She put 3 cookies on each plate. How many cookies did she serve?

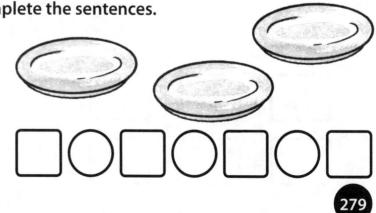

Mom served $\boxed{}$ cookies.

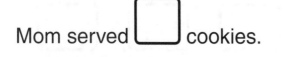

Write the time.

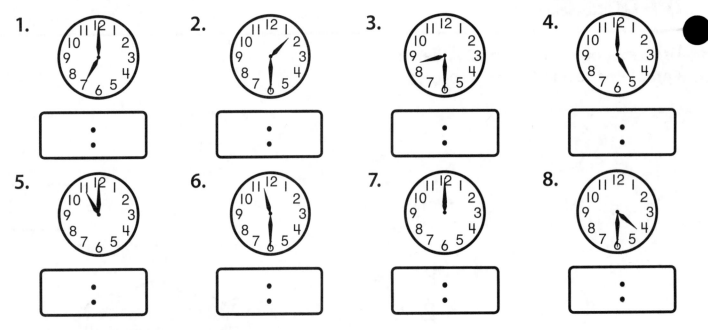

1.
2.
3.
4.
5.
6.
7.
8.

Write the number represented.
Circle the single cubes to make pairs. Circle *even* or *odd*.

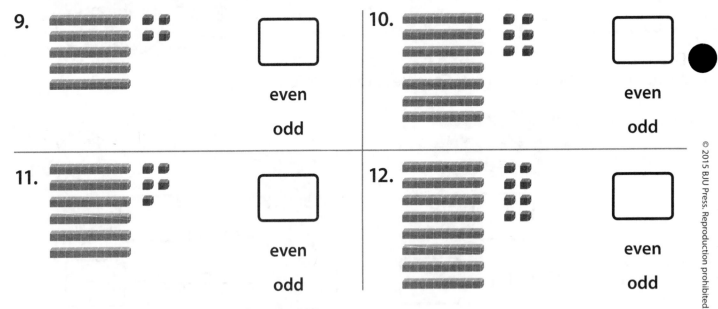

9.
even

odd

10.
even

odd

11.
even

odd

12.
even

odd

Write the related facts for the fact family.

13.

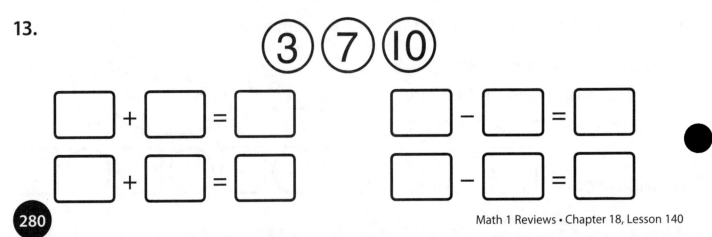

③ ⑦ ⑩

☐ + ☐ = ☐   ☐ − ☐ = ☐

☐ + ☐ = ☐   ☐ − ☐ = ☐

Fact Families for Doubles

Write an addition sentence for the picture.
Write the related subtraction sentence.

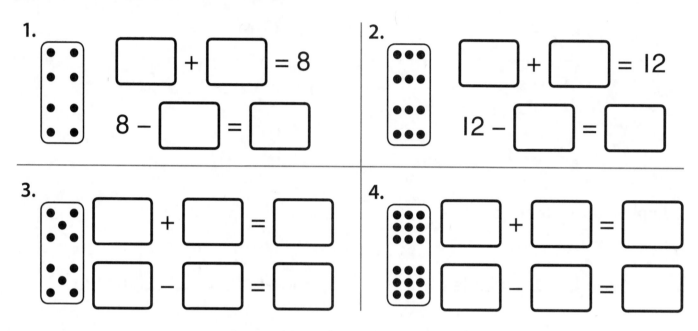

1.

☐ + ☐ = 8

8 − ☐ = ☐

2.

☐ + ☐ = 12

12 − ☐ = ☐

3.

☐ + ☐ = ☐

☐ − ☐ = ☐

4.

☐ + ☐ = ☐

☐ − ☐ = ☐

● Draw dots to picture the story. Complete the sentences.

5. Mom had 12 stamps. She used 6 stamps. How many stamps does mom have left?

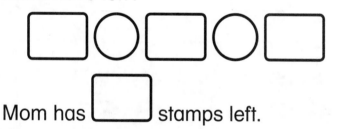

Mom has ☐ stamps left.

6. The cowboy bought 14 horses. He put 7 in the barn. How many horses are still outside?

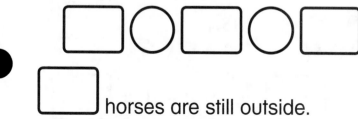

☐ horses are still outside.

Circle the longest object. Put an *X* on the shortest object.

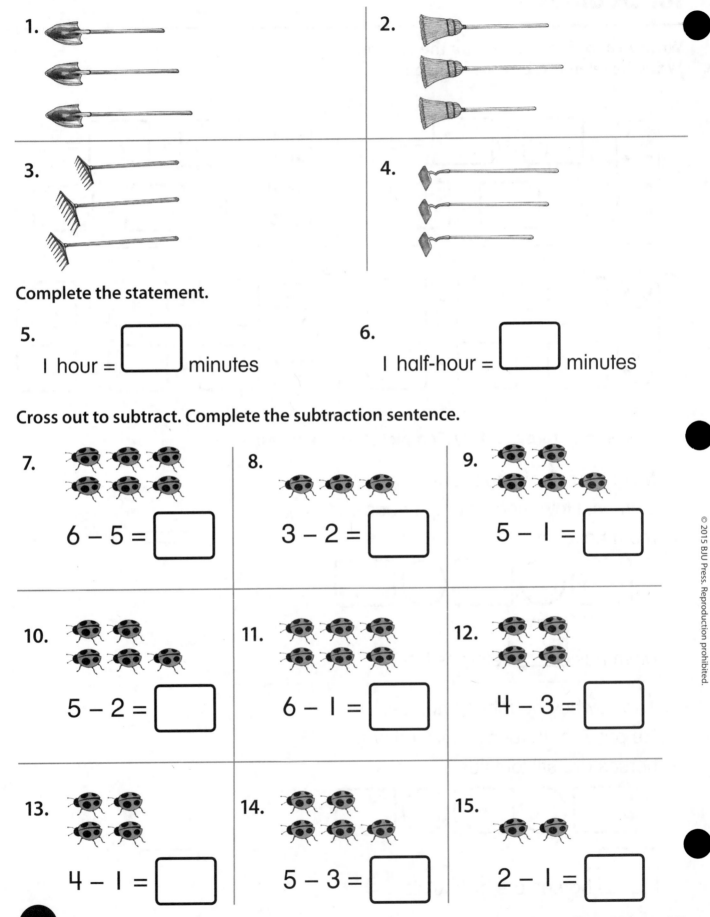

1.

2.

3.

4.

Complete the statement.

5.

I hour = ☐ minutes

6.

I half-hour = ☐ minutes

Cross out to subtract. Complete the subtraction sentence.

7.

$6 - 5 =$ ☐

8.

$3 - 2 =$ ☐

9.

$5 - 1 =$ ☐

10.

$5 - 2 =$ ☐

11.

$6 - 1 =$ ☐

12.

$4 - 3 =$ ☐

13.

$4 - 1 =$ ☐

14.

$5 - 3 =$ ☐

15.

$2 - 1 =$ ☐

Fact Families for 13 & 14; Missing Addend

Write the numbers for the fact family.
Complete the related facts.

1.

◯ ◯ ◯

$7 + 7 = \boxed{}$

$14 - 7 = \boxed{}$

2.

◯ ◯ ◯

$4 + 9 = \boxed{}$

$9 + 4 = \boxed{}$

$13 - 4 = \boxed{}$

$13 - 9 = \boxed{}$

Write the related facts for the fact family.

3.

⑥ ⑦ ⑬

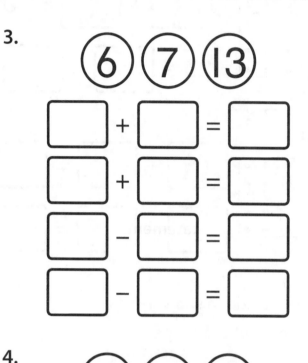

4.

⑤ ⑨ ⑭

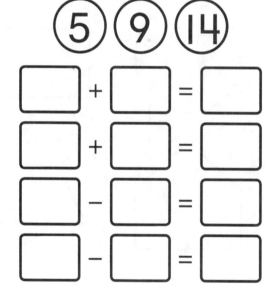

Complete the sentences.

5. Dad planted 8 rows of green beans.
   He needs to plant 14 rows altogether.
   How many more rows does Dad
   need to plant?

   Dad needs to plant $\boxed{}$ more rows.

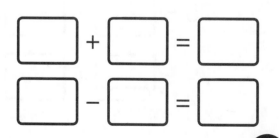

Write an addition sentence for the picture.
Write the related subtraction sentence.

1.
$$\boxed{} + \boxed{} = 20$$
$$20 - \boxed{} = \boxed{}$$

2.
$$\boxed{} + \boxed{} = 18$$
$$18 - \boxed{} = \boxed{}$$

3.
$$\boxed{} + \boxed{} = \boxed{}$$
$$\boxed{} - \boxed{} = \boxed{}$$

4.
$$\boxed{} + \boxed{} = \boxed{}$$
$$\boxed{} - \boxed{} = \boxed{}$$

Draw a line to show halves.
Color $\frac{1}{2}$ of the shape.

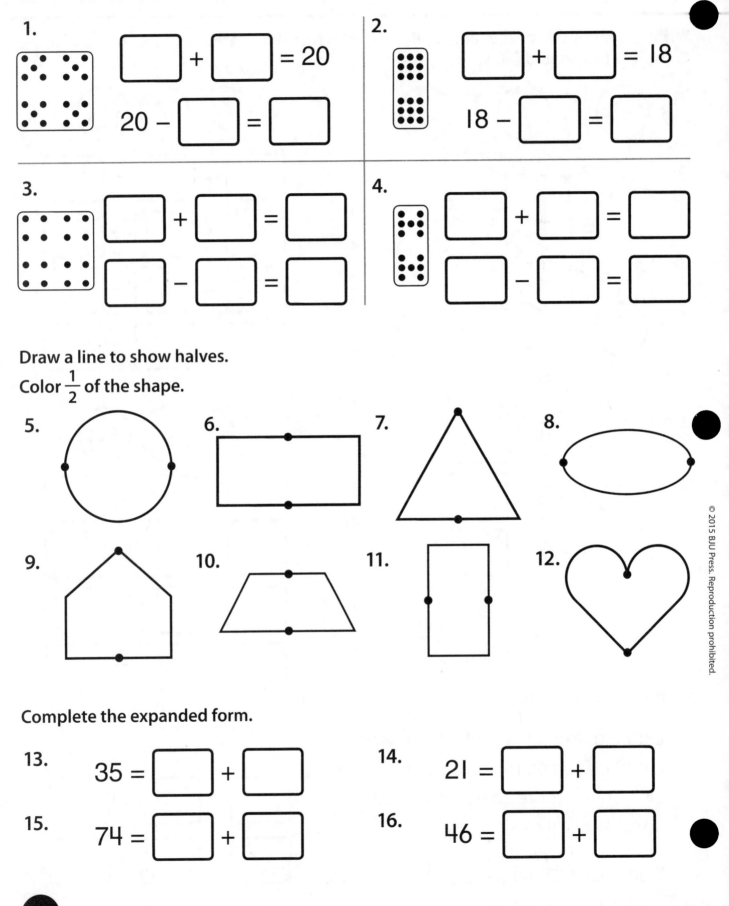

5.

6.

7.

8.

9.

10.

11.

12.

Complete the expanded form.

13. $35 = \boxed{} + \boxed{}$

14. $21 = \boxed{} + \boxed{}$

15. $74 = \boxed{} + \boxed{}$

16. $46 = \boxed{} + \boxed{}$

Fact Families for 15 & 16

Write the numbers for the fact family. Complete the related facts.

1.

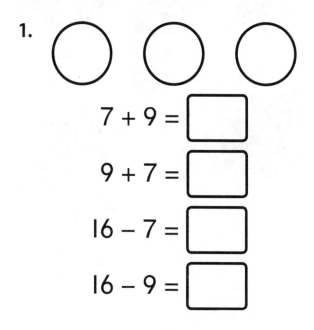

$7 + 9 = \boxed{}$

$9 + 7 = \boxed{}$

$16 - 7 = \boxed{}$

$16 - 9 = \boxed{}$

Write the related facts for the fact family.

2.

(6) (9) (15)

$\boxed{} + \boxed{} = \boxed{}$

$\boxed{} + \boxed{} = \boxed{}$

$\boxed{} - \boxed{} = \boxed{}$

$\boxed{} - \boxed{} = \boxed{}$

Draw coins to picture the story. Complete the sentences.

3. Sam put 7 coins in his bank. His mom put 8 coins in his bank. How many coins were put in the bank?

$\boxed{}$ coins were put in the bank.

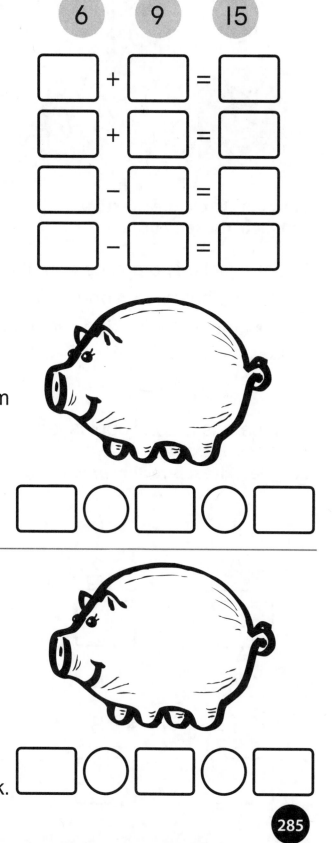

4. There were 16 coins in the bank. Jessica took 9 coins out of the bank. How many coins are left?

There are $\boxed{}$ coins left in the bank.

Circle each figure that will roll.

1.
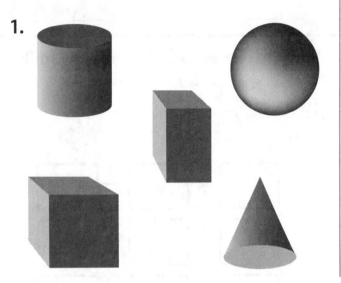

Circle each figure that will stack.

2.
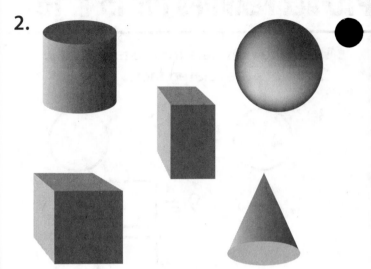

Draw dots to picture the story.
Complete the sentences.

3. Jane picked 16 apples from the tree.
   Her mother used 6 apples for a pie.
   How many apples does Jane have
   left?

   Jane has ☐ apples left.

☐○☐○☐

Complete the subtraction problems.

4.
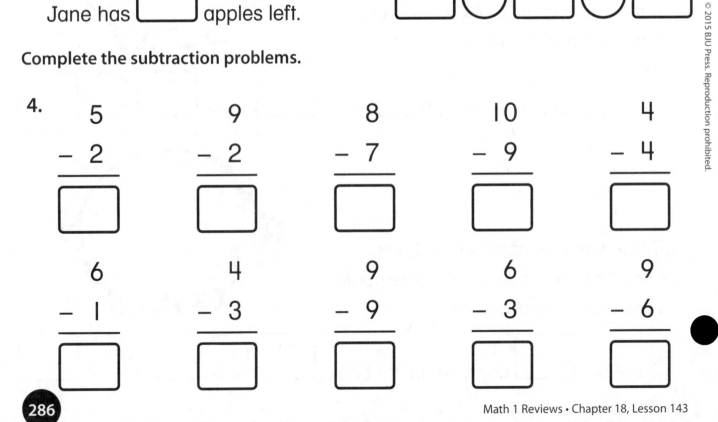

$$5 - 2 = \boxed{}$$ $$9 - 2 = \boxed{}$$ $$8 - 7 = \boxed{}$$ $$10 - 9 = \boxed{}$$ $$4 - 4 = \boxed{}$$

$$6 - 1 = \boxed{}$$ $$4 - 3 = \boxed{}$$ $$9 - 9 = \boxed{}$$ $$6 - 3 = \boxed{}$$ $$9 - 6 = \boxed{}$$

Fact Families for 17 & 18; Problem Solving

_____

- - - - - - - - - - -

Write the related facts for the fact families.

1.

9 9 18

☐ + ☐ = ☐

☐ − ☐ = ☐

2.

8 9 17

☐ + ☐ = ☐

☐ + ☐ = ☐

☐ − ☐ = ☐

☐ − ☐ = ☐

Draw circles to picture the story.
Complete the sentences.

3. Sally stopped to pet 2 dogs. Then 3 more dogs came to be petted. How many dogs did Sally pet?

☐ ○ ☐ ○ ☐

Sally petted ☐ dogs.

After being petted, 2 dogs ran away to chase a cat. How many dogs are still with Sally?

☐ ○ ☐ ○ ☐

There are ☐ dogs still with Sally.

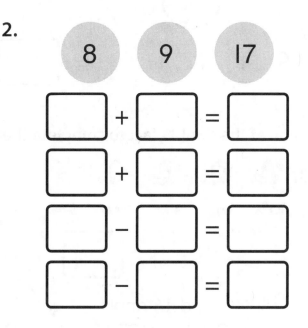

Use a strategy to combine 2 addends.
Complete the addition sentence.

1.

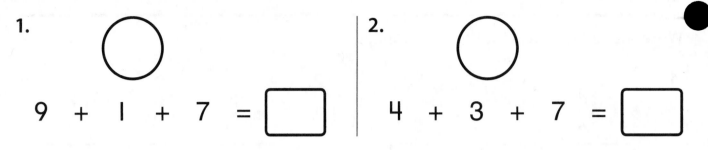

$9 + 1 + 7 = \boxed{}$

2.

$4 + 3 + 7 = \boxed{}$

Think of the double fact to complete the near double fact.

3.

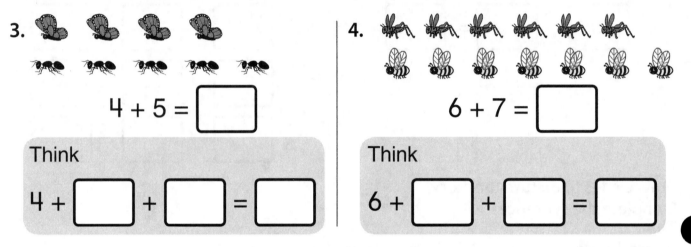

$4 + 5 = \boxed{}$

Think

$4 + \boxed{} + \boxed{} = \boxed{}$

4.

$6 + 7 = \boxed{}$

Think

$6 + \boxed{} + \boxed{} = \boxed{}$

Complete the subtraction problems.

5.

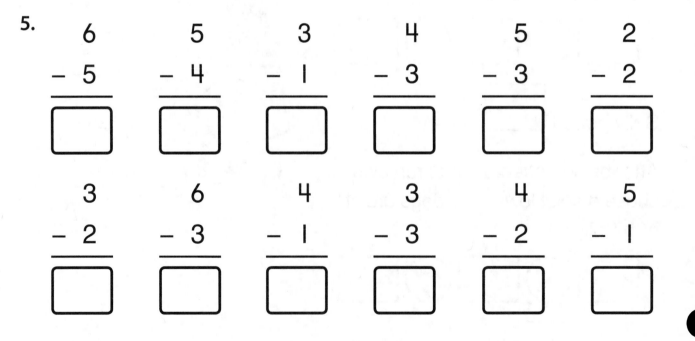

$\begin{array}{r} 6 \\ -\ 5 \\ \hline \end{array}$
$\begin{array}{r} 5 \\ -\ 4 \\ \hline \end{array}$
$\begin{array}{r} 3 \\ -\ 1 \\ \hline \end{array}$
$\begin{array}{r} 4 \\ -\ 3 \\ \hline \end{array}$
$\begin{array}{r} 5 \\ -\ 3 \\ \hline \end{array}$
$\begin{array}{r} 2 \\ -\ 2 \\ \hline \end{array}$

$\begin{array}{r} 3 \\ -\ 2 \\ \hline \end{array}$
$\begin{array}{r} 6 \\ -\ 3 \\ \hline \end{array}$
$\begin{array}{r} 4 \\ -\ 1 \\ \hline \end{array}$
$\begin{array}{r} 3 \\ -\ 3 \\ \hline \end{array}$
$\begin{array}{r} 4 \\ -\ 2 \\ \hline \end{array}$
$\begin{array}{r} 5 \\ -\ 1 \\ \hline \end{array}$

Chapter 18 Review

Draw the part being added to 7, 8, or 9.
Think of making 10. Complete the addition sentence.

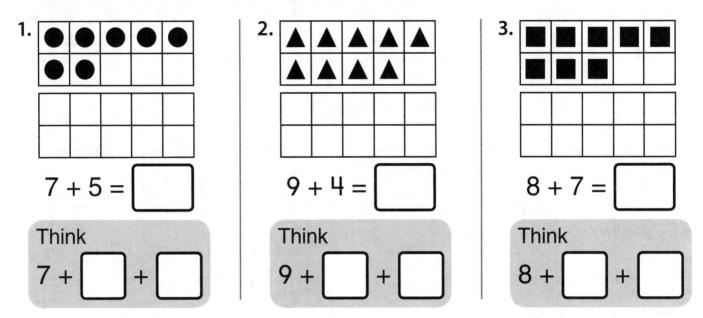

1. 7 + 5 = ☐

Think
7 + ☐ + ☐

2. 9 + 4 = ☐

Think
9 + ☐ + ☐

3. 8 + 7 = ☐

Think
8 + ☐ + ☐

● Think of the double fact to complete the near double fact.

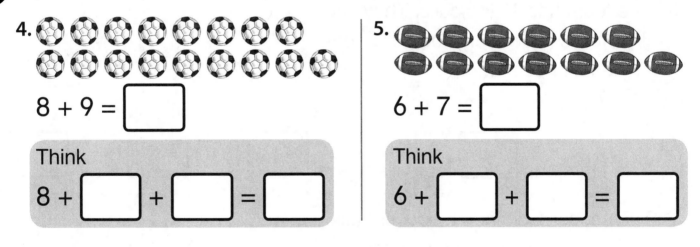

4. 8 + 9 = ☐

Think
8 + ☐ + ☐ = ☐

5. 6 + 7 = ☐

Think
6 + ☐ + ☐ = ☐

Use a strategy to combine 2 addends.
Complete the addition sentence.

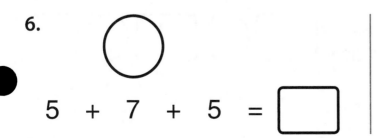

6. ○

5 + 7 + 5 = ☐

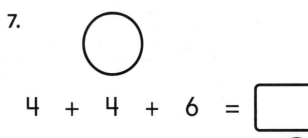

7. ○

4 + 4 + 6 = ☐

Write the related facts for the fact families.

8.

8   8   16

□ + □ = □   □ − □ = □

9.

7   8   15

□ + □ = □   □ − □ = □

□ + □ = □   □ − □ = □

Draw squares to picture the story.
Complete the sentences.

10. The team had 12 footballs. They lost 4 footballs. How many footballs does the team have now?

The team has □ footballs now.   □ ○ □ ○ □

11. The soccer team had 6 soccer balls. The coach bought 5 more soccer balls. How many soccer balls does the team have now?

The team has □ soccer balls now.   □ ○ □ ○ □

Cumulative Review

Write the number that comes *before*, *after*, or *between*.

1. (28) ( ) (30)

2. (52) ( )

3. [ ] [66]

4. ♡21 ♡ ♡23

5. [ ] [93]

6. (35) ( )

Draw shapes to extend the pattern.

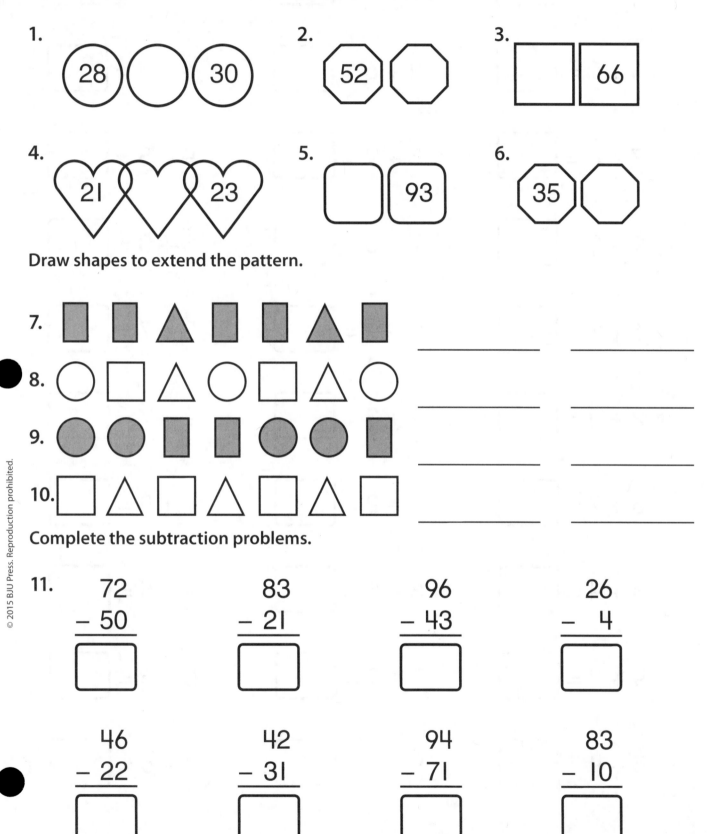

7.

8.

9.

10.

Complete the subtraction problems.

11.
$$\begin{array}{r} 72 \\ -\ 50 \\ \hline \end{array}$$

$$\begin{array}{r} 83 \\ -\ 21 \\ \hline \end{array}$$

$$\begin{array}{r} 96 \\ -\ 43 \\ \hline \end{array}$$

$$\begin{array}{r} 26 \\ -\ 4 \\ \hline \end{array}$$

$$\begin{array}{r} 46 \\ -\ 22 \\ \hline \end{array}$$

$$\begin{array}{r} 42 \\ -\ 31 \\ \hline \end{array}$$

$$\begin{array}{r} 94 \\ -\ 71 \\ \hline \end{array}$$

$$\begin{array}{r} 83 \\ -\ 10 \\ \hline \end{array}$$

Complete the addition sentences.

12.

6 + 7 = ☐   5 + 2 = ☐   6 + 6 = ☐

3 + 9 = ☐   4 + 6 = ☐   6 + 5 = ☐

7 + 0 = ☐   5 + 9 = ☐   4 + 8 = ☐

9 + 2 = ☐   7 + 5 = ☐   3 + 3 = ☐

6 + 3 = ☐   9 + 4 = ☐   3 + 7 = ☐

2 + 8 = ☐   9 + 3 = ☐   9 + 7 = ☐

5 + 7 = ☐   6 + 2 = ☐   6 + 9 = ☐

8 + 4 = ☐   3 + 5 = ☐   9 + 5 = ☐

4 + 2 = ☐   7 + 9 = ☐   5 + 6 = ☐

5 + 4 = ☐   9 + 6 = ☐   7 + 6 = ☐

Count Quarters & Pennies

_____

- - - - - - - - - - - - - - - - - -

_____

Write the value of the coin.

quarter

1. [ ] ¢

2. [ ] ¢

25¢

3. [ ] ¢

4. [ ] ¢

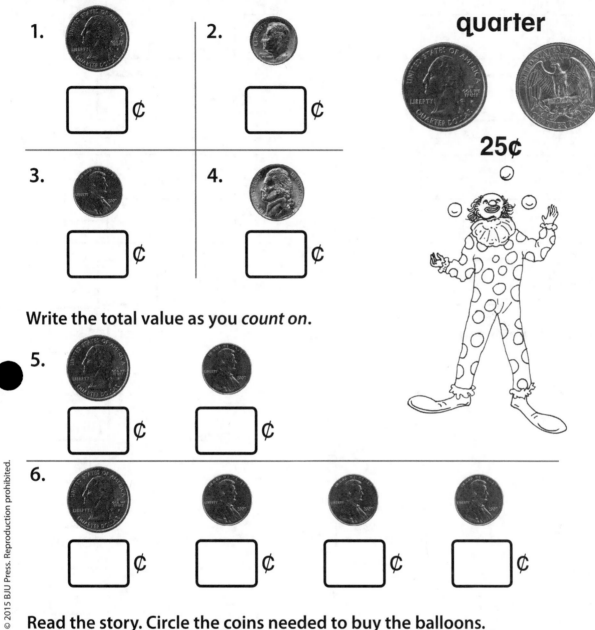

Write the total value as you _count on_.

5. [ ] ¢   [ ] ¢

6. [ ] ¢   [ ] ¢   [ ] ¢   [ ] ¢

Read the story. Circle the coins needed to buy the balloons.

7. Matthew and Jackson each want to buy some balloons.

Matthew   Jackson

28¢

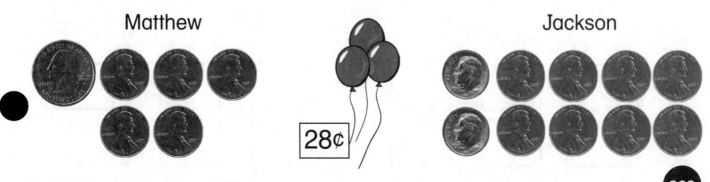

Use 2 colors to picture the addends.
Count on from 5 to add. Complete the addition sentence.

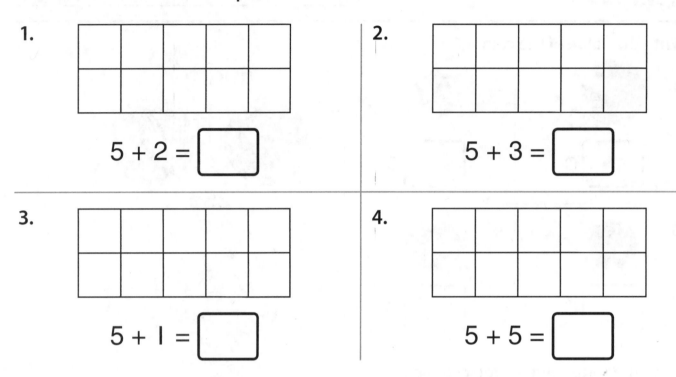

1. 5 + 2 = ☐

2. 5 + 3 = ☐

3. 5 + 1 = ☐

4. 5 + 5 = ☐

Draw a line to match the number to its number word.

5.
0   two
1   five
2   zero
3   one
4   three
5   four

6.
6   eight
7   nine
8   six
9   ten
10   seven

Write the related facts for the fact family.

7.

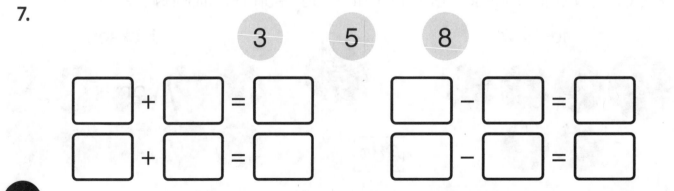

☐ + ☐ = ☐   ☐ – ☐ = ☐

☐ + ☐ = ☐   ☐ – ☐ = ☐

Compare Nickels & Quarters

_____

Write the value of the coin.

1. 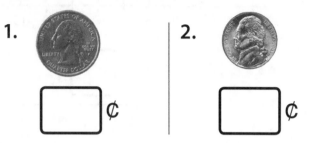 [   ] ¢

2. [   ] ¢

Write the value of each set.
Write >, <, or = to compare.

3. [   ] ¢ ◯ [   ] ¢

4. [   ] ¢ ◯ [   ] ¢

5. [   ] ¢ ◯ [   ] ¢

Read the story. Circle the coins needed to buy each flower.
Answer the question.

6. Jan wants to buy 2 flowers.

20¢

How much money does Jan have left? [   ] ¢

Draw back jumps to subtract.
Complete the subtraction sentence.

1.

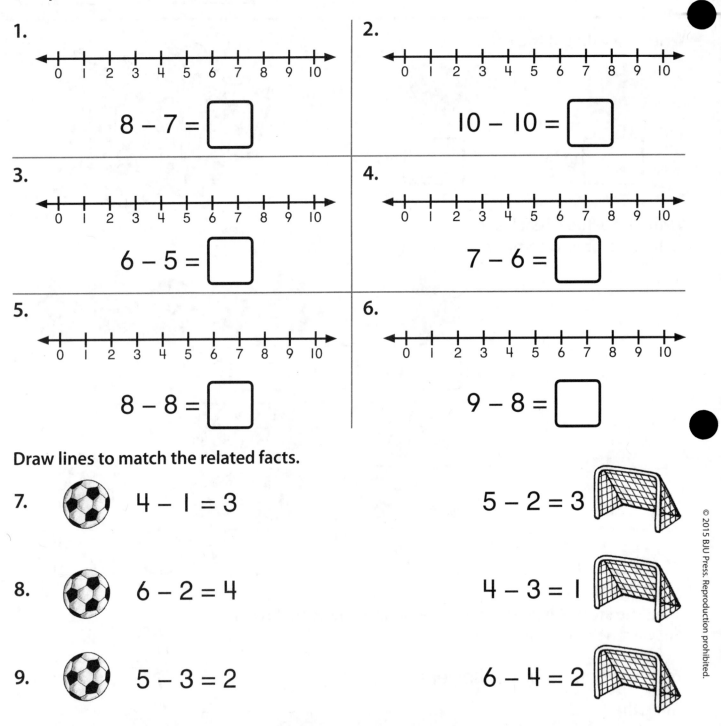

$8 - 7 = \boxed{}$

2.

$10 - 10 = \boxed{}$

3.

$6 - 5 = \boxed{}$

4.

$7 - 6 = \boxed{}$

5.

$8 - 8 = \boxed{}$

6.

$9 - 8 = \boxed{}$

Draw lines to match the related facts.

7. $\qquad 4 - 1 = 3$

$5 - 2 = 3$

8. $\qquad 6 - 2 = 4$

$4 - 3 = 1$

9. $\qquad 5 - 3 = 2$

$6 - 4 = 2$

Count to 100 by 5s. Write the missing numbers.

10.

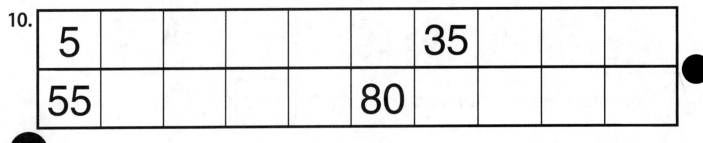

5					35		
55				80			

Count Quarters & Dimes

Write the value of the coin.

1. [ ] ¢

2. [ ] ¢

Write the total value as you *count on*.

3. [ ] ¢ [ ] ¢ [ ] ¢ [ ] ¢

4. [ ] ¢ [ ] ¢ [ ] ¢ [ ] ¢ [ ] ¢ [ ] ¢ [ ] ¢

5. [ ] ¢ [ ] ¢ [ ] ¢ [ ] ¢ [ ] ¢

Circle the coins needed to buy each item.

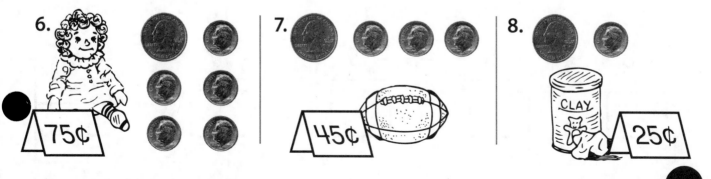

6. 75¢

7. 45¢

8. CLAY 25¢

Mark the number.

1. 40 + 7 =   37 ○   40 ○   47 ○   76 ○

2. 20 + 9 =   20 ○   29 ○   30 ○   45 ○

3. 60 + 3 =   26 ○   63 ○   81 ○   91 ○

Complete the expanded form.

4. 35 = [ ] + [ ]

5. 21 = [ ] + [ ]

6. 74 = [ ] + [ ]

7. 46 = [ ] + [ ]

Complete the addition problems.

8.
```
   9        7        8        8        9
+  9     +  8     +  9     +  7     +  8
-----    -----    -----    -----    -----
[   ]    [   ]    [   ]    [   ]    [   ]
```

Complete the subtraction problems.

9.
```
  15       17       18       15       17
-  8     -  8     -  9     -  7     -  9
-----    -----    -----    -----    -----
[   ]    [   ]    [   ]    [   ]    [   ]
```

One Hundred Cents

Write the value of the coin.

1. 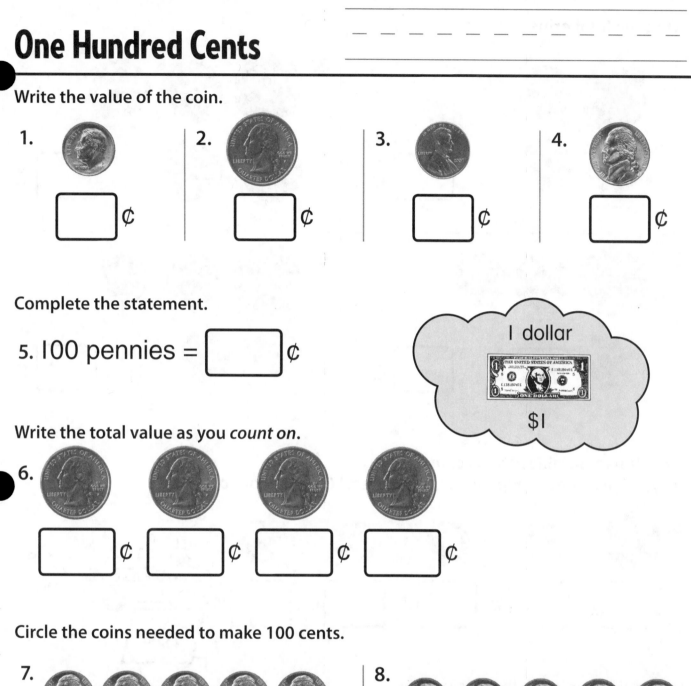 ⬜ ¢

2. ⬜ ¢

3. ⬜ ¢

4. ⬜ ¢

Complete the statement.

5. 100 pennies = ⬜ ¢

I dollar

$1

Write the total value as you *count on*.

6. ⬜ ¢   ⬜ ¢   ⬜ ¢   ⬜ ¢

Circle the coins needed to make 100 cents.

7.

8.

Write the total value.

1. 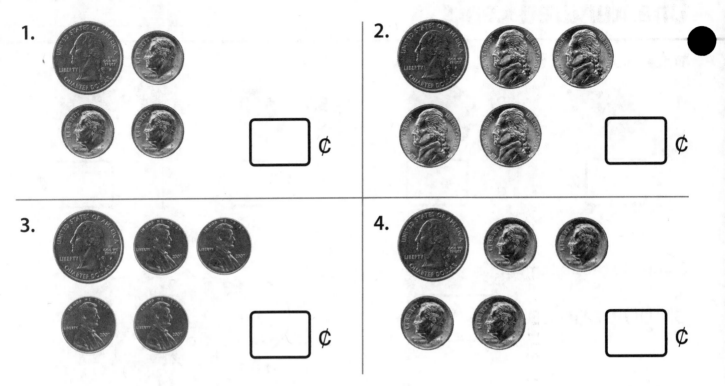 □ ¢

2. □ ¢

3. □ ¢

4. □ ¢

Write the total value as you *count on*.
Do you have enough money to buy the item? Circle *yes* or *no*.

5. 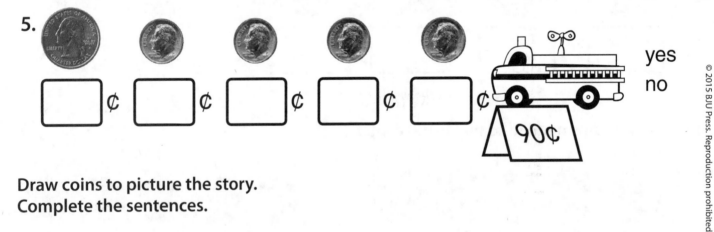 □ ¢ □ ¢ □ ¢ □ ¢ □ ¢

yes
no

Draw coins to picture the story.
Complete the sentences.

6. Jan had 30 cents in her bank.
Her mother gave her 3 dimes.
How much money does she
have now?

Jan has □ cents now.

□ ¢ ○ □ ¢ ○ □ ¢

Chapter 19 Review

Write the value of each coin.
Draw a line to match each coin to its name.

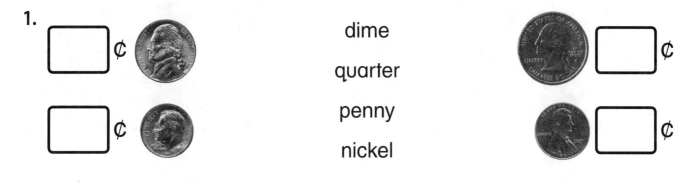

1.

⬜ ¢

⬜ ¢

dime

quarter

penny

nickel

⬜ ¢

⬜ ¢

Write the total value as you *count on*.
Do you have enough money to buy the item? Circle *yes* or *no*.

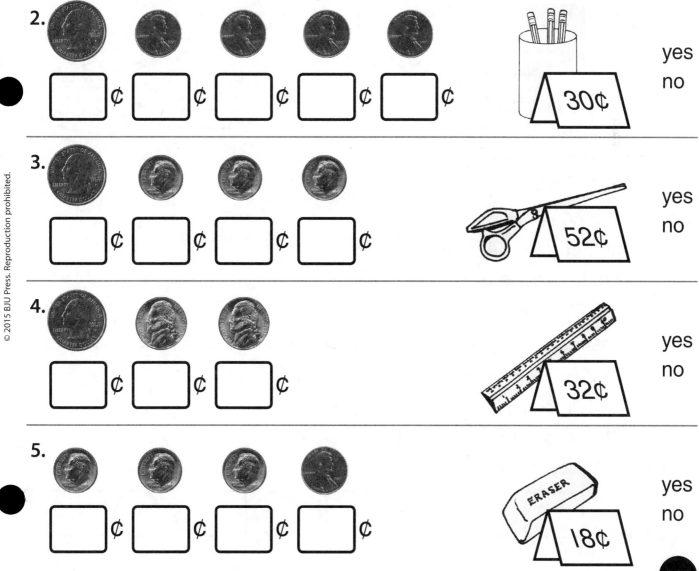

2. ⬜ ¢ ⬜ ¢ ⬜ ¢ ⬜ ¢ ⬜ ¢   30¢   yes   no

3. ⬜ ¢ ⬜ ¢ ⬜ ¢ ⬜ ¢   52¢   yes   no

4. ⬜ ¢ ⬜ ¢ ⬜ ¢   32¢   yes   no

5. ⬜ ¢ ⬜ ¢ ⬜ ¢ ⬜ ¢   18¢   yes   no

Circle the coins needed to buy each item.

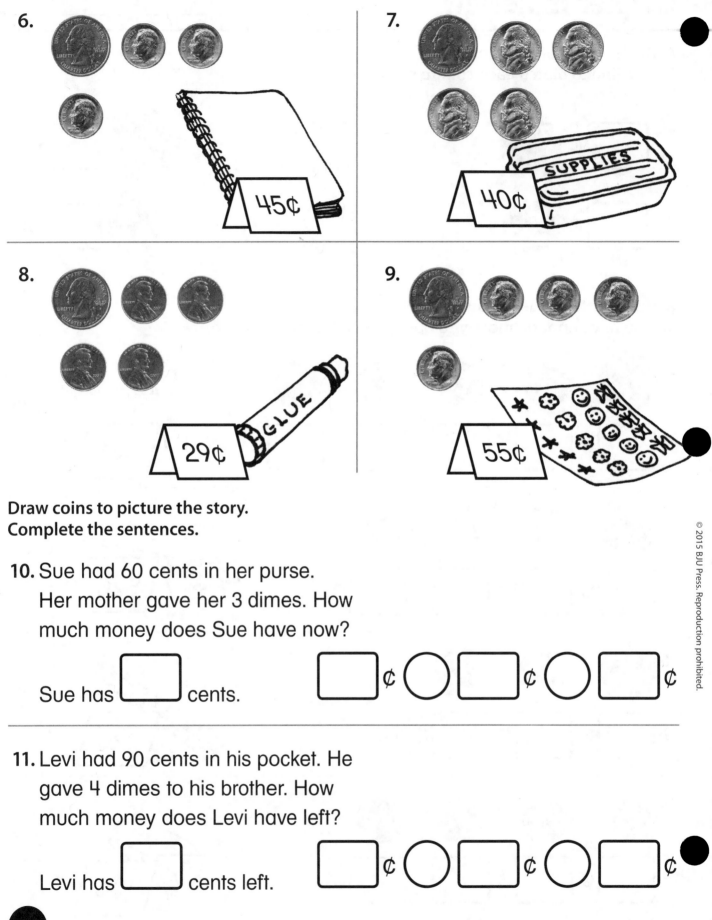

6.

45¢

7.

SUPPLIES

40¢

8.

GLUE

29¢

9.

55¢

Draw coins to picture the story.
Complete the sentences.

10. Sue had 60 cents in her purse.
Her mother gave her 3 dimes. How
much money does Sue have now?

Sue has ☐ cents.

☐ ¢ ○ ☐ ¢ ○ ☐ ¢

11. Levi had 90 cents in his pocket. He
gave 4 dimes to his brother. How
much money does Levi have left?

Levi has ☐ cents left.

☐ ¢ ○ ☐ ¢ ○ ☐ ¢

Cumulative Review

Complete the addition problem.

1. 43
   + 33
   ☐

2. 61
   + 24
   ☐

3. 33
   + 16
   ☐

4. 74
   + 25
   ☐

Mark the value of the underlined digit.

5. | 77<u>5</u> | ○ 500   ○ 50   ○ 5

6. | <u>2</u>34 | ○ 200   ○ 20   ○ 2

7. | 1<u>8</u>6 | ○ 800   ○ 80   ○ 8

8. | <u>9</u>23 | ○ 900   ○ 90   ○ 9

Draw circles to picture the story.
Complete the sentences.

9. Grandma folded 5 towels.
    She folded 4 wash cloths.
    How many items did she fold?

    Grandma folded ☐ items.   ☐ ○ ☐ ○ ☐

10. Jess had 5 rings. While she
    was playing, she lost 3 rings. How
    many rings does Jess have left?

    Jess has ☐ rings left.   ☐ ○ ☐ ○ ☐

11. Solve the number problems. Use the key to color.

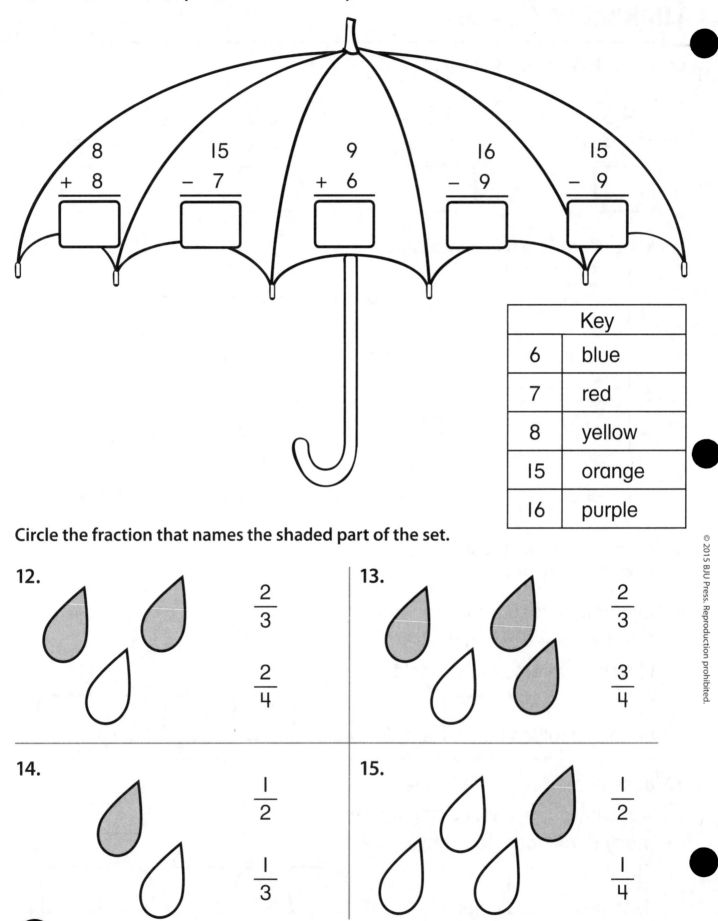

8	15	9	16	15
+ 8	− 7	+ 6	− 9	− 9

Key	
6	blue
7	red
8	yellow
15	orange
16	purple

Circle the fraction that names the shaded part of the set.

12. $\dfrac{2}{3}$ $\dfrac{2}{4}$

13. $\dfrac{2}{3}$ $\dfrac{3}{4}$

14. $\dfrac{1}{2}$ $\dfrac{1}{3}$

15. $\dfrac{1}{2}$ $\dfrac{1}{4}$

Time to the Half-Hour

_____

Write the missing numbers to show counting the minutes by 5s.

1.

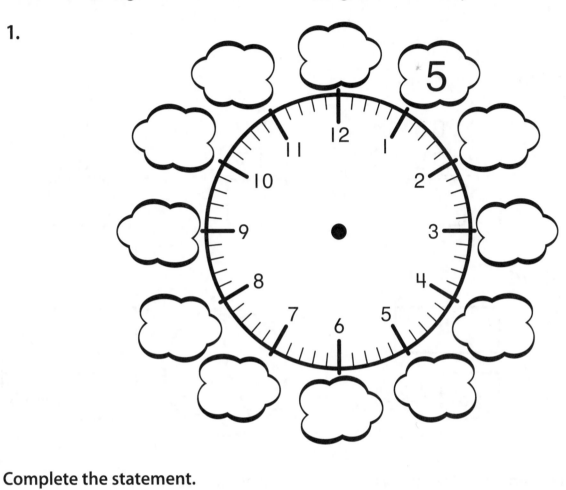

Complete the statement.

2. I hour = [ ] minutes

3. I half-hour = [ ] minutes

Write the times.

4.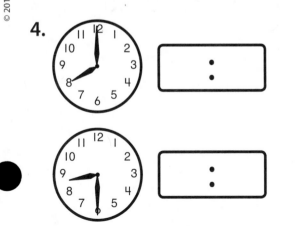

5.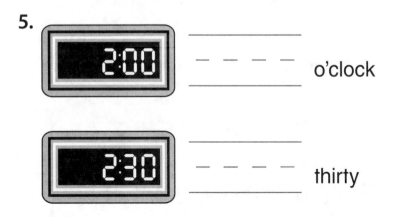

_____ o'clock

_____ thirty

Write the missing addends to complete the addition sentences.

1. $3 + \boxed{} = 10$ $5 + \boxed{} = 14$ $9 + \boxed{} = 9$

Complete the subtraction problems.

2.
$$\begin{array}{r} 47 \\ -\ 15 \\ \hline \end{array}$$
$\boxed{}$

$$\begin{array}{r} 86 \\ -\ 35 \\ \hline \end{array}$$
$\boxed{}$

$$\begin{array}{r} 29 \\ -\ 17 \\ \hline \end{array}$$
$\boxed{}$

$$\begin{array}{r} 49 \\ -\ 34 \\ \hline \end{array}$$
$\boxed{}$

Write the time 2 ways.

3. 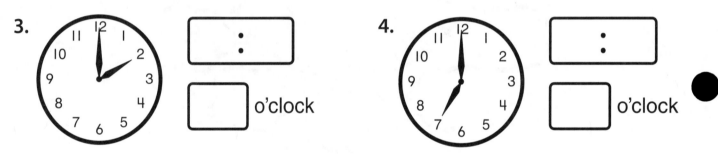 $\boxed{\ :\ }$ $\boxed{}$ o'clock

4. $\boxed{\ :\ }$ $\boxed{}$ o'clock

Mark the number sequence that shows counting by even numbers.

5. ○ 14, 15, 16, 17, 18   ○ 3, 6, 9, 12, 15

   ○ 8, 10, 12, 14, 16   ○ 5, 10, 15, 20, 25

Write the number that extends the pattern.

6. 3 7 7 5 3 7 7 5 3 7 7 $\boxed{}$

7. 8 0 4 8 0 4 8 0 4 8 0 $\boxed{}$

Elapsed Time

Circle the time passed.
Use the time schedule to answer the question.

1.

Piano Practice Schedule			
Day	Start	Finish	Time Passed
Monday	3:00	3:30	30 minutes 1 hour
Wednesday	4:30	5:00	30 minutes 1 hour
Friday	4:30	5:30	30 minutes 1 hour

2. Which practice was longer?

○ Wednesday   ○ Friday

3. Which practice was shorter?

○ Monday   ○ Friday

Draw the hour hand to show the elapsed time.
Write the times.

4.   I Hour Later   5.   Half-Hour Later

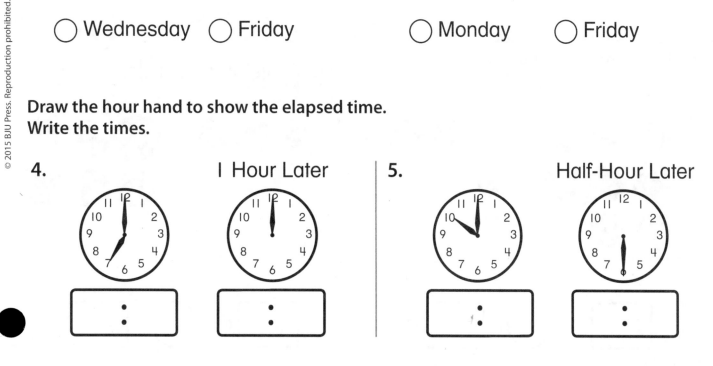

Draw the shape that extends the pattern.

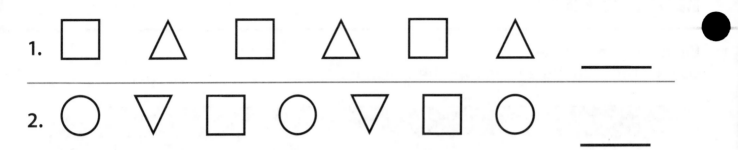

1. ☐ △ ☐ △ ☐ △ _____

2. ○ ▽ ☐ ○ ▽ ☐ ○ _____

Write the total value as you *count on*.

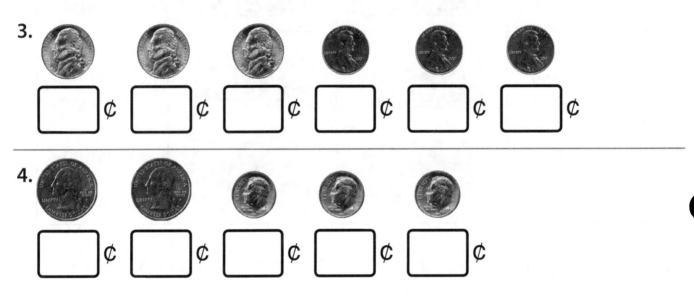

3. ☐¢ ☐¢ ☐¢ ☐¢ ☐¢ ☐¢

4. ☐¢ ☐¢ ☐¢ ☐¢ ☐¢

Write the value of each set.
Write >, <, or = to compare.

> is greater than   < is less than

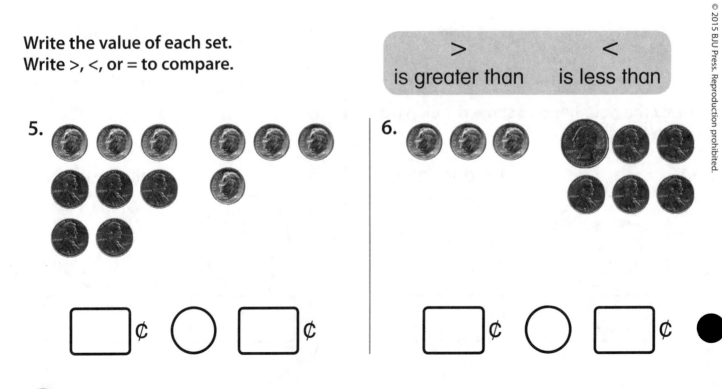

5. ☐¢ ○ ☐¢

6. ☐¢ ○ ☐¢

More Elapsed Time

Read the story. Show the times on the clocks.
Complete the sentence.

1. Ava had ball practice at 4:30. The practice lasted a half-hour. What time did practice end?

   The practice ended at ☐ o'clock.

   Practice Started

   Practice Ended

2. The ball game started at 6:00. It lasted 1 hour. What time did the game end?

   The game ended at ☐ o'clock.

   Game Started

   Game Ended

3. The game ended at 8:30. It took the Smiths a half-hour to travel home. What time did they arrive at home?

   They arrived home at ☐ o'clock.

   End of Game

   Arrived at Home

Show that 1 hour has passed.

4.

5.

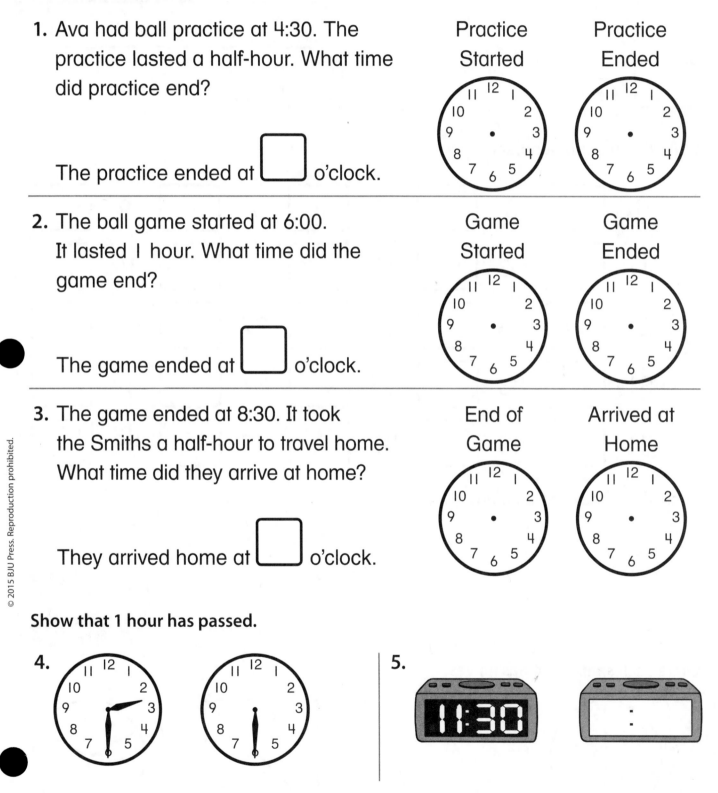

Write the length.

1.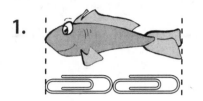

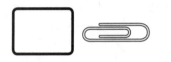

[ ] 🖇️

2.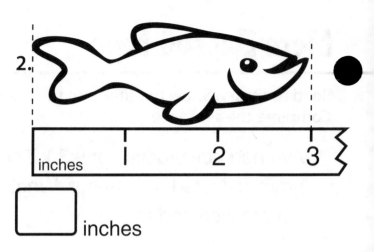

[ ] inches

Write the missing numbers.

3.

1 [ ] 3 [ ] 5 [ ] 7 [ ] 9 [ ]

11 [ ] 13 [ ] 15 [ ] 17 [ ] 19 [ ]

21 [ ] 23 [ ] 25 [ ] 27 [ ] 29 [ ]

31 [ ] 33 [ ] 35 [ ] 37 [ ] 39 [ ]

41 [ ] 43 [ ] 45 [ ] 47 [ ] 49 [ ]

Circle the container that holds less.

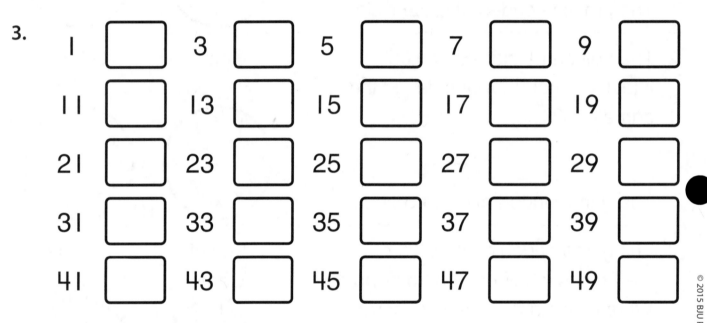

4.   5.   6.

Circle each shape that has halves.

7.

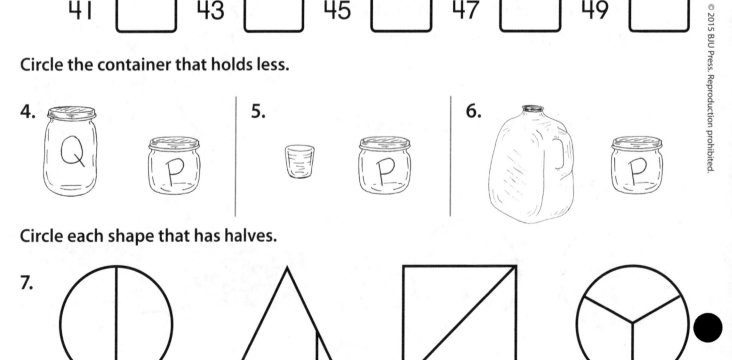

Order Time & Events

Number the times in order.

1.

4:00

3:00

3:30

2.

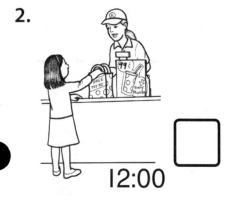

12:00

1:00

12:30

Number the events in order.

3.

4.

Read the story. Show the time on the clock. Write the time.

1. Haley went to school at 8 o'clock.

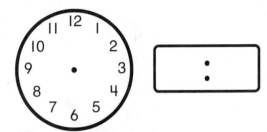

2. Haley has a music lesson at ten thirty.

Draw a line to show halves.

3.

4.

5.

Circle the temperature.

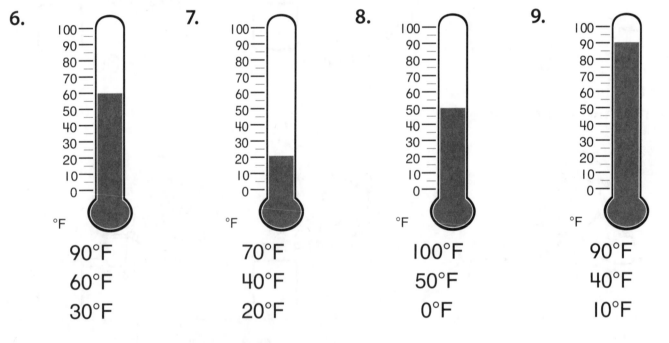

6. 90°F
    60°F
    30°F

7. 70°F
    40°F
    20°F

8. 100°F
    50°F
    0°F

9. 90°F
    40°F
    10°F

Complete the subtraction problems.

10.

97	83	58	49	74
− 34	− 12	− 20	− 25	− 24

Estimate Time

Read the story. Mark the clock.

1. Diego leaves for school a little before 8 o'clock.

   ◯   ◯   ◯

2. Dad eats lunch just after 1 o'clock each day.

   ◯   ◯   ◯

3. The Jones family walks to church between 6 o'clock and 7 o'clock.

   ◯   ◯   ◯

Use the time schedule to answer the question.

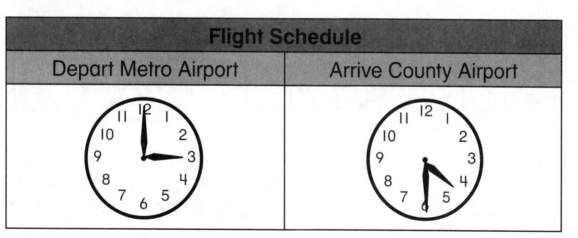

Flight Schedule	
Depart Metro Airport	Arrive County Airport

4. The Walker family arrived at Metro airport at 2:00. How long will they wait before the plane departs?

   ◯ 1 hour   ◯ 1 half-hour

5. How long will the flight take?

   ◯ 1 hour and 30 minutes

   ◯ 2 hours and 30 minutes

Write the time.

1.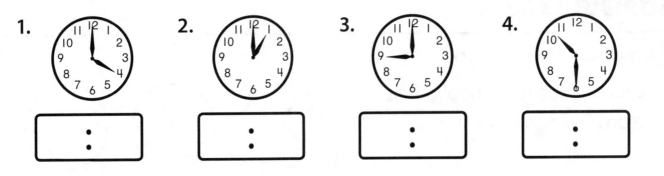

┌─────────┐
│   :   │
└─────────┘

2.

┌─────────┐
│   :   │
└─────────┘

3.

┌─────────┐
│   :   │
└─────────┘

4.

┌─────────┐
│   :   │
└─────────┘

Read the story. Show the time.

5. Jamile has lunch at 12:00.

6. Chloe goes to bed at 8 o'clock.

7. The family eats supper at 5:30.

Number the events in order.

8.

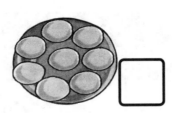

Write > or < to compare.

> is greater than   < is less than

9. 40 ◯ 70

10. 35 ◯ 25

11. 40 ◯ 45

12. 64 ◯ 54

13. 28 ◯ 18

14. 29 ◯ 30

Calendars

Mark the day that comes next.

1.
Sunday
- ◯ Monday
- ◯ Tuesday

2.
Wednesday
- ◯ Tuesday
- ◯ Thursday

3.
Thursday
- ◯ Friday
- ◯ Saturday

Mark the month that comes next.

4.
January
- ◯ February
- ◯ March

5.
July
- ◯ June
- ◯ August

6.
September
- ◯ October
- ◯ November

Use the calendar to answer the question.

June						
Sunday	Monday	Tuesday	Wednesday	Thursday	Friday	Saturday
			1	2	3	4
5	6	7	8	9	10	11
12	13	14	15	16	17	18
19 Father's Day	20	21	22	23	24	25
26	27	28	29	30		

7. What day is June 18?   ◯ Monday   ◯ Thursday   ◯ Saturday

8. What day is Flag Day?   ◯ Sunday   ◯ Monday   ◯ Tuesday

9. How many Sundays are in the month?   ◯ 3   ◯ 4   ◯ 5

Put an *X* on each Thursday.

1.

April						
Sunday	Monday	Tuesday	Wednesday	Thursday	Friday	Saturday
1	2	3	4	5	6	7
8	9	10	11	12	13	14
15	16	17	18	19	20	21
22	23	24	25	26	27	28
29	30					

Use the calendar to answer the question.

2. On what day does this month begin? ○ Sunday ○ Monday

3. What is the date of the last Monday? ○ 29 ○ 30 ○ 31

4. What day is April 18? ○ Monday ○ Tuesday ○ Wednesday

Cross out to subtract. Complete the subtraction problem.

5.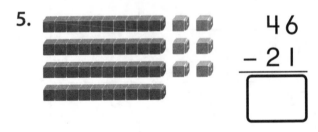
$$\begin{array}{r} 46 \\ -\ 21 \\ \hline \end{array}$$

6.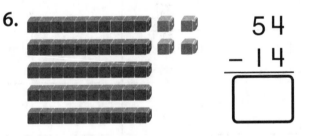
$$\begin{array}{r} 54 \\ -\ 14 \\ \hline \end{array}$$

Use the picture graph to answer the question.

7. On which day were the most apples sold?

○ Monday   ○ Thursday

○ Tuesday   ○ Friday

○ Wednesday

Apples Sold	
Monday	🍎🍎🍎🍎🍎
Tuesday	🍎🍎🍎
Wednesday	🍎🍎🍎
Thursday	🍎🍎🍎🍎
Friday	🍎🍎
🍎 = one apple	

Chapter 20 Review

Write the time.

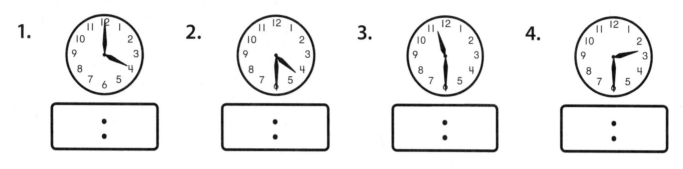

1.

2.

3.

4.

Draw the hour hand to show the elapsed time.

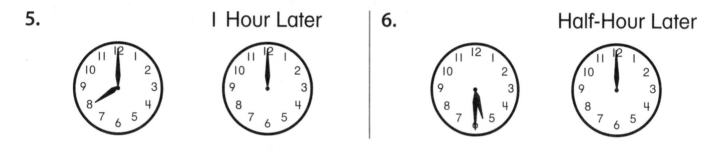

5.

I Hour Later

6.

Half-Hour Later

Circle the time passed.
Use the time schedule to answer the question.

7.

Choir Practice Schedule			
Class	Start	Finish	Time Passed
Grade I	1:00	2:00	30 minutes I hour
Grade 2	2:00	2:30	30 minutes I hour
Grade 3	3:00	3:30	30 minutes I hour

8. Which grade has the longest practice time?

     ◯ Grade I   ◯ Grade 2   ◯ Grade 3

9. Which grade has choir practice last?

     ◯ Grade I   ◯ Grade 2   ◯ Grade 3

Read the story. Show the times on the clock. Write the times.

10. Children's choir practice begins at 5 o'clock. Choir practice ends a half-hour later.

Begins

Ends

11. The evening service at church begins at 7 o'clock. It ends 1 hour later.

Begins

Ends

Put an X on each Wednesday.

12.

October						
Sunday	Monday	Tuesday	Wednesday	Thursday	Friday	Saturday
			1	2	3	4
5	6	7	8	9	10	11
12	13	14	15	16	17	18
19	20	21	22	23	24	25
26	27	28	29	30	31	

Use the calendar to answer the question.

13. How many days are in this month? ○ 29 ○ 30 ○ 31

14. What day is October 12? ○ Sunday ○ Monday ○ Tuesday

15. On what day does this month end? ○ Friday ○ Saturday

Cumulative Review

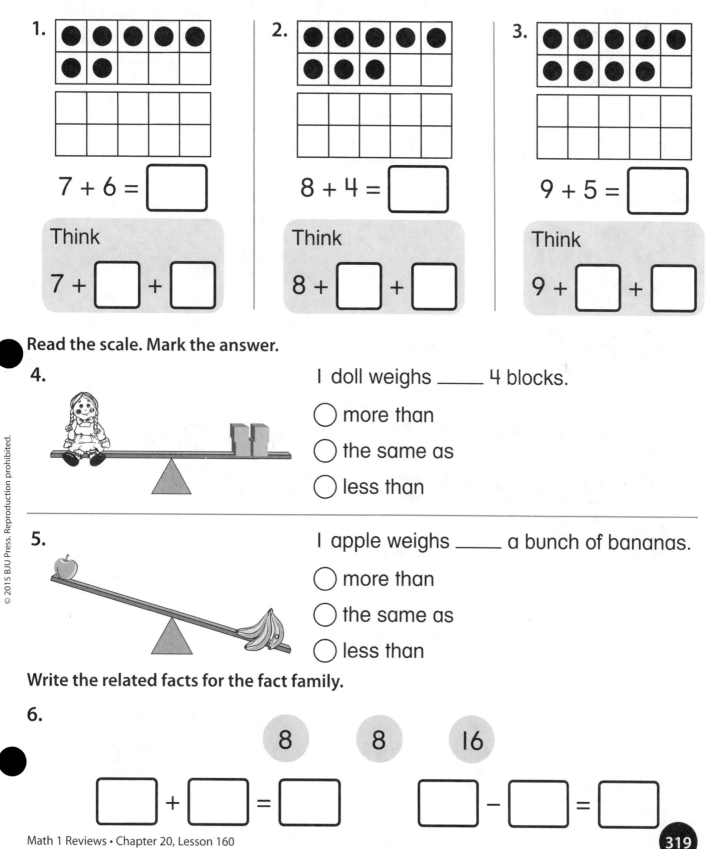

Draw the part being added to 7, 8, or 9.
Think of making 10. Complete the addition sentence.

1.

7 + 6 = ☐

Think

7 + ☐ + ☐

2.

8 + 4 = ☐

Think

8 + ☐ + ☐

3.

9 + 5 = ☐

Think

9 + ☐ + ☐

Read the scale. Mark the answer.

4.

I doll weighs ____ 4 blocks.

◯ more than
◯ the same as
◯ less than

5.

I apple weighs ____ a bunch of bananas.

◯ more than
◯ the same as
◯ less than

Write the related facts for the fact family.

6.

8   8   16

☐ + ☐ = ☐   ☐ – ☐ = ☐

Draw the number of jars that 2 jugs can fill.
Use the key.
Complete the sentence.

I jug fills 2 jars.

7.

 =

2 jugs can fill ☐ jars.

Write the total value.

8. 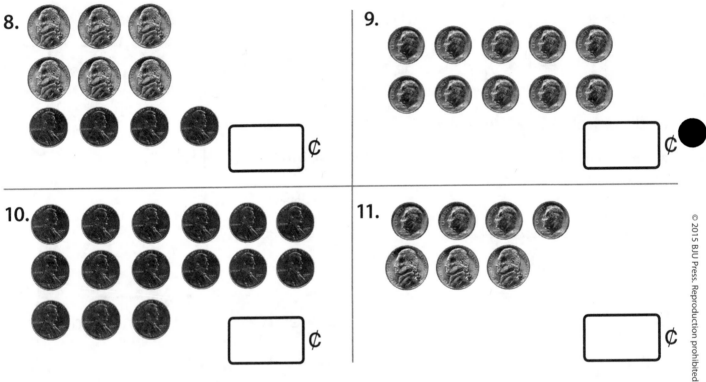 ___ ¢

9. ___ ¢

10. ___ ¢

11. ___ ¢

Circle the container that holds more.
Draw a line under the container that holds less.

12.

13.

Combine to Make 10

Write the expanded form of the problem.
Combine addends to make 10. Complete the addition sentence.

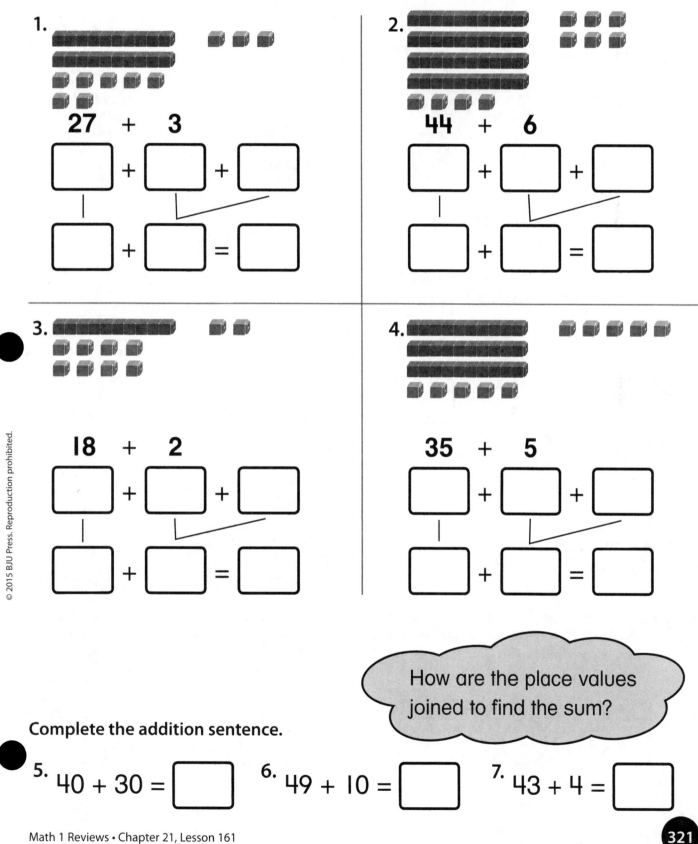

1.

27 + 3

☐ + ☐ + ☐

☐ + ☐ = ☐

2.

44 + 6

☐ + ☐ + ☐

☐ + ☐ = ☐

3.

18 + 2

☐ + ☐ + ☐

☐ + ☐ = ☐

4.

35 + 5

☐ + ☐ + ☐

☐ + ☐ = ☐

How are the place values joined to find the sum?

Complete the addition sentence.

5. 40 + 30 = ☐

6. 49 + 10 = ☐

7. 43 + 4 = ☐

Circle each figure that has at least 1 flat surface.

1.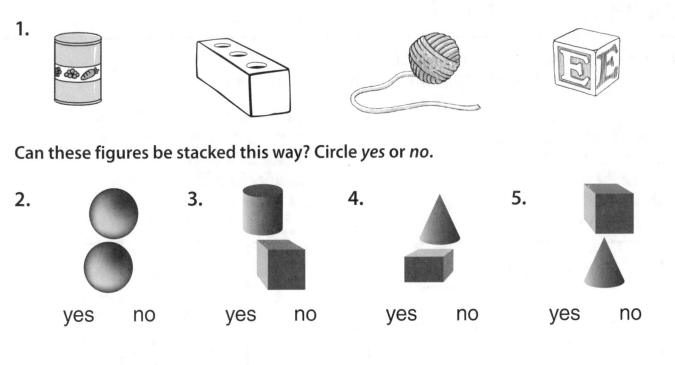

Can these figures be stacked this way? Circle *yes* or *no*.

2.   yes   no

3.   yes   no

4.   yes   no

5.   yes   no

Write the number of hundreds, tens, and ones.
Write the number represented.

6.

⬜ hundreds   ⬜ tens   ⬜ ones

⬜

Write the number represented.
Write > or < to compare.

> | > | < |
> |----|----|
> | is greater than | is less than |

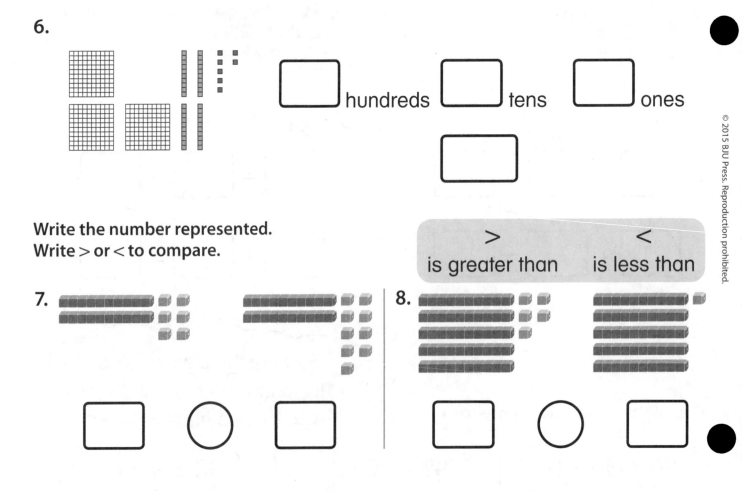

7. ⬜ ◯ ⬜

8. ⬜ ◯ ⬜

Group and Rename

Write the number of tens and ones.
Circle 10 ones and rename.
Complete the addition sentence.

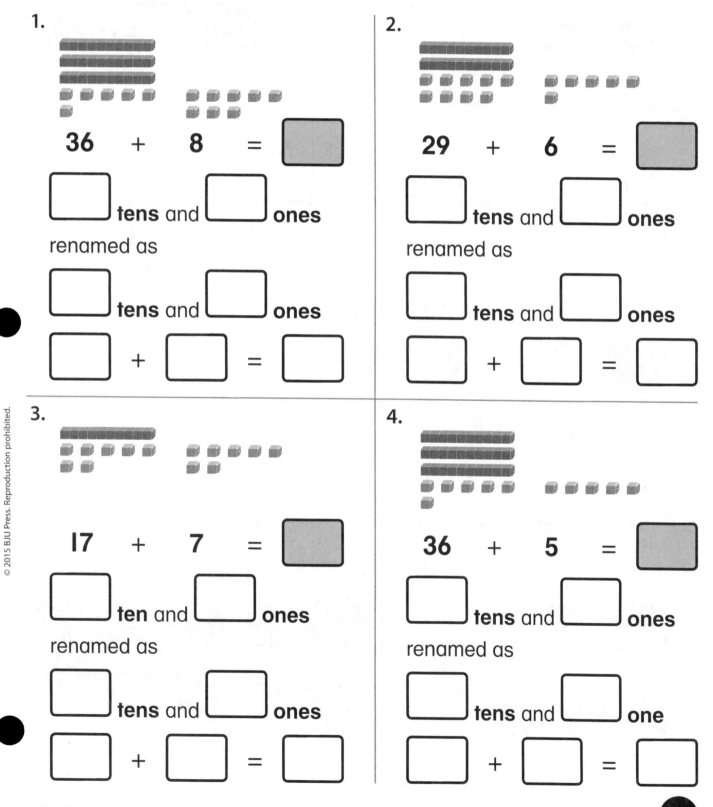

1.

36 + 8 =

☐ **tens** and ☐ **ones**

renamed as

☐ **tens** and ☐ **ones**

☐ + ☐ = ☐

2.

29 + 6 =

☐ **tens** and ☐ **ones**

renamed as

☐ **tens** and ☐ **ones**

☐ + ☐ = ☐

3.

17 + 7 =

☐ **ten** and ☐ **ones**

renamed as

☐ **tens** and ☐ **ones**

☐ + ☐ = ☐

4.

36 + 5 =

☐ **tens** and ☐ **ones**

renamed as

☐ **tens** and ☐ **one**

☐ + ☐ = ☐

Write the missing numbers.

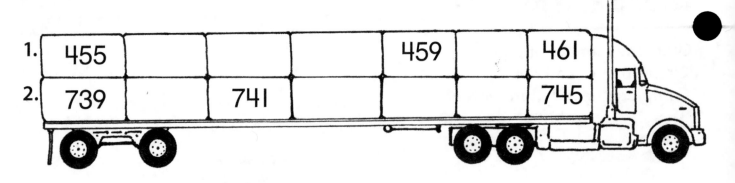

| 1. | 455 | | | | 459 | | 461 |
| 2. | 739 | | 741 | | | | 745 |

Complete the addition problem.

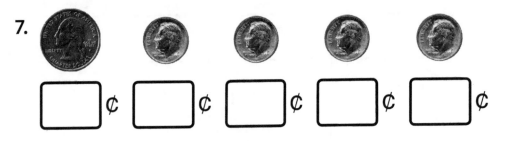

3.
$$\begin{array}{r} 91 \\ +8 \\ \hline \end{array}$$

4.
$$\begin{array}{r} 31 \\ +42 \\ \hline \end{array}$$

5.
$$\begin{array}{r} 63 \\ +11 \\ \hline \end{array}$$

6.
$$\begin{array}{r} 53 \\ +5 \\ \hline \end{array}$$

Write the total value as you *count on*.

7. ⬜ ¢ ⬜ ¢ ⬜ ¢ ⬜ ¢ ⬜ ¢

Circle the coins needed to buy each item.

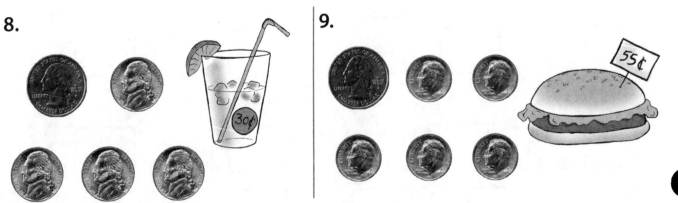

8.

9.

Rename to Add

Circle 10 ones and rename.
Complete the addition problem.

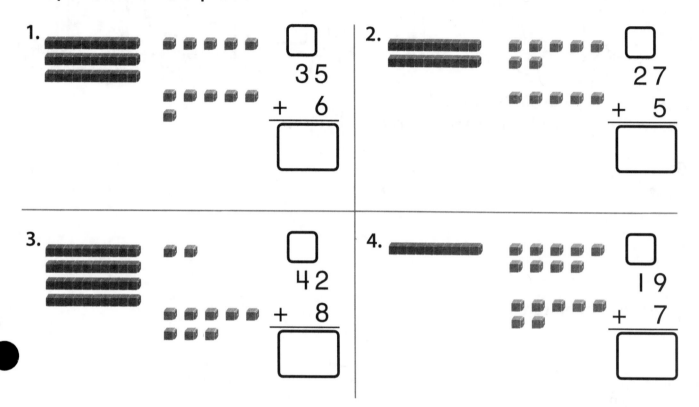

1. $\square$
     3 5
     + 6
     $\square$

2. $\square$
     2 7
     + 5
     $\square$

3. $\square$
     4 2
     + 8
     $\square$

4. $\square$
     1 9
     + 7
     $\square$

Picture the story. Complete the sentences.

5. Jason counted 16 black sheep at the farm. He also counted 8 white sheep. How many sheep did Jason count?

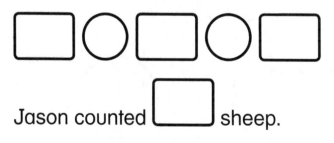

Jason counted $\square$ sheep.

Complete the subtraction problem.

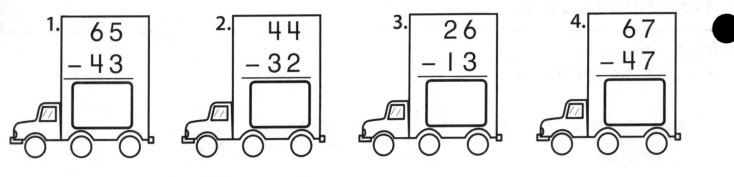

1. 65 − 43 =

2. 44 − 32 =

3. 26 − 13 =

4. 67 − 47 =

Draw a line to connect the stars.
Measure the line with an inch ruler. Write the length.

5.
★   ★   ☐ inches

6.
★   ★ ☐ inches

Circle the temperature.

7.
70°F

60°F

50°F

8.
40°F

30°F

20°F

Write the time.

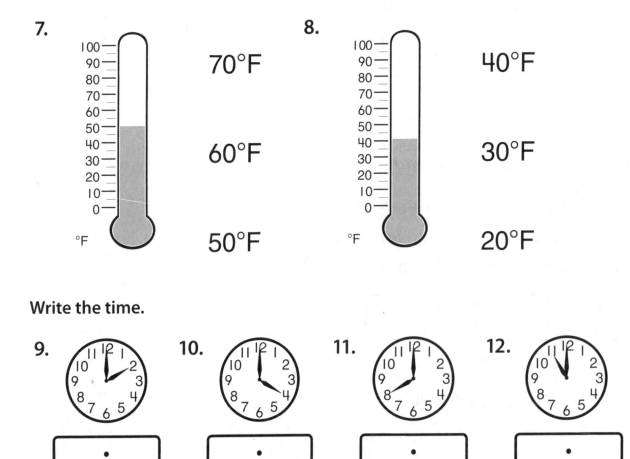

9.

10.

11.

12.

Rename to Add

Complete the addition problem. Rename if needed.
Circle *yes* or *no* to answer the question.

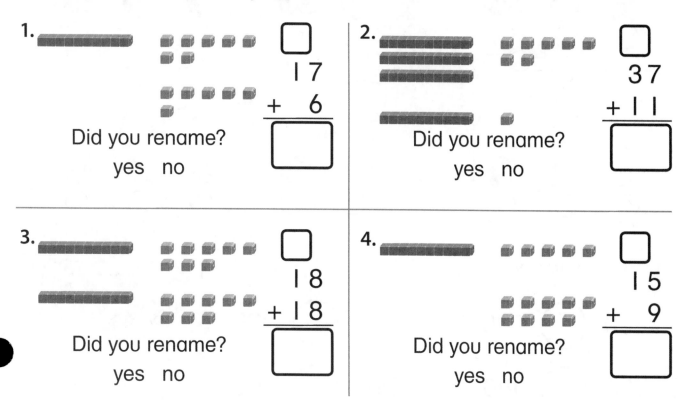

1.
☐
17
+ 6
☐

Did you rename?
yes   no

2.
☐
37
+11
☐

Did you rename?
yes   no

3.
☐
18
+18
☐

Did you rename?
yes   no

4.
☐
15
+ 9
☐

Did you rename?
yes   no

Picture the addition sentence. Complete the sentence.

5.   14 + 17 = ☐

Complete the addition problem.

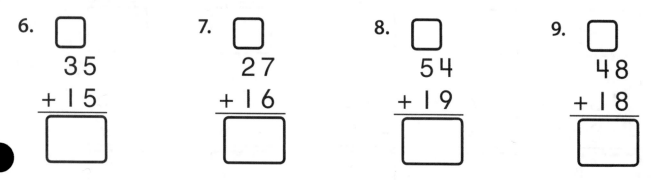

6.
☐
35
+15
☐

7.
☐
27
+16
☐

8.
☐
54
+19
☐

9.
☐
48
+18
☐

Mark the figure that has the same attributes as the object.

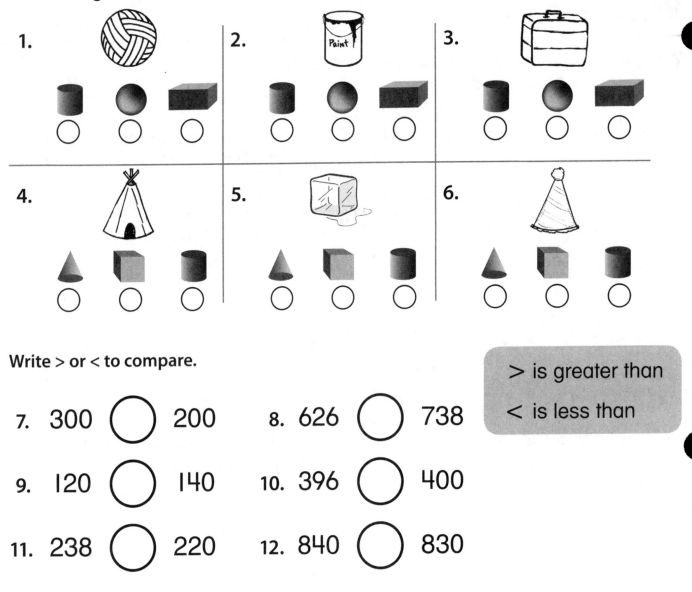

1.

2.

3.

4.

5.

6.

Write > or < to compare.

7. 300 ◯ 200

8. 626 ◯ 738

9. 120 ◯ 140

10. 396 ◯ 400

11. 238 ◯ 220

12. 840 ◯ 830

Complete the subtraction problems.

13.

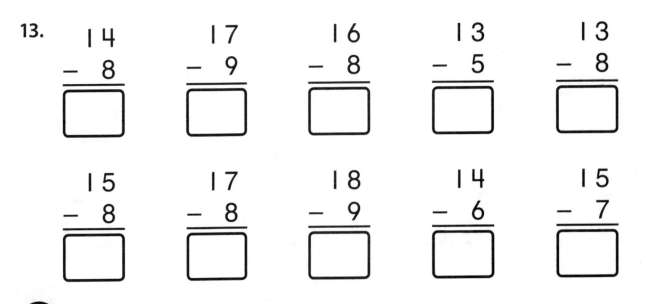

$$14 - 8 =$$

$$17 - 9 =$$

$$16 - 8 =$$

$$13 - 5 =$$

$$13 - 8 =$$

$$15 - 8 =$$

$$17 - 8 =$$

$$18 - 9 =$$

$$14 - 6 =$$

$$15 - 7 =$$

Ungroup and Rename

Write the number of tens and ones. Circle 1 ten and rename.

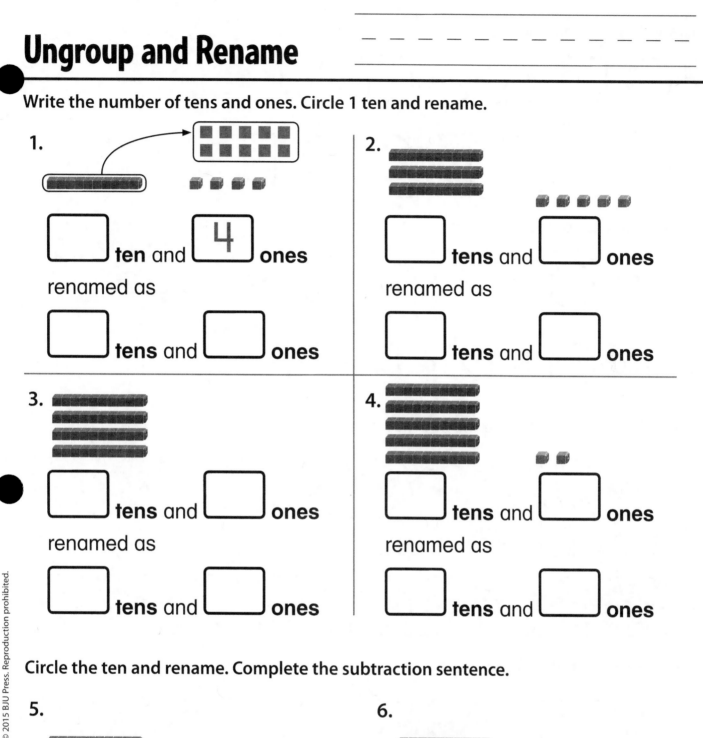

1. [   ] **ten** and [4] **ones**
   renamed as
   [   ] **tens** and [   ] **ones**

2. [   ] **tens** and [   ] **ones**
   renamed as
   [   ] **tens** and [   ] **ones**

3. [   ] **tens** and [   ] **ones**
   renamed as
   [   ] **tens** and [   ] **ones**

4. [   ] **tens** and [   ] **ones**
   renamed as
   [   ] **tens** and [   ] **ones**

Circle the ten and rename. Complete the subtraction sentence.

5. $10 - 6 = $ [   ]

6. $10 - 7 = $ [   ]

Complete the sentence.

7. I ten has the same value as [   ] ones.

Draw shapes to extend the pattern.

1. ◯ ▢ △ ◯ ▢ △ ◯ ____ ____

2. ◯ ◯ ▢ ▢ ◯ ◯ ▢ ____ ____

Write > or < to compare.

> is greater than
< is less than

3. 195 ◯ 643

4. 356 ◯ 456

5. 700 ◯ 500

6. 903 ◯ 890

Color the sun yellow beside the day that comes next.

7.

Monday	☀ Sunday	☀ Tuesday
Wednesday	☀ Tuesday	☀ Thursday
Friday	☀ Saturday	☀ Sunday

Circle the month that comes next.

8.

April	March	May
July	June	August
September	October	November
November	January	December

Rename to Subtract

Rename to subtract. Complete the sentences.

1. Cheryl had 22 balloons. She gave 5 of them to Matt. How many balloons does she have left?

   Cheryl has ⬜ balloons.

   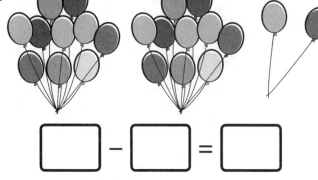

   ⬜ − ⬜ = ⬜

2. Mom put 12 cookies on a tray. Bob and Tom ate 7 of the cookies. How many cookies are left?

   There are ⬜ cookies left.

   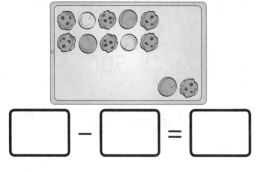

   ⬜ − ⬜ = ⬜

Complete the sentences.

3. Mom bought 3 boxes of crayons. Each box had 10 crayons. How many crayons are there in all?

   ⬜ ◯ ⬜ ◯ ⬜ ◯ ⬜

   There are ⬜ crayons in all.

   7 crayons fell on the floor. How many crayons are still in the boxes?

   ⬜ ◯ ⬜ ◯ ⬜

   There are ⬜ crayons still in the boxes.

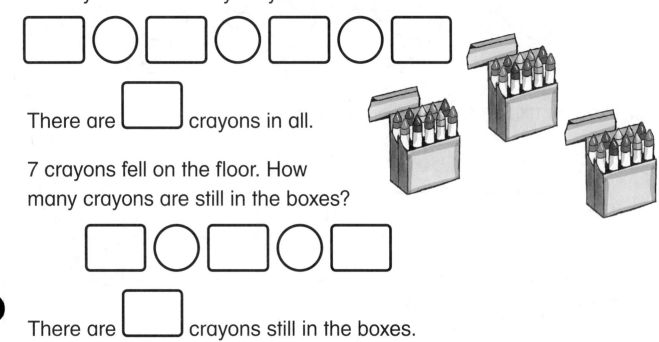

Write the number of hundreds, tens, and ones.

1.

Hundreds	Tens	Ones

2.

Hundreds	Tens	Ones

Color to show the named part of the set.

3. $\dfrac{3}{4}$

4. $\dfrac{1}{2}$

5. $\dfrac{2}{4}$

Count to 900 by 100s. Write the missing numbers.

6.

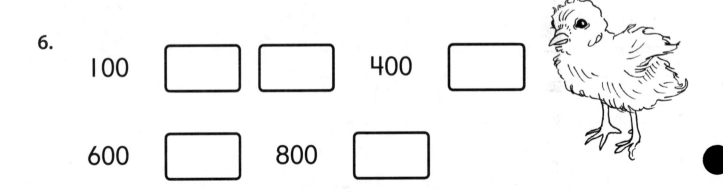

100 ☐ ☐ 400 ☐

600 ☐ 800 ☐

Check Subtraction with Addition

Complete the sentences.
Use addition to check your work.

1. There are 21 shapes. 8 of the shapes are circles. How many are not circles?

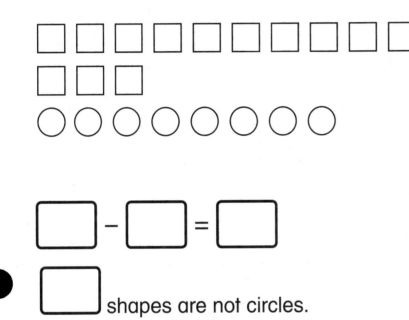

$\boxed{} - \boxed{} = \boxed{}$

$\boxed{}$ shapes are not circles.

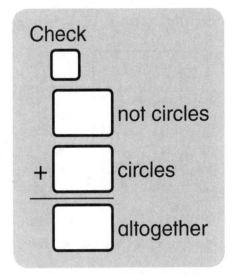

Check

$\boxed{}$
$\boxed{}$ not circles
$+ \boxed{}$ circles
$\overline{}$
$\boxed{}$ altogether

Rename to complete the subtraction sentence.
Use addition to check your work.

2.

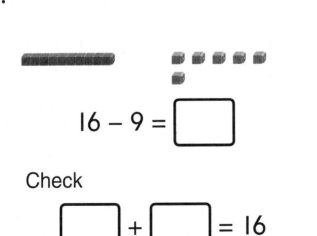

$16 - 9 = \boxed{}$

Check

$\boxed{} + \boxed{} = 16$

3.

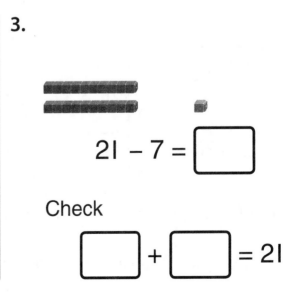

$21 - 7 = \boxed{}$

Check

$\boxed{} + \boxed{} = 21$

Write the total value as you *count on*.

1.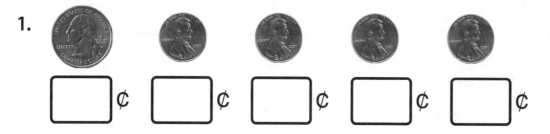

[ ] ¢   [ ] ¢   [ ] ¢   [ ] ¢   [ ] ¢

Complete the subtraction problem.

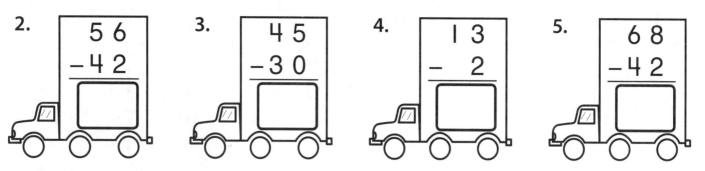

2.
```
  5 6
- 4 2
```

3.
```
  4 5
- 3 0
```

4.
```
  1 3
-   2
```

5.
```
  6 8
- 4 2
```

Use the calendar to answer the question.

☀ **July** ☀

Sunday	Monday	Tuesday	Wednesday	Thursday	Friday	Saturday
			1	2	3	4
5	6	7	8	9	10	11
12	13	14	15	16	17	18
19	20	21	22	23	24	25
26	27	28	29	30	31	

6. What month is this?   ◯ April   ◯ July

7. What is the date of the second Wednesday?   ◯ 20   ◯ 8

8. What day is July 19?   ◯ Sunday   ◯ Wednesday

Chapter 21 Review

Write the number of tens and ones.
Circle 10 ones and rename.
Complete the addition sentence.

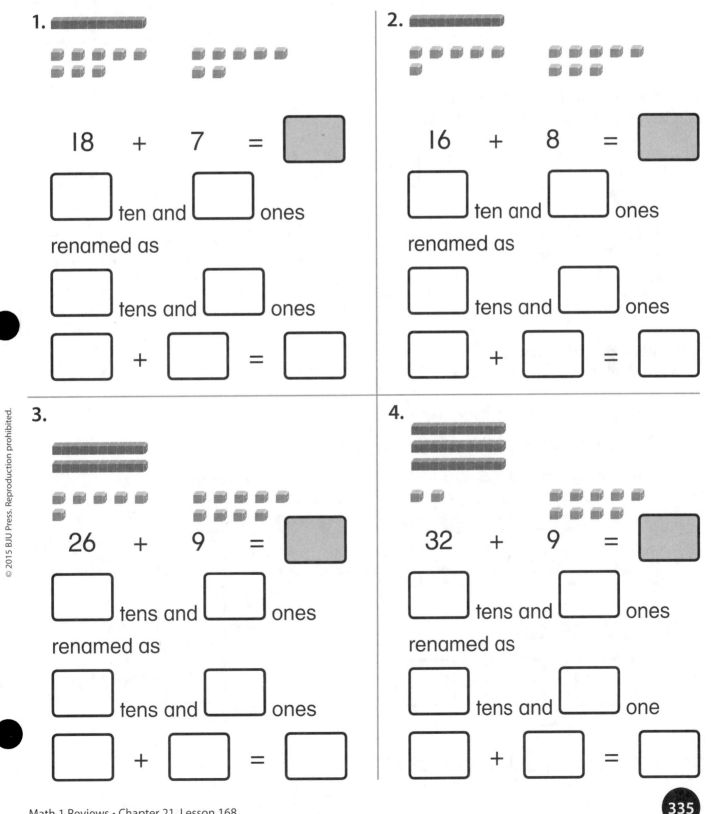

1.

18 + 7 = ☐

☐ ten and ☐ ones

renamed as

☐ tens and ☐ ones

☐ + ☐ = ☐

2.

16 + 8 = ☐

☐ ten and ☐ ones

renamed as

☐ tens and ☐ ones

☐ + ☐ = ☐

3.

26 + 9 = ☐

☐ tens and ☐ ones

renamed as

☐ tens and ☐ ones

☐ + ☐ = ☐

4.

32 + 9 = ☐

☐ tens and ☐ ones

renamed as

☐ tens and ☐ one

☐ + ☐ = ☐

Complete the addition problem. Rename if needed.

5.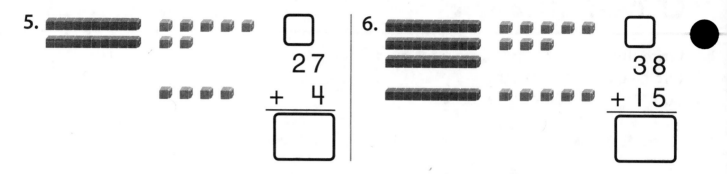

27
+ 4
☐

6. 38
+15
☐

Complete the addition problem.
Circle _yes_ or _no_ to answer the question.

7. ☐
   37
  +27
   ☐   Did you
        rename?
        yes   no

8. ☐
   75
  +18
   ☐   Did you
        rename?
        yes   no

9. ☐
   54
  +22
   ☐   Did you
        rename?
        yes   no

Complete the sentences.
Use addition to check your work.

10. Mother baked 24 cupcakes.
    The family ate 9 of them after supper.
    How many cupcakes are left?

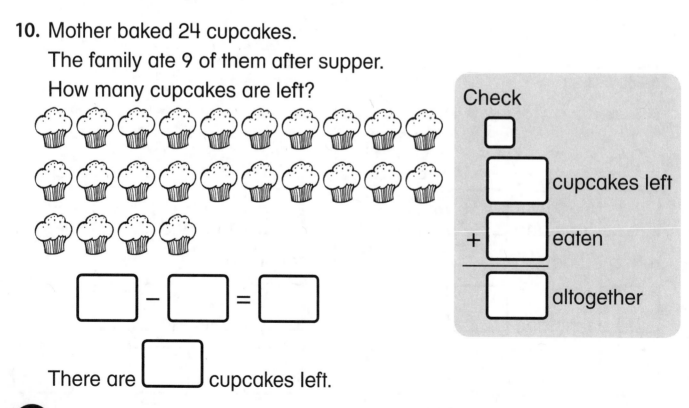

Check

☐

☐ cupcakes left

+ ☐ eaten

☐ altogether

☐ − ☐ = ☐

There are ☐ cupcakes left.

Cumulative Review

Complete the subtraction problems.

1.
```
  9 7        3 8        5 9        6 8
- 6 4      - 1 7      - 4 2      - 2 1
```

Complete the addition problems.

2.
```
  8 7        6 5        3 6        4 7
+ 1 2      + 1 3      + 6 0      + 2 2
```

Write the number represented.
Circle the single cubes to make pairs.
Circle *even* or *odd*.

3.

even

odd

4.

even

odd

Write the time.

5.   6.   7.   8.   9.

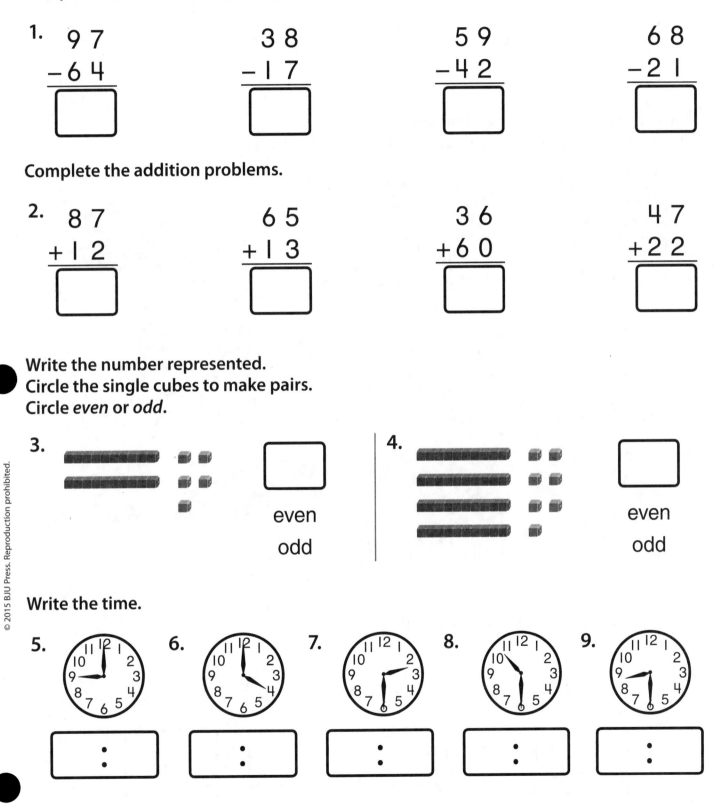

Underline the digit in the tens place.
Use the clues to write the numbers.

10. 10 Less [ ] 326 10 More [ ] | **11.** 10 Less [ ] 861 10 More [ ]

Write the total value as you *count on*.
Do you have enough money to buy the item? Circle *yes* or *no*.

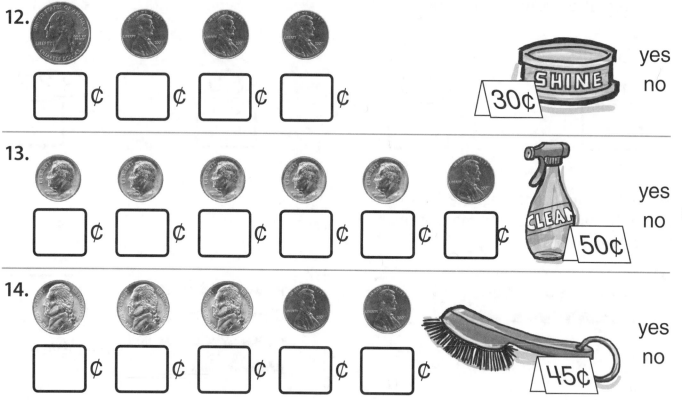

12. [ ]¢ [ ]¢ [ ]¢ [ ]¢   SHINE 30¢   yes no

13. [ ]¢ [ ]¢ [ ]¢ [ ]¢ [ ]¢ [ ]¢   CLEAN 50¢   yes no

14. [ ]¢ [ ]¢ [ ]¢ [ ]¢ [ ]¢   45¢   yes no

Write the related facts for the fact family.

15.

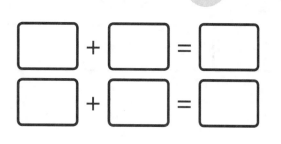

8   9   17

[ ] + [ ] = [ ]   [ ] – [ ] = [ ]

[ ] + [ ] = [ ]   [ ] – [ ] = [ ]

Count to 120

Write the missing numbers.
Count by 5s. Color each counted number yellow.
Count by 10s. Circle each counted number.
Draw a red box around the number 57.
Color the number 1 more than 57 green and the number 1 less than 57 orange.
Color the number 10 more than 57 purple and the number 10 less than 57 blue.

1	2		4		6	7	8		10
		13	14			17	18	19	20
21			24			27	28		30
31	32	33	34		36	37		39	40
41	42	43	44	45	46	47		49	
51	52		54	55	56	57	58	59	60
	62	63	64	65	66	67		69	70
71		73	74	75	76	77	78		80
81	82			85	86	87	88	89	90
91	92	93	94	95		97	98	99	100
		103	104	105	106	107	108	109	110
111	112	113		115	116		118	119	120

Write the number represented.

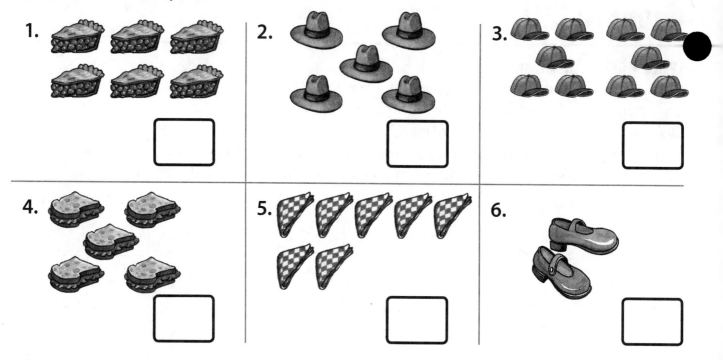

1. ☐

2. ☐

3. ☐

4. ☐

5. ☐

6. ☐

Complete the addition problems.

7.

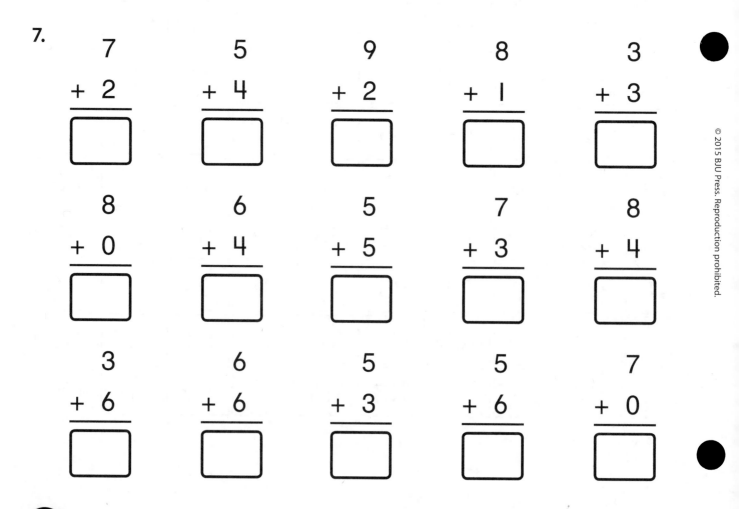

$$7 + 2 = \boxed{}$$ $$5 + 4 = \boxed{}$$ $$9 + 2 = \boxed{}$$ $$8 + 1 = \boxed{}$$ $$3 + 3 = \boxed{}$$

$$8 + 0 = \boxed{}$$ $$6 + 4 = \boxed{}$$ $$5 + 5 = \boxed{}$$ $$7 + 3 = \boxed{}$$ $$8 + 4 = \boxed{}$$

$$3 + 6 = \boxed{}$$ $$6 + 6 = \boxed{}$$ $$5 + 3 = \boxed{}$$ $$5 + 6 = \boxed{}$$ $$7 + 0 = \boxed{}$$

Compare Numbers

Picture each number. Write > or < to compare.

1.

18 ◯ 13

2.

40 ◯ 50

3.

27 ◯ 30

4.

12 ◯ 9

Complete the sentence.

5. 14 is 1 less than ☐ .

6. 22 is 1 more than ☐ .

7. 31 is 1 more than ☐ .

8. 20 is 10 more than ☐ .

9. 4 is 10 less than ☐ .

10. 19 is 10 more than ☐ .

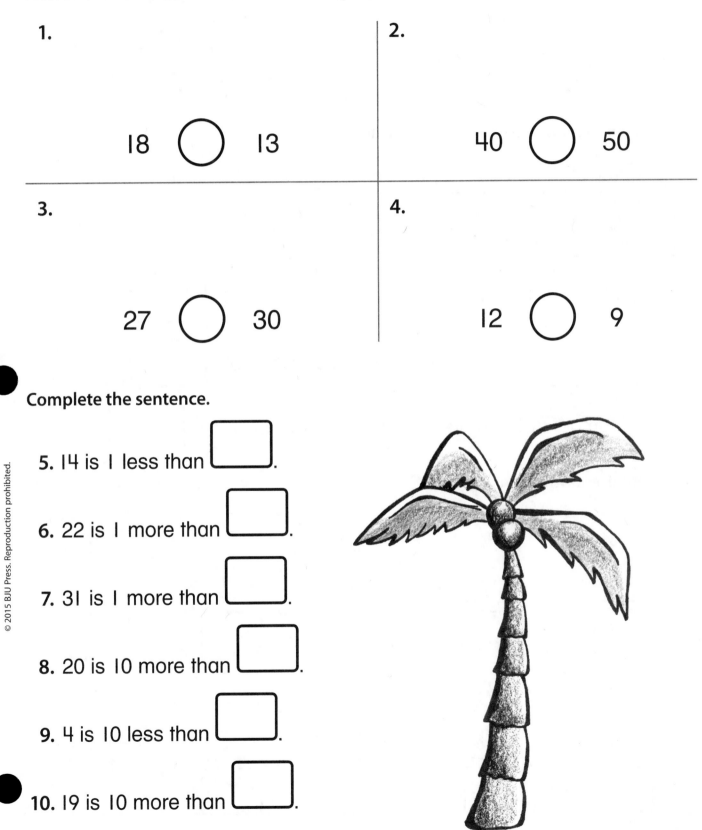

Write >, <, or = to compare.

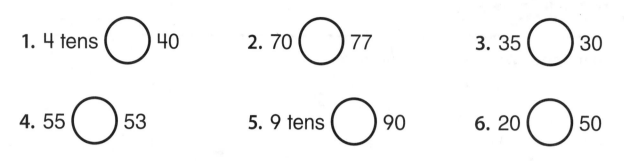

1. 4 tens ◯ 40

2. 70 ◯ 77

3. 35 ◯ 30

4. 55 ◯ 53

5. 9 tens ◯ 90

6. 20 ◯ 50

Write the number pictured. Answer the questions.

7.
Hundreds	Tens	Ones

[   ]

What number is 1 more than the number pictured? [   ]

What number is 10 less than the number pictured? [   ]

What number is 100 more than the number pictured? [   ]

Complete the subtraction problems.

8.

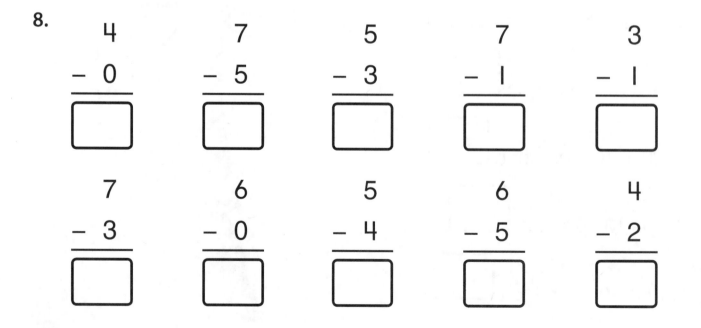

```
   4        7        5        7        3
 - 0      - 5      - 3      - 1      - 1
 [  ]     [  ]     [  ]     [  ]     [  ]

   7        6        5        6        4
 - 3      - 0      - 4      - 5      - 2
 [  ]     [  ]     [  ]     [  ]     [  ]
```

Shapes

Draw a line to match the name to the shape.
Draw a line to match the shape to its attributes.

1.

triangle ●

rectangle ●

circle ●

square ●

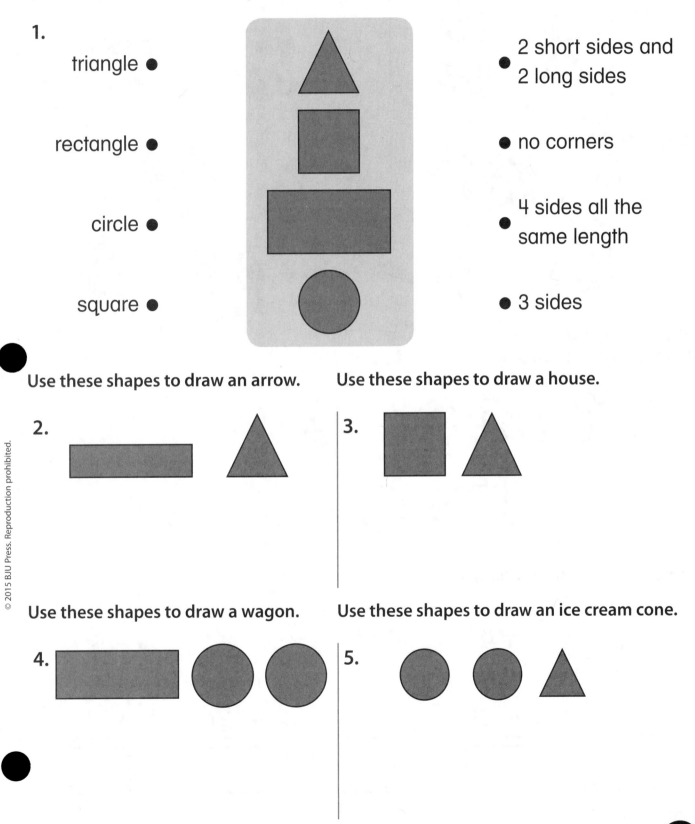

● 2 short sides and 2 long sides

● no corners

● 4 sides all the same length

● 3 sides

Use these shapes to draw an arrow.

2.

Use these shapes to draw a house.

3.

Use these shapes to draw a wagon.

4.

Use these shapes to draw an ice cream cone.

5.

Put an X on the object that does not belong.

1.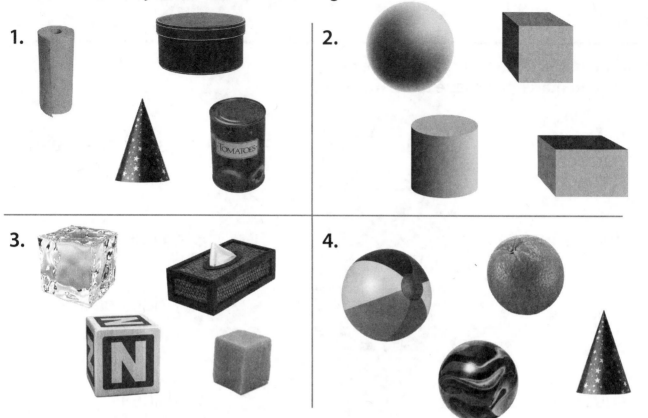

2.

3.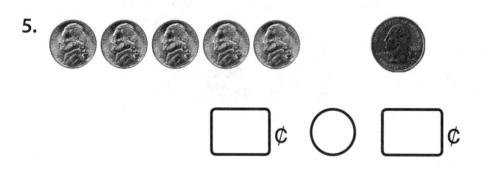

4.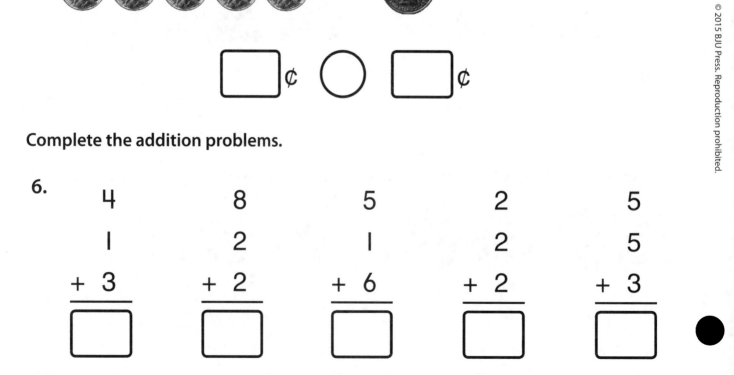

Write the value of each set.
Write >, <, or = to compare.

5.

[ ] ¢ ◯ [ ] ¢

Complete the addition problems.

6.
```
   4        8        5        2        5
   1        2        1        2        5
 + 3      + 2      + 6      + 2      + 3
 ────     ────     ────     ────     ────
```
[ ]   [ ]   [ ]   [ ]   [ ]

Measurement

Mark the answer.

Line A

Line B

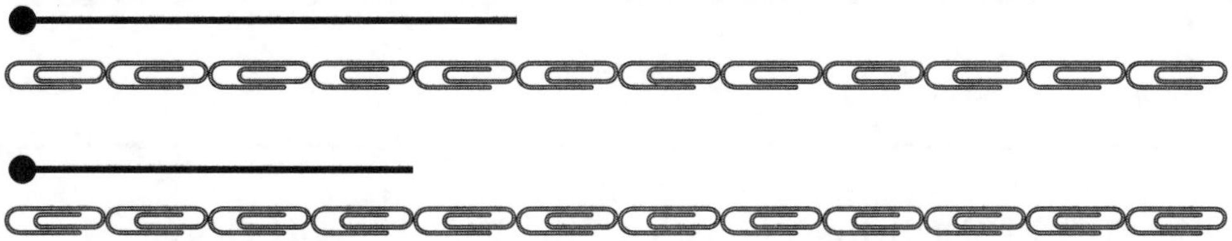

1. How long is Line A?   ○ 3 ⊂⊃   ○ 4 ⊂⊃   ○ 5 ⊂⊃

2. How long is Line B?   ○ 3 ⊂⊃   ○ 4 ⊂⊃   ○ 5 ⊂⊃

3. How much shorter is Line B than Line A?   ○ 1 ⊂⊃   ○ 2 ⊂⊃   ○ 3 ⊂⊃

Read the story. Draw Line C. Complete the sentence.

4. Sam wants Line C to be 2 ⊂⊃ longer than Line B.

Line C

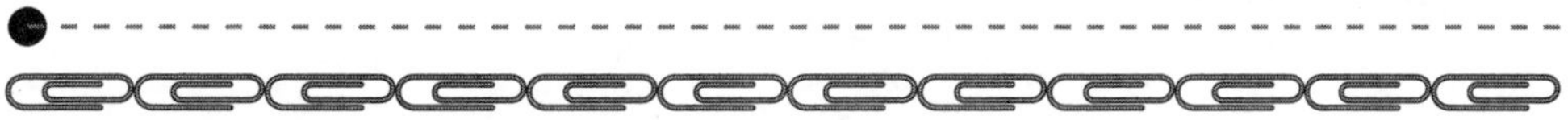

Line C is [ ] ⊂⊃ long.

Draw a line that is 8 paper clips long.

5.

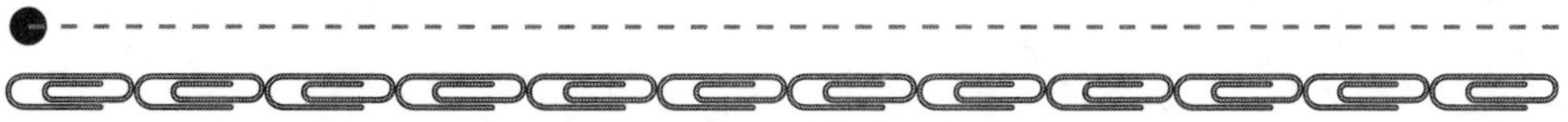

**Read the story. Mark the correct statement.
Fill in the measurement if needed.**

1.

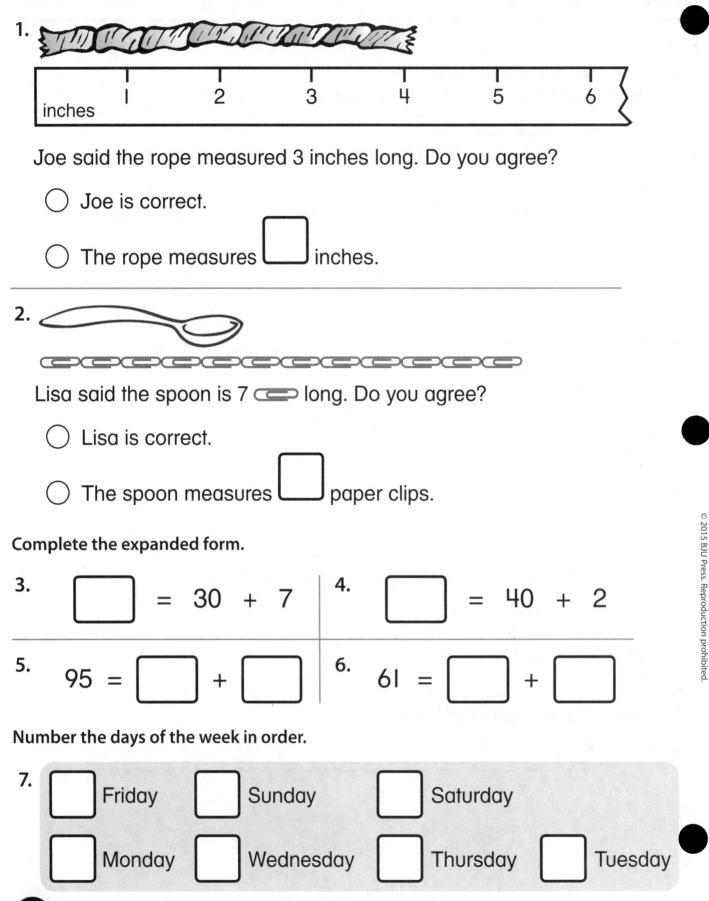

Joe said the rope measured 3 inches long. Do you agree?

◯ Joe is correct.

◯ The rope measures ☐ inches.

2.

Lisa said the spoon is 7 ◔ long. Do you agree?

◯ Lisa is correct.

◯ The spoon measures ☐ paper clips.

Complete the expanded form.

3. ☐ = 30 + 7   4. ☐ = 40 + 2

5. 95 = ☐ + ☐   6. 61 = ☐ + ☐

Number the days of the week in order.

7. ☐ Friday   ☐ Sunday   ☐ Saturday

☐ Monday   ☐ Wednesday   ☐ Thursday   ☐ Tuesday

Equal Parts

Color $\frac{1}{2}$ of the shape.

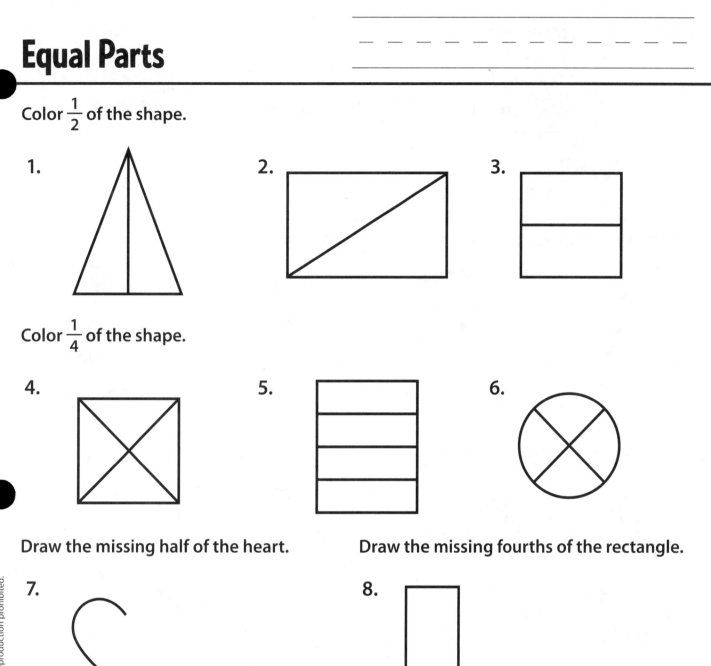

1.

2.

3.

Color $\frac{1}{4}$ of the shape.

4.

5.

6.

Draw the missing half of the heart.

Draw the missing fourths of the rectangle.

7.

8.

Read the story. Draw lines to show the equal parts.
Mark the answer.

9.

Mom cut the sandwich for 2 children to share equally. What part of the sandwich did each child get?

I half	I third	I fourth
◯	◯	◯

Circle to complete the sentence.

1. 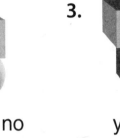 I fourth of a sandwich is [smaller / larger] than I half.

Can these figures be stacked this way? Circle *yes* or *no*.

2.

yes   no

3.

yes   no

4.

yes   no

5.

yes   no

Circle the fraction that names the part of flying birds in the set.

6.

$\frac{1}{2}$

$\frac{3}{4}$

7.

$\frac{1}{4}$

$\frac{1}{2}$

Complete the addition problem.

8.
```
  23
+ 44
```
☐

9.
```
  56
+ 20
```
☐

10.
```
  33
+ 13
```
☐

11.
```
  71
+ 10
```
☐

Time; Charts & Graphs

_____

Mark the answer.

Sunday	Monday	Tuesday	Wednesday	Thursday	Friday	Saturday
	1	2	3	4	5	6
7	8	9	10 Ann's Birthday	11	12	13
14	15	16	17	18	19	20 Zoo Trip
21	22	23 Sam's Game	24	25	26	27
28	29	30	31			

May

1. What day of the week is the trip to the zoo?

   Friday ○   Saturday ○   Sunday ○

2. Which Tuesday is Sam's baseball game?

   the first Tuesday ○   the fourth Tuesday ○   the fifth Tuesday ○

3. What day is Ann's birthday?

   Thursday, May 10 ○   Wednesday, June 10 ○   Wednesday, May 10 ○

Use the picture graph to answer the question.
Make a tally chart from the data.

Favorite Lunch Foods	
Pizza	🍕 🍕 🍕 🍕 🍕 🍕 🍕
Burgers	🍔 🍔 🍔 🍔
Hot dogs	🌭 🌭 🌭 🌭 🌭 🌭

Each picture equals 1 student's choice.

1. How many people chose pizza? ☐

2. How many fewer people chose hot dogs than pizza? ☐

3. How many more people chose pizza than burgers? ☐

4. How many people chose hot dogs? ☐

5.

Favorite Lunch Foods		
Set	Tally	Total
🍕 Pizza		
🍔 Burgers		
🌭 Hot dogs		

Write the number that comes *before*, *after*, or *between*.

6. ☐ 19

7. ☐ 57

8. 20 ☐

9. 63 ☐

10. 34 ☐ 36

11. 71 ☐ 73

Addition & Subtraction

Write an addition sentence for the picture.
Write a related subtraction sentence.

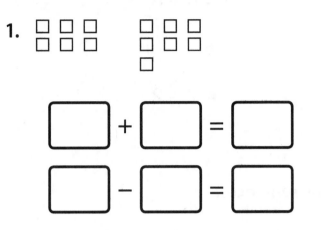

1. $\boxed{} + \boxed{} = \boxed{}$

$\boxed{} - \boxed{} = \boxed{}$

2. $\boxed{} + \boxed{} = \boxed{}$

$\boxed{} - \boxed{} = \boxed{}$

Complete the related facts for the fact family.

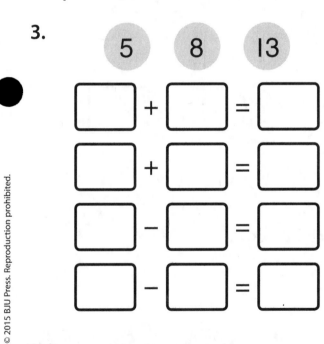

3. ⑤ ⑧ ⑬

$\boxed{} + \boxed{} = \boxed{}$

$\boxed{} + \boxed{} = \boxed{}$

$\boxed{} - \boxed{} = \boxed{}$

$\boxed{} - \boxed{} = \boxed{}$

4. ⑧ ⑨ ⑰

$\boxed{} + \boxed{} = \boxed{}$

$\boxed{} + \boxed{} = \boxed{}$

$\boxed{} - \boxed{} = \boxed{}$

$\boxed{} - \boxed{} = \boxed{}$

Write >, <, or = to compare.

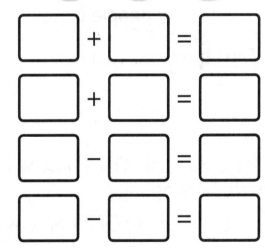
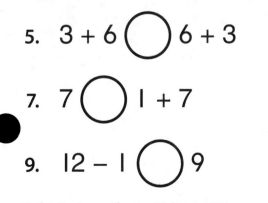

5. $3 + 6 \bigcirc 6 + 3$

6. $5 \bigcirc 8 - 2$

7. $7 \bigcirc 1 + 7$

8. $14 + 1 \bigcirc 20$

9. $12 - 1 \bigcirc 9$

10. $6 + 4 + 1 \bigcirc 13$

Draw a line to match the clue to the numbers.

1.

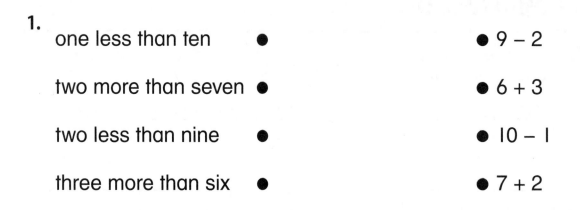

one less than ten ●   ● 9 – 2

two more than seven ●   ● 6 + 3

two less than nine ●   ● 10 – 1

three more than six ●   ● 7 + 2

Draw squares to picture the story. Complete the sentences.

2. Digit made 6 ham sandwiches.
He made 4 cheese sandwiches.
How many sandwiches did he make in all?

Digit made ☐ sandwiches.   6 ◯ 4 = ☐

**Read the story. Circle the coins needed to buy each hair bow.
Answer the question.**

3. Elsa wants to buy 2 hair bows.

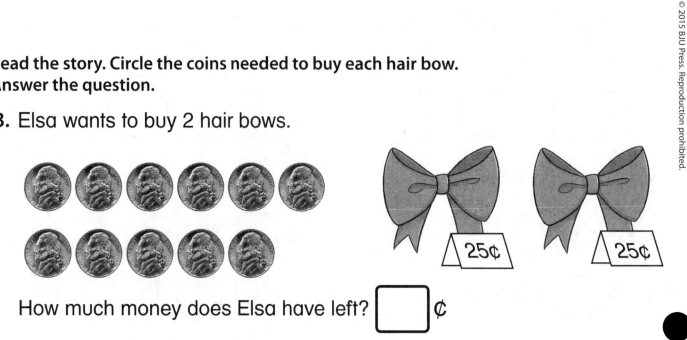

25¢   25¢

How much money does Elsa have left? ☐ ¢

2-Digit Addition

Write the number of tens and ones. Complete the addition sentence.

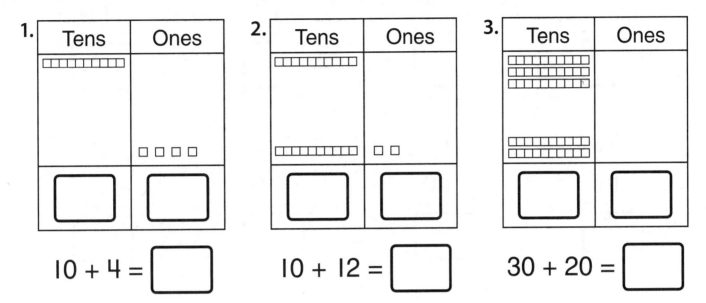

1.

Tens	Ones

$10 + 4 = \boxed{}$

2.

Tens	Ones

$10 + 12 = \boxed{}$

3.

Tens	Ones

$30 + 20 = \boxed{}$

Write the addition sentence for the picture.

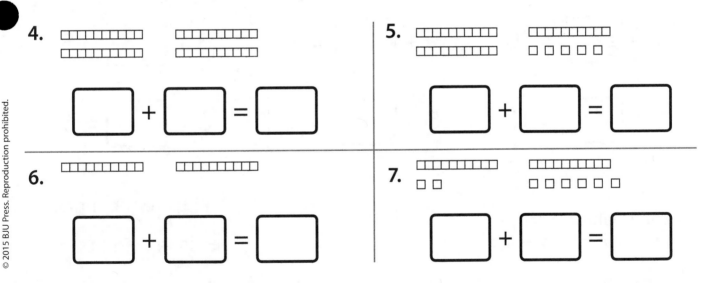

4. $\boxed{} + \boxed{} = \boxed{}$

5. $\boxed{} + \boxed{} = \boxed{}$

6. $\boxed{} + \boxed{} = \boxed{}$

7. $\boxed{} + \boxed{} = \boxed{}$

Complete the addition sentence.

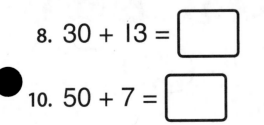

8. $30 + 13 = \boxed{}$

9. $45 + 10 = \boxed{}$

10. $50 + 7 = \boxed{}$

11. $13 + 12 = \boxed{}$

Complete the addition problems.

1.

$$25 + 4 = \boxed{}$$

$$42 + 3 = \boxed{}$$

$$64 + 12 = \boxed{}$$

$$30 + 60 = \boxed{}$$

$$53 + 15 = \boxed{}$$

$$77 + 10 = \boxed{}$$

$$29 + 20 = \boxed{}$$

$$45 + 31 = \boxed{}$$

Write the missing addends to complete the addition sentences.

2. $9 + \boxed{} = 10$ $7 + \boxed{} = 9$ $3 + \boxed{} = 5$

$8 + \boxed{} = 10$ $5 + \boxed{} = 11$ $6 + \boxed{} = 6$

> \> is greater than
>
> \< is less than

Write the value of each set.
Write >, <, or = to compare.

3.

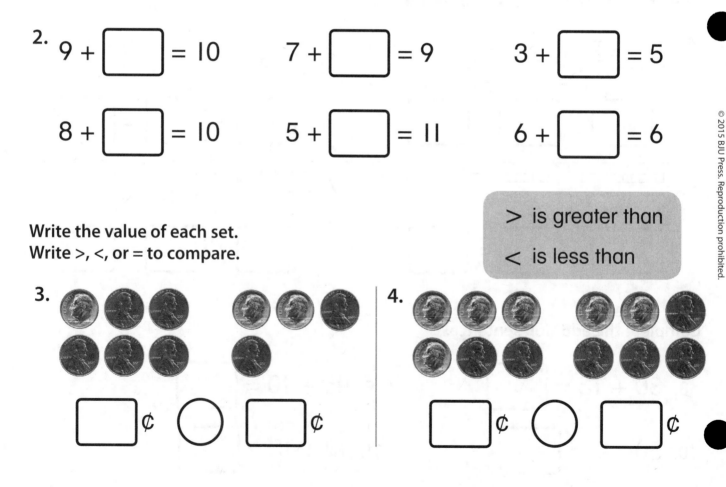

$\boxed{}$ ¢ ◯ $\boxed{}$ ¢

4.

$\boxed{}$ ¢ ◯ $\boxed{}$ ¢

Rename to Add

Circle 10 ones and rename. Complete the addition problem.

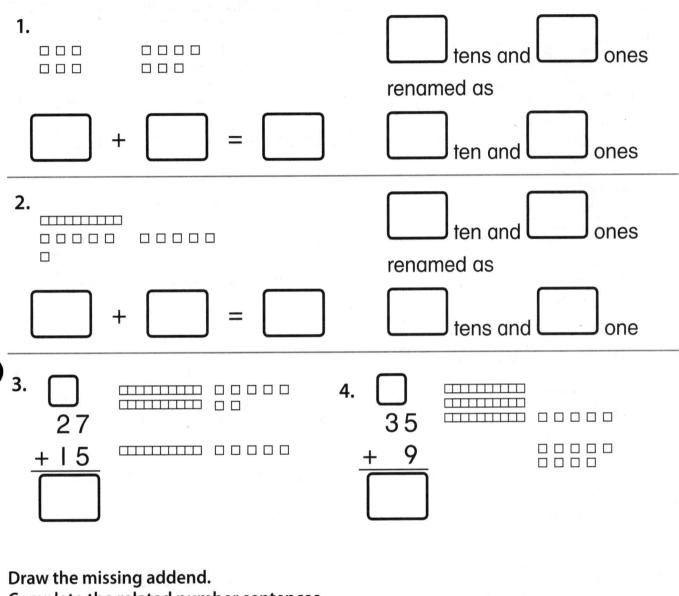

1.

☐ tens and ☐ ones renamed as

☐ + ☐ = ☐

☐ ten and ☐ ones

2.

☐ ten and ☐ ones renamed as

☐ + ☐ = ☐

☐ tens and ☐ one

3.
☐
27
+ 1 5
☐

4.
☐
3 5
+ 9
☐

Draw the missing addend.
Complete the related number sentences.

5.

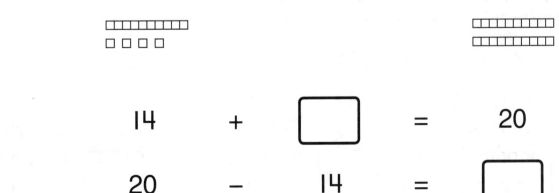

14 + ☐ = 20

20 − 14 = ☐

**Write the number of hundreds, tens, and ones.
Write the number represented.**

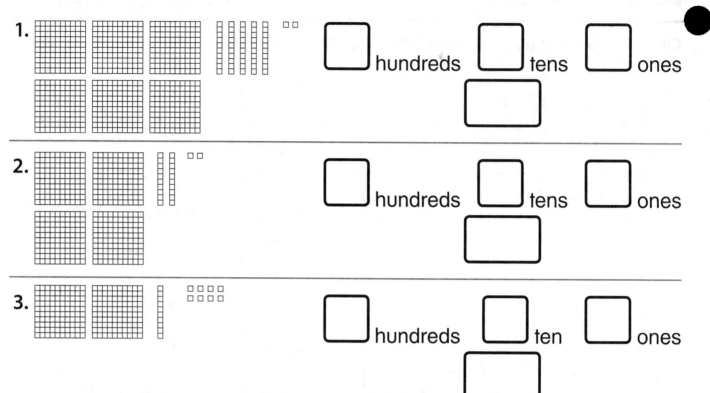

1. ☐ hundreds ☐ tens ☐ ones
   ☐

2. ☐ hundreds ☐ tens ☐ ones
   ☐

3. ☐ hundreds ☐ ten ☐ ones
   ☐

Complete the expanded form.

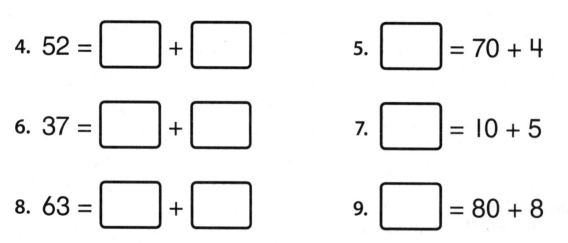

4. $52 = \boxed{} + \boxed{}$

5. $\boxed{} = 70 + 4$

6. $37 = \boxed{} + \boxed{}$

7. $\boxed{} = 10 + 5$

8. $63 = \boxed{} + \boxed{}$

9. $\boxed{} = 80 + 8$

**Complete the addition problem. Rename if needed.
Circle *yes* or *no* to answer the question.**

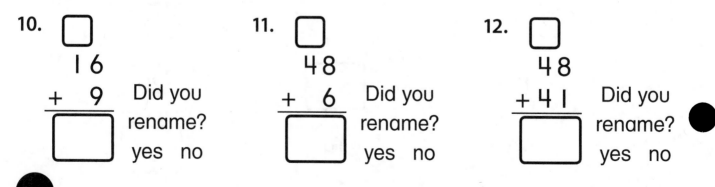

10. ☐
$$\begin{array}{r} 1\,6 \\ +\ \ 9 \\ \hline \boxed{} \end{array}$$
Did you rename?
yes   no

11. ☐
$$\begin{array}{r} 4\,8 \\ +\ \ 6 \\ \hline \boxed{} \end{array}$$
Did you rename?
yes   no

12. ☐
$$\begin{array}{r} 4\,8 \\ +4\,1 \\ \hline \boxed{} \end{array}$$
Did you rename?
yes   no

More Addition & Subtraction

Complete the addition problems.

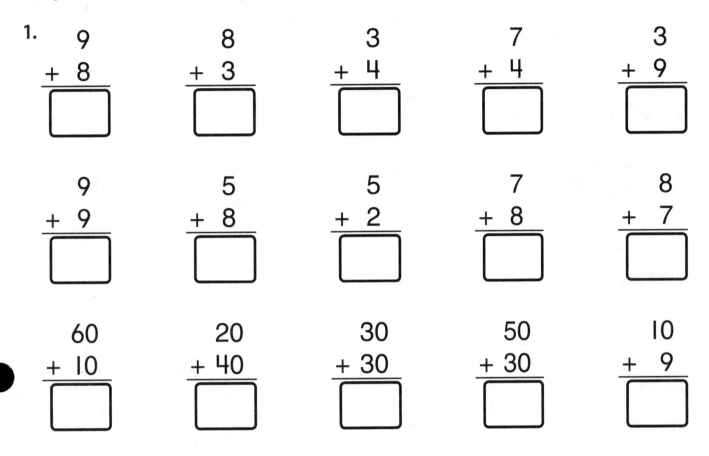

1.

9	8	3	7	3
+ 8	+ 3	+ 4	+ 4	+ 9

9	5	5	7	8
+ 9	+ 8	+ 2	+ 8	+ 7

60	20	30	50	10
+ 10	+ 40	+ 30	+ 30	+ 9

Complete the subtraction problems.

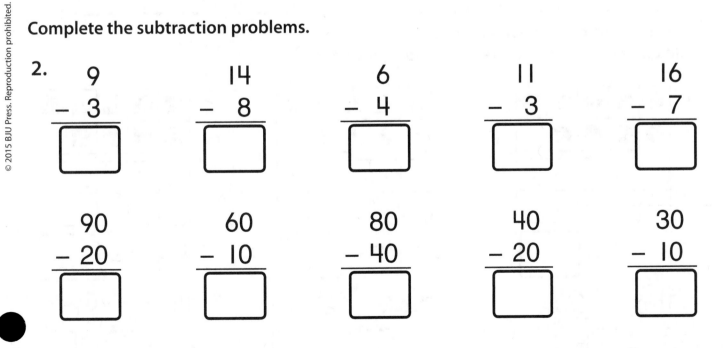

2.

9	14	6	11	16
– 3	– 8	– 4	– 3	– 7

90	60	80	40	30
– 20	– 10	– 40	– 20	– 10

Circle the correct measuring tool.

1. How long is the snake?

2. What object weighs more?

3. How warm is the soup?

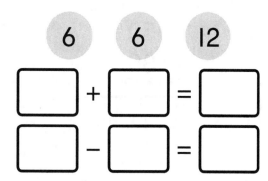 

4. How much water is in the tank?

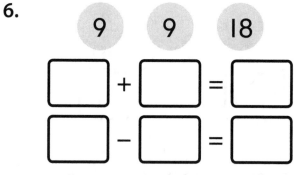

Write the related facts for the fact family.

5.

(6) (6) (12)

☐ + ☐ = ☐

☐ – ☐ = ☐

6.

(9) (9) (18)

☐ + ☐ = ☐

☐ – ☐ = ☐

Draw the part being added to 9.
Think of making 10. Complete the addition sentence.

7.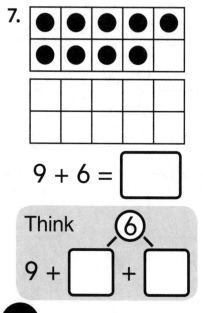

9 + 6 = ☐

Think (6)

9 + ☐ + ☐

8.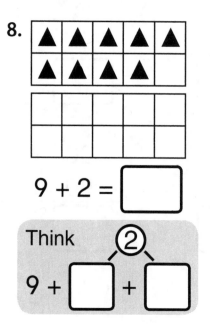

9 + 2 = ☐

Think (2)

9 + ☐ + ☐

9.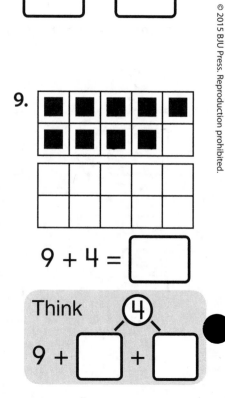

9 + 4 = ☐

Think (4)

9 + ☐ + ☐

Story Problems

Draw coins to picture the story.
Complete the sentences.

1. Stephen has 9 pennies. He needs
17 pennies. How many more
pennies does he need?

He needs ⬜ more pennies.

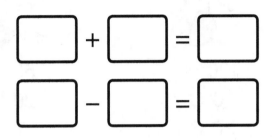

Write the lengths to complete the story.
Complete the sentences.

2.

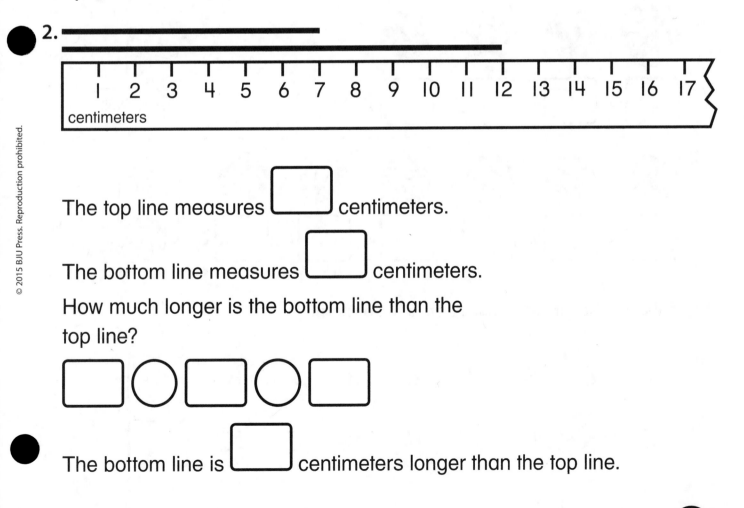

The top line measures ⬜ centimeters.

The bottom line measures ⬜ centimeters.

How much longer is the bottom line than the
top line?

⬜ ◯ ⬜ ◯ ⬜

The bottom line is ⬜ centimeters longer than the top line.

Circle the temperature.

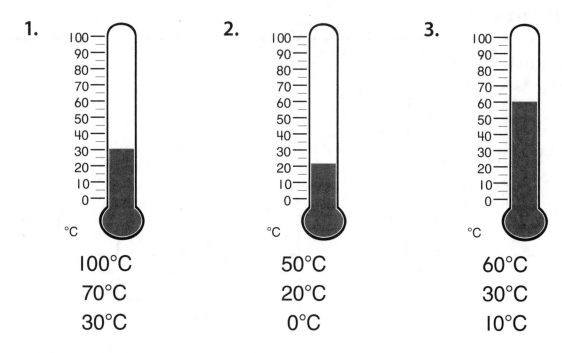

1.	2.	3.
100°C	50°C	60°C
70°C	20°C	30°C
30°C	0°C	10°C

Write the total value as you *count on*.
Do you have enough money to buy the item? Circle *yes* or *no*.

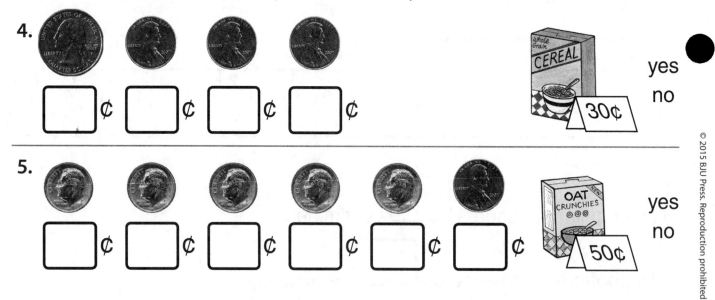

4. ☐¢ ☐¢ ☐¢ ☐¢   yes   no

5. ☐¢ ☐¢ ☐¢ ☐¢ ☐¢ ☐¢   yes   no

Write the number or letter that extends the pattern.

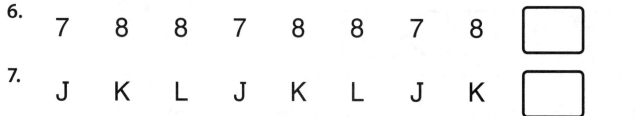

6. 7 8 8 7 8 8 7 8 ☐

7. J K L J K L J K ☐

Photo Credits

Cover
(denim background) PhotoDisc, Inc.; (linen background) © iStockphoto.com/rusm; (patch border) © iStockphoto.com/TinaFields

Front Matter
(patch border) © iStockphoto.com/TinaFields

Chapter 3
54 (all coins) BJU Press

Chapter 6
81, 83, 85, 87–92 (all coins) BJU Press

Chapter 7
96, 100, 102 (all coins) BJU Press

Chapter 8
116, 118, 125 (all coins) BJU Press

Chapter 9
132, 134 (all coins), 141 (penny front, nickel—front and back, dime—front and back) BJU Press; 141 (penny back) United States Mint

Chapter 10
144, 160 (all coins) BJU Press

Chapter 12
179–80, 184, 186 BJU Press

Chapter 13
190 (all coins), 193, 194, 195, 197 (penny front, dime—front and back) BJU Press; 193, 194, 195, 197 (penny back) United States Mint

Chapter 14
202 (all coins), 210 (penny front, nickel—front and back, dime front) BJU Press; 210 (penny back) United States Mint

Chapter 15
230 (penny front, dime—front and back) BJU Press; 230 (penny back) United States Mint; 234 (paper) Iamnee/iStock/Thinkstock; 234 (party hat) © iStockphoto.com/ScrappinStacy; 234 (3D puzzle) Achim Prill/iStock/Thinkstock; 234 (book) thongseedary/iStock/Thinkstock

Chapter 18
274 (all coins) BJU Press

Chapter 19
293, 295, 297, 299–302 (all coins) BJU Press

Chapter 20
308, 320 (all coins) BJU Press

Chapter 21
324, 334, 338 (all coins) BJU Press

Chapter 22
344 (paper towel) BJU Photo Services; 344 (hat box) pjmorley/iStock/Thinkstock; 344 (party hat) Nastco/iStock/Thinkstock; 344 (can of vegetables) PhotoObjects.net/Thinkstock; 344 (ice cube) Yura Tikhonovskyy/Hemera/Thinkstock; 344 (tissue box) skynavin/iStock/Thinkstock; 344 (toy cube) koya79/iStock/Thinkstock; 344 (cheese cube) john shepherd/iStock/Thinkstock; 344 (beach ball) Stepan_Bormotov/iStock/Thinkstock; 344 (orange) anna1311/iStock/Thinkstock; 344 (marble) John_Brueske/iStock/Thinkstock; 344, 352, 354, 360 (all coins) BJU Press